D0119642

Subsurface Drainage Practices

ILRI publication 60

Subsurface Drainage Practices

Guidelines for the implementation, operation and maintenance of subsurface pipe drainage systems

By H.J. Nijland, F.W. Croon and H.P. Ritzema[1]

[1] With the support of the following drainage experts: Dr. Safwat Abdel Dayem,
Dr. Muhammad N. Bhutta and Dr. K.V.G.K. Rao.

This book is published in the Alterra-ILRI Publication Series. The main characteristic of this series is that the books are "practical" in the sense that they can be used in the day-to-day work of those professionals (mostly engineers) who are involved in irrigation and drainage.

Nijland, H.J., F.W. Croon and H.P. Ritzema, 2005. *Subsurface Drainage Practices: Guidelines for the implementation, operation and maintenance of subsurface pipe drainage systems.* Wageningen, Alterra, ILRI Publication no. 60, pp. 608.

Keywords: subsurface drainage, planning, organization, implementation, operation, maintenance.

ISBN 90 327 0340 4

NUR 910

This publication can be ordered by paying € 40,- to bank account number 36 70 54 612 by name of Alterra Wageningen, IBAN number NL 83 RABO 036 70 54 612, Swift number RABO2u nl. Please refer to ILRI Publication 60. This amount is including tax (where applicable) and handling costs.

The aims of Alterra-ILRI are:
- To collect information on land reclamation and improvement from all over the world;
- To disseminate this knowledge through publications, courses, and consultancies;
- To contribute - by supplementary research - towards a better understanding of the land and water problems in developing countries.

Preface

Drainage of agricultural lands is an instrument for production growth, a safeguard for sustainable investment in irrigation and a tool for conservation of land resources. In global terms, drainage in the developing countries is still far of being adequate or sufficient. Out of the 1500 million ha of cropped lands (irrigated and rainfed) of the world, only about 14% is provided by some form of drainage. The total area in need of artificial drainage can be roughly estimated by 300 million ha mainly in the arid and tropical humid zones of the developing countries. Projections of crop production to meet the food and fibre needs of the world during the next 25 years shows that drainage should be improved in at least 10 -15 million ha which would imply investing at least € 750 million annually. It is expected that one third of this area will be provided with subsurface drainage systems.

Subsurface drainage is a form of drainage that was widely introduced in Europe and North America in the twentieth century. In the developing countries, Egypt stands as the country with largest area provided with subsurface drainage (about 2.5 million ha). Countries such as Pakistan, China, Turkey and India however are also providing subsurface drainage to large tracts of their irrigated lands. The world experience in subsurface drainage over the past decades provide a wide range of lessons learned and offers great opportunity to identify best practices. Although the technological advances and the scientific research offered a lot of innovations to subsurface drainage, organizational and institutional aspect of drainage project proved to be equally important for achieving the development objectives. Most of this knowledge and experience however is hidden in the so-called "*grey literature*" (unpublished reports) and in the mind of few experts who have not got the chance to integrate this vast experience and offer it to the next generation of projects. The purpose of this handbook is to made this knowledge and experiences readily available.

This handbook focuses on the construction process of subsurface pipe drainage systems. It includes a discussion of planning, organisation, and installation techniques and contains guidelines and relevant information for improving the quality of pipe drainage installation. The emphasis is on lessons learned from past experiences and how new projects can benefit from these experiences. The handbook is meant for operational managers, field and office staff of drainage organisations, both public and private, involved in the planning, installation and management of pipe drainage systems.

This handbook has been compiled based on experiences with the development and implementation of pipe drainage techniques and systems over a period of approximately 50 years in four continents. The manual has been written under the responsibility of the Alterra-ILRI, International Institute for Land Reclamation and Improvement by Ir. Henk Nijland of the Netherlands Ministry of Transport, Public Works and Water Management, Ir. Frank W. Croon of Croon Consult, formerly of Arcadis Euroconsult and Ir. Henk Ritzema of Alterra-ILRI, based on the experiences of the authors and their organisations in the implementation of subsurface drainage systems in many parts of the world. As the reference material is not readily available for most readers, the authors have prepared a bibliography with a brief description of the most important published background information.

The contents of the handbook could not have been realised without the direct contribution of the following drainage experts:

Name	Post/Company/Organisation
Dr. Safwat Abdel Dayem	Drainage Adviser, The World Bank, Washington, USA
Dr. Muhammad N. Bhutta	Director, International Waterlogging and Salinity Research Institute/IWASRI, Lahore, Pakistan
Dr. K.V.G.K. Rao	Drainage Adviser, Hyderabad, India

Next to these direct contributions the techniques and methodologies described in this book are based on the knowledge and experiences of the following persons, who have indirectly contributed to the content:

Name	Company/Organisation
Ir. F. P. A. C. van Berkom	Alterra-ILRI, Wageningen, The Netherlands
Ir. J.C. Cavelaars	Formerly at Arcadis-Euroconsult, Arnhem, The Netherlands
Ir. J.P. Driessen	Formerly at Arcadis-Euroconsult, Arnhem, The Netherlands
Ing. G. Harmsen	Wavin Overseas, Dedemsvaart, The Netherlands
Ir. E.H. Kloosterboer	Government Service for Land and Water Use, Utrecht, The Netherlands
Ing. F.W. Lampe	Formerly Steenbergen Hollanddrain, Klaaswaal, The Netherlands
Ing. O. Offringa	Formerly Government Service for Land and Water Use, Lelystad, The Netherlands
Ing. J. Penninkhof	Formerly IJsselmeerpolders Development Authority, Lelystad, The Netherlands
Ir. J. Vos	Formerly IJsselmeerpolders Development Authority, Lelystad, The Netherlands
Ing. J. de Weert	Formerly at Larenco, The Netherlands
Mr. H. Koppert	Steenbergen Holland Drain, Klaaswaal, The Netherlands
Mr. W. de Waard	Steenbergen Holland Drain, Klaaswaal, The Netherlands

Beside these people, we like to thank the following staff who contributed to the preparation of this handbook:

Language editor	Mrs. Ninette de Zylva
Drawings	Jos Rietstap Vormgeving
Design and Layout	Graphic Design & DTP team, Alterra

Furthermore this publication could not have been printed without the financial support of:
- Department of Science and Knowledge Transfer, Ministry for Agriculture, Nature and Food Quality, The Netherlands;
- Institute for Inland Water Management and Waste Water Treatment (RIZA), Lelystad, The Netherlands, Ministry of Transport, Public Works and Water Management, The Netherlands;
- Arcadis Euroconsult, The Netherlands;
- Homburg Drainage Machinery, The Netherlands;
- Horman Drainagefilters, The Netherlands;
- Steenbergen Holland Drain, The Netherlands;
- Mastenbroek, UK.

We want to thank everyone who was involved in the production of this book. It is our belief that their combined efforts will facilitate the further introduction of pipe drainage in the world and through this contribute to a better, more sustainable, use of the world's precious land and water resources.

Wageningen, January 2005   Ir. Henk Nijland
                                  Ir. Frank W. Croon
                                  Ir. Henk Ritzema

Contents

Preface   **5**

Preamble   **15**

**Part I   Implementation of subsurface drainage systems:
           the Process   25**

I.1   Implementation Process for Subsurface Drainage Systems   27
         I.1.1 Main steps and players in the implementation process   27
         I.1.2 Step 1: Policy preparation and decision-making   28
         I.1.3 Step 2: Technical, organisational and administrative preparation   30
         I.1.4 Step 3: Actual implementation   37
         I.1.5 Step 4: Handing-over to beneficiaries and operation & maintenance   44

I.2   Implementation Modes and Tender Procedures   45
         I.2.1 Implementation modes   45
         I.2.2 Tender procedures   50

I.3   Layout Options for Subsurface Drainage Systems   57
         I.3.1 Layout considerations during the various steps of the
                implementation process   57
         I.3.2 Elements of a drainage system   57
         I.3.3 Considerations for the selection of a layout   58
         I.3.4 Pumping   59
         I.3.5 Layout options of subsurface field drainage systems   60
         I.3.6 Quantitative comparison of different layout systems   65

I.4   Materials for subsurface drainage systems   69
         I.4.1 Considerations on material selection during the various steps of
                the implementation process   69
         I.4.2 Pipes for field drains   70
         I.4.3 Pipes for collector drains   80
         I.4.4 Envelopes   81
         I.4.5 Structures and pumps   86

I.5   Installation Equipment for Subsurface Drainage Systems   91
         I.5.1 Introduction   91
         I.5.2 General considerations on the selection of installation equipment   92
         I.5.3 Hydraulic excavator/backhoe   93
         I.5.4 Trencher drainage machines   94
         I.5.5 Trenchless drainage machines   100
         I.5.6 Comparison of capacities and cost of drainage installation machinery   106

I.5.7 Specialised drain installation machinery 108
I.5.8 Specialised drain installation support equipment 111

I.6 Installation of Subsurface Drainage Systems 115
I.6.1 Introduction 115
I.6.2 Installation methods 115
I.6.3 Machinery and equipment requirements for mechanical installation 118
I.6.4 Organisation and staff requirements for mechanical installation 119
I.6.5 Planning and preparatory aspects for subsurface drainage installation 123
I.6.6 Steps in pipe drain installation 124
I.6.7 Site clean-up 133

I.7 Quality Control in Drainage Construction 135
I.7.1 Quality control process 135
I.7.2 Quality control of drainage materials 137
I.7.3 Quality control of installation 138
I.7.4 Checking of the functioning of the drainage system 140
I.7.5 Post installation quality checks 140
I.7.6 Post construction performance assessment 143

I.8 Operation and maintenance of drainage systems 145
I.8.1 Introduction 145
I.8.2 Decisions during the planning stage of the implementation process 145
I.8.3 Operation of subsurface drainage systems 146
I.8.4 Maintenance of subsurface drainage systems 146
I.8.5 Cost of operation and maintenance 151

I.9 Cost of Subsurface Drainage Systems 153
I.9.1 General 153
I.9.2 Considerations for determining cost, benefits and financing of
drainage projects 154
I.9.3 Estimating the cost of drainage projects 159
I.9.4 Investments for the creation of a drainage industry 161
I.9.5 Cost calculation of the pre-construction activities 165
I.9.6 Construction costs 168
I.9.7 Cost of operation and maintenance of subsurface systems 177

**Part II Detailed instructions for the implementation of
subsurface drainage systems** 179

General Introduction to Part II 181

II-A Panning and Supporting Research 187
A.1 Network Planning for the Construction of Subsurface Drainage Systems 189

| | A.2 | Operational Monitoring for Machine Performance | 197 |
| | A.3 | Time and Motion Studies | 201 |

II-B | **Cost Calculations** | | **205**
	B.1	Methodology for the Calculation of Staff Costs	207
	B.2	Methodology for the Calculation of the Cost of Equipment and Machinery	209
	B.3	Methodology for the Calculation of the Cost of Transport	213
	B.4	Methodology for the Calculation of the Cost of Raw Materials	215

II-C | **Installation of Subsurface Drainage Systems** | | **217**
| | Preamble | | 219 |

II-C/1 | **Organisation of the Implementation of Subsurface Drainage Systems** | | **223**
	C.1	Requirements for the Implementation of Singular Drainage Systems	227
	C.2	Requirements for the Implementation of Composite Drainage Systems	229
	C.3	Tasks Descriptions for Key Installation Staff	231

II-C/2 | **Machinery and Equipment** | | **237**
	C.4	Description of Trenchers	239
	C.5	Maintenance of Trenchers	245
	C.6	Adjustment of the Trench Box and Digging Chain	253
	C.7	Minimising the Operation Costs of Trenchers	259
	C.8	Operation of Trenchers for Corrugated Plastic Drain Pipe Installation	263
	C.9	Working with a Liftable Trench Box	267
	C.10	Description of Trenchless Drainage Machines	271
	C.11	Maintenance of Trenchless Drainage Machines	275
	C.12	Operation of Trenchless Drainage Machines	283
	C.13	Description of Laser Equipment for Grade Control	287
	C.14	Management of Laser Equipment for Grade Control	291
	C.15	Determining the Extension of Laser Mast on Trencher	295
	C.16	Verification of Correctness of Laser Transmitter in the Field	297
	C.17	Manual Grade Control in the Absence of Laser Equipment	299
	C.18	Description and Maintenance of Gravel Trailers	303

II-C/3 | **Installation of Pipe Drainage Systems** | | **305**
	C.19	Preparatory Activities	307
	C.20	Sequence of Drain Installation	311
	C.21	Setting Out of Field	317
	C.22	Site Preparation	321
	C.23	Installation of Drains	325

C.24 Installation Drains in Saturated and/or Unstable Subsoils 331
C.25 Installation in Fields with Standing Surface Water 333
C.26 Installation of Field Drains Starting from an Open Ditch 335
C.27 Installation of Outlets of Field Drains into Open Ditches 339
C.28 Installation of Sumps at the Start of Collector Drains 341
C.29 Levels of Manholes and Starting Levels for Trencher for Field
      Drain Installation 343
C.30 Installation of Manholes and Starting Holes for Field Drains
      (Composite Systems) 349
C.31 Installation of Connections and Joints 353
C.32 Completion of Manhole/Sump Installation 355
C.33 Backfilling of Trenches 359
C.34 Cleaning Up of Site after Installation 363
C.35 Application of Gravel 365
C.36 Manual Installation of Drains 373
C.37 Manual Installation in Trenches Dug by Excavators 379
C.38 Wrapping a Synthetic Sheet Envelope around the Pipes in the Field 385

II-D   Practical Aspects of Quality Control   387
D.1   Quality Control of Drainage Materials 391
D.2   Quality Control of Installation of Pipe Drainage Systems 397
D.3   Checking the Functionality of Composite Drainage Systems 403
D.4   Methodology for Checking the Grade of Installed Drain and Collector
      Pipes during Installation 407
D.5   Post Construction Verification of Drain Pipes 413

II-E   Maintenance of Drainage Systems   419
E.1   Checking the Functioning of Subsurface Drainage Systems 421
E.2   Principles of Flushing of Subsurface Drains 427
E.3   Management, Maintenance and Repair of High Pressure Flushers 433
E.4   Flushing of Collector Drains 435
E.5   Flushing of Field Drains from a Ditch 439
E.6   Flushing of Field Drains from a Manhole 443

Part III Case Studies   447

China   451
1   Introduction 453
2   Distribution of Areas with Drainage Problems 453
3   Historical Developments 454
4   Pipe Drainage in China 457
5   Development of Pipe Drainage in China 459
6   Technical Aspects of Pipe Drainage Systems in China 461
7   Challenges for the Further Development of Pipe Drainage in China 464

Egypt   **467**
    1   Background   469
    2   Organisation   470
    3   Planning   477
    4   Drainage Materials   478
    5   Installation   484
    6   Operational Research   488
    7   Capacity Building   498

India   **501**
    1   Background   503
    2   Organisation   504
    3   Planning   505
    4   Drainage Materials   506
    5   Installation Equipment   509
    6   Examples of Large-scale Drainage Projects   509

The Netherlands   **525**
    1   Background   527
    2   Organisation of the Water Management   529
    3   Drainage Materials   536
    4   Manual Installation   540
    5   Quality Control   543

Pakistan   **545**
    1   Background   547
    2   Organisation   548
    3   Drainage Materials   549
    4   Installation   551
    5   Examples of Large-scale Drainage Projects   554

Bibliography   **565**

Glossary   **575**

Index   **587**

Preamble

Implementation of pipe drainage systems

Over the past decades land drainage has evolved as a mature technique to control water logging and salinity and to reclaim agricultural lands. Where drainage has been applied it has proven to be a technically and economically feasible methodology to increase yields and consequently the income of farmers. As a secondary effect it safeguards the productivity of the soil and protects the environment from deterioration.

Of the different drainage methodologies such as open drainage, well drainage and pipe drainage[2], pipe drainage is the most advantageous solution for large areas in the world. Applied on a large scale, it can effectively solve the drainage problems at relatively moderate costs with a minimum of interference to agricultural practices and existing infrastructure. Maintenance of properly constructed pipe drainage systems has proven to be far less problematical than maintenance of other forms of drainage.

The background and theories of drainage and the effects have been amply described in the available literature, for instance ILRI Publication no. 16 *Drainage Principles and Applications* (see the bibliography for more background information). The theories are well known and generally well understood, yet the implementation of pipe drainage for water logging and/or salinity control is still not common knowledge. Furthermore, although the various aspects of the implementation are described in the literature, starting up the routine implementation remains a rather time-consuming and complex process during which small mistakes can have disastrous and costly consequences.

This handbook serves as a guideline for those who have a role in the process of implementing (pipe) drainage systems. Aspects and experiences of the implementation process of pipe drainage systems are summarised in Part I of this handbook. Part II presents the details of the construction of drainage systems and is specially meant for the people working in or with the construction, like contractors or specialised entities, field engineers and supervisors. Finally, Part III presents case studies from various countries describing available information on the introduction of pipe drainage systems in Egypt, Pakistan, China, India and the Netherlands.

---

[2] In the literature pipe drainage is often referred to as "tile drainage". Please consult the glossary for the definitions used in this handbook.

Objectives and effects of agricultural drainage

The overall objective of agricultural drainage, as part of agricultural water management, is to enhance crop growth and to maintain the soil productivity. The immediate objectives of agriculture drainage are (Figure 1):

- To remove excess surface and subsurface water;
- To remove excess soluble salts with the (excess) water from the drained soil profile;
- To maintain groundwater levels at a desired level.

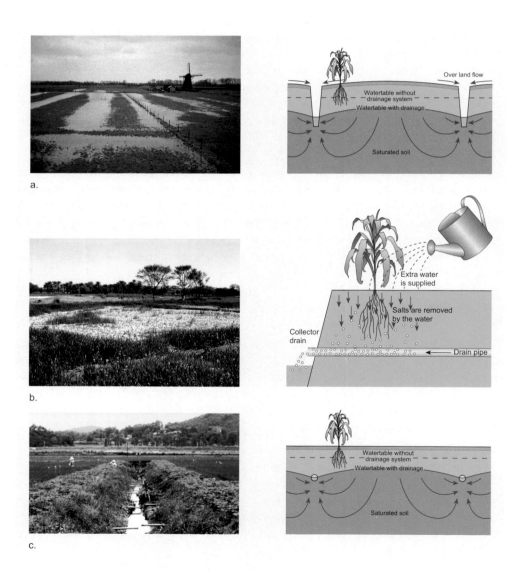

Figure 1   Objectives of drainage are: (a) to remove excess water, (b) to control salinity and (c) to maintain the watertable at a desired level

Drainage systems are man-made systems that are only implemented when natural drainage is insufficient for a satisfactory form of agriculture. Areas with limited natural drainage requiring artificial drainage are usually located in coastal plains, river valleys and inland plains where in the humid regions rainfall exceeds evaporation, or in arid regions where the (inevitable) inefficient use of irrigation water has caused water logging and secondary salinisation. Pipe drainage systems have proved to be an essential and relatively cheap method to restore the productivity of agricultural lands, especially in arid and semi-arid zones. These agricultural (pipe) drainage systems can be used for:

- Reclamation of new land with a groundwatertable and/or soil salinity that is too high;
- Controlling groundwater levels at desired depths and soil salinity at desired levels;
- Restoring the productivity of water logged and/or salinised lands to their potential levels.

Under specific conditions, these systems also create conditions under which:

- Accessibility to the field for (mechanised) farm operations is better assured;
- More crops per year can be grown;
- A larger range of crops can be grown;
- Higher value crops can be cultivated.

Finally, secondary benefits of agricultural drainage systems are:

- Facilitation of sanitation: lowering of groundwater levels in an area will facilitate the sanitation of houses and/or population centres;
- Health improvement: lowering groundwatertables and removing stagnant water can under specific conditions control malaria, bilharzias etc.;
- Improvement of access and trafficability of an area: lowering groundwatertables and removing surface water will improve the general accessibility in an area;
- Improvement of environmental conditions: lower groundwatertables and reduced salinity in an area will stop or reverse environmental deterioration.

The costs of pipe drainage systems vary from place to place depending on the local physical and economic conditions. Generally speaking, the cost of large-scale pipe drainage systems fluctuates between € 750 and € 1500 per ha.[3]

The need for drainage

Drainage plays an essential part in food production while safeguarding the investments in irrigation and conserving land resources. During the second half of the 20th Century, drainage was implemented in about 150 million hectares of under-producing and naturally waterlogged or salinised lands, mainly in Europe, North America, Middle East and to a lesser extent Asia. This resulted in important improvements that contributed to a considerable increase of food

---

[3] In this handbook all prices are in euro (€ 1.00 = US $ 1.00) in 2002 prices except when stated otherwise.

production. Drainage has also contributed to agricultural intensification and diversification and as such has made the agricultural sector more competitive and financially sustainable. In global terms, however, drainage is still far of being adequate or sufficient. Out of the worldwide 1500 million ha of cropped land (irrigated and rainfed), only about 14% is provided with some form of artificial drainage (Figure 2a). Consequently large parts of existing agricultural land still suffer from inadequate drainage and/or salinisation, e.g. in arid and semi-arid areas some 20 to 30 million ha suffer from irrigation induced degradation resulting in water logging and high soil salinity.

To be able to feed the growing world population and to banish hunger from the world, food production needs to be doubled within 25 years. The majority of this increase will have to come from investment in improved irrigation and drainage practices in existing agricultural areas (Figure 2.b). This includes the reclamation of areas that are already equipped with irrigation facilities, by using piped subsurface drainage systems and improved water management, which can relatively cheaply restore these areas to their full production potential. To fulfil this task, it is estimated that drainage is to be improved on at least 10-15 million ha.

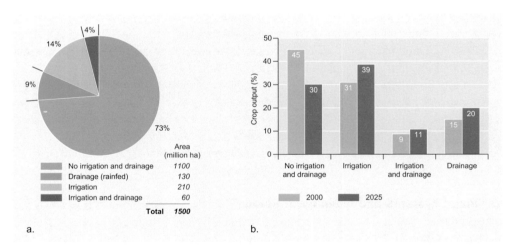

a.   b.

Figure 2   *Drainage plays an essential part to sustain food production: (a) Worldwide agricultural areas equipped with and without irrigation and/or drainage systems, and; (b) Agricultural output (crop yield) from agricultural land with and without irrigation and drainage facilities now (2000) and in 2025 (Source ICID Statistics, 2003)*

History of pipe drainage technology

Subsurface drainage has a long history, the oldest known systems date back some 9000 years in Mesopotamia. Drain pipes were already in use some 4000 years ago in the lower Indus Valley and bamboo pipes were used as drains in ancient times in China.

Pipe drainage in modern times started in the United Kingdom in the 17th Century in the form of trenches filled with bushes or stones. The first clay pipes were produced in 1810, followed by concrete pipes a few decades later. Starting around 1940, the prevailing empirical knowledge of drainage and salinity control gained a solid theoretical footing. A breakthrough in pipe drainage technology also occurred in the 1940s when rigid plastic pipes were introduced followed by corrugated PVC and PE pipes in the 1960s. Nowadays, corrugated PE or PVC is considered to be the preferred standard.

Mechanised installation developed rapidly from the 1940s onwards (Figure 3). Nowadays, highly effective drainage machines that install the drain pipes in trenches (trenchers) with almost perfect depth and grade control are on the market. Moreover, trenchless drainage machines that were developed after the 1970s have proved to be very cost effective for the installation of corrugated PVC pipes to relative shallow depth. Laser technology for semi-automatic depth and grade control has, in the meantime, become standard for mechanised installation.

The necessary envelop material around the field drains originally consisted of locally available materials like stones, gravel or straw. In arid areas the technique for the use of granular envelopes has been further developed to such a degree that effective granular envelopes can be designed for most soils. In practice, granular envelopes are often expensive, installation is cumbersome and error prone and requires almost perfect logistic management during installation. Moreover, gravel cannot be used when installation is done with trenchless equipment. Alternatively pre-wrapped envelopes of synthetic material have been under development for some decades. Pre-wrapped envelopes made of artificial fibre are presently almost universally used in Europe, in some areas of the United States and in Egypt. Since the specifications of envelopes are very soil specific and soils are rather variable, the specifications and effectiveness of envelopes have to be proven in field trials in the areas where they are to be applied.

Drainage systems and drainage methods

In humid regions the primary goal of agricultural drainage is to lower the water content of the rootzone to provide adequate aeration following excessive rainfall or irrigation. A secondary goal is to provide site access and trafficability for timely planting and harvesting. Under these conditions open drainage systems are the most common, but dictated by agricultural practices, more and more in combination with subsurface drainage to lower groundwater levels quickly after rainstorms or at the end of the rainy season.

In arid and semi-arid regions the primary goal of agricultural drainage is to remove the accumulated salts from the rootzone and to control the secondary salinisation by lowering groundwater levels. These goals can be achieved by both pipe and open drains, in most cases pipe drains are the most practical solution.

There are field drainage and main drainage systems. The field drainage system controls the groundwater level in the field and removes the excess rain or irrigation water. The main drainage

Figure 3   History of mechanised installation of subsurface pipe drainage systems

systems convey the water to the outlets of the drainage basins. Field drainage systems can be either surface or subsurface drainage systems. Surface drainage systems are applied when overland flow or water ponding occurs on the soil surface (Figure 1a). Subsurface drainage systems are usually applied when there are problems with excessively shallow watertables and/or secondary salinisation (Figure 1c). There are four types of subsurface drainage systems (Figure 4):

- Tubewell drainage (vertical drainage, also called well drainage);
- Mole drainage (horizontal drainage);
- Open drainage (horizontal drainage, also called ditch drainage), and;
- Pipe drainage (horizontal drainage, also called tile drainage).

Tubewell drainage systems
A tubewell drainage system consists of a network of tubewells to lower the watertable, including provisions for running the pumps, and surface drains to dispose of the excess water. Tubewell drainage is used in areas with a high soil permeability and preferably fresh groundwater that can be reused for irrigation. The system is operation and maintenance intensive and requires a continuous diesel or electrical power supply.

Mole drainage systems
A mole drain is an unlined underground drainage channel, formed by pulling a solid object, usually a solid cylinder with a wedge-shaped point at the end, through the soil at the proper slope and depth, without a trench having to be dug. Mole drainage is applied only under very specific conditions, mainly in stable clayey soils. The effect of mole drainage is a rapid removal of excess water from the surface layers, rather than at controlling the watertable as such. The mole drains have a life span of only a few years and have to be renewed frequently.

Open drainage systems
An open drain is a channel with an exposed water surface that conveys overland flow as well as subsurface flow. Open drains combine surface and subsurface drainage functions. The main disadvantages of open drainage systems are: (i) land loss; (ii) interference with the irrigation; (iii) splitting-up of the land into small units; (iv) hampering (mechanised) farming operation; and (v) relatively frequent maintenance requirements.

Pipe drainage systems
A pipe drain is a buried pipe (regardless of material, size or shape) that conveys excess groundwater to control the watertable at a desired depth. Pipe drainage systems are installed in the soil below the plough layer (normally > 0.70 m depth) and therefore have the advantage of not interfering with the farm operations. The land can be farmed right over the drain and there is no loss of farming area. Maintenance requirements are minimal if the systems are properly constructed. If overland drainage flows occur, shallow open drains are additionally required.

Subsurface pipe drainage systems can be divided into: (i) singular and (ii) composite systems. In a singular pipe drainage system, the field drains are buried perforated pipes that discharge

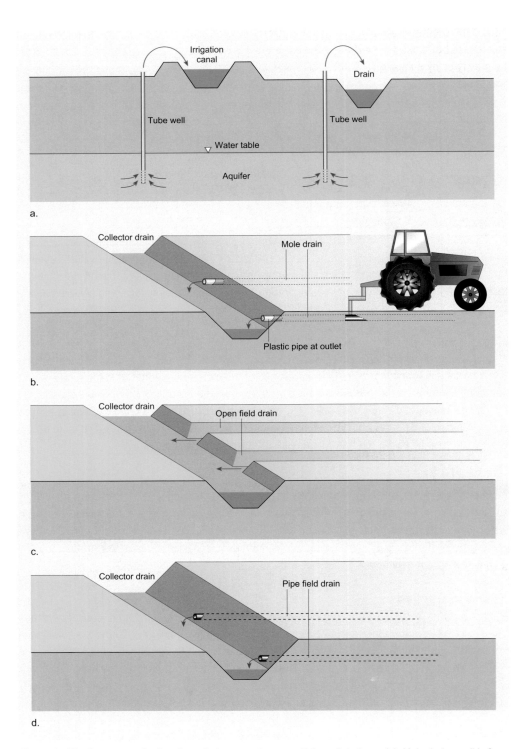

a.

b.

c.

d.

Figure 4   The four types of subsurface drainage systems are Tubewell drainage (a), Mole drainage (b), Open drainage (c) and Pipe drainage (d)

into open collector drains (Figure 5a). In a composite pipe drainage system, the collector drains also consist of closed or perforated pipes that in turn discharge into an open main drain either by gravity or by pumping. The collector system itself may be composed of sub-collectors and a main collector.

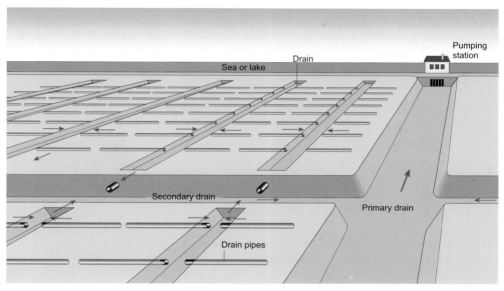

a.

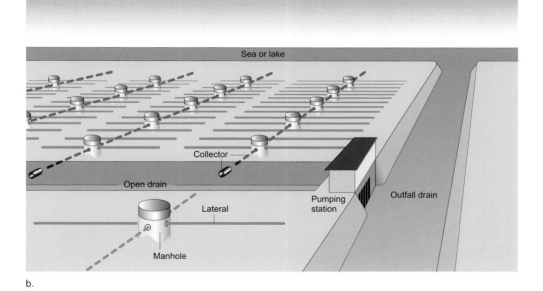

b.

Figure 5   Subsurface drainage system can be: a) single subsurface drainage system, for example The Netherlands, or b) composite subsurface drainage system, for example Egypt

The structure of the handbook

This handbook focuses on the construction process of subsurface pipe drainage systems. Since the construction process is part of the total implementation process, a description of the implementation process is also included. Because there is already a wealth of manuals and literature available on parts of the implementation process (see Bibliography), the authors have tried to avoid any duplication. Wherever relevant, references to existing sources are made provided that they are easily accessible.

This handbook is organised as follows:

Part I: The Implementation of pipe drainage systems: the process

Part I describes the process to be followed for the implementation of subsurface pipe drainage systems. This part is meant for all people concerned with part or the whole process of the implementation of subsurface pipe drainage systems. Part I aspires to give guidelines for carrying out all the required activities; it also provides suggestions for decisions for the implementation mode and how these can be prepared. Part I focuses on drainage systems that are implemented with important governmental participation and/or financing.

Part II: The Implementation of pipe drainage systems: the construction

Part II is a guideline for the actual installation of subsurface pipe drainage systems. It is chiefly meant for those who are involved in the actual construction process.

Part III: The Implementation of pipe drainage systems: Case histories

Part III presents the salient features of the history and present practices of the implementation of and the start up of the implementation process of pipe drainage systems in various countries, such as Egypt, China, India, Pakistan and the Netherlands. This part is intended as reference. The most relevant experiences in these countries have been used to compile Part I and Part II.

Part I

Implementation of subsurface drainage systems: the Process

Part I describes the process to be followed for the implementation of subsurface pipe drainage systems. This part is meant for all people concerned with part or the whole process of the implementation of subsurface pipe drainage systems. Part I aspires to give guidelines for carrying out all the required activities; it also provides suggestions for decisions for the implementation mode and how these can be prepared. Part I focuses on drainage systems that are implemented with important governmental participation and/or financing.

I.1 Implementation Process for Subsurface Drainage Systems

I.1.1 Main steps and players in the implementation process

This chapter discusses the implementation process of subsurface drainage projects. Proper planning is essential because drainage usually involves substantial long-term investments of capital and other costs. In the implementation process, four main steps can be distinguished, i.e. (Figure 6):

- Step 1: Policy preparation and decision-making;
- Step 2: Technical, organisational and administrative preparation;
- Step 3: Actual implementation: field investigations, design, planning & budgeting, tendering and construction;
- Step 4: Handing-over and operation & maintenance.

Numerous stakeholders are involved in the implementation process, i.e.: the farmers who are the main beneficiaries, the government, planning and implementation authorities, drainage contractors, suppliers of drainage materials and machinery, each with their own specific interest. For each step, however, one authority will have the overall responsibility: the national or regional government in the policy and decision-making process, a planning authority in the preparation, a implementation authority for the actual implementation and of course the farmers or their representatives to operate and maintain the system.

The importance of the different steps depends on the extent of the development of the subsurface pipe drainage in the country concerned and on how the country is organised. In a country where pipe drainage is a routine matter, the national government has probably already got a

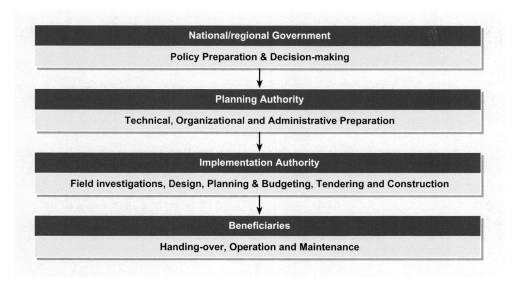

Figure 6   The main steps and responsible organisations in the drainage implementation process

standard policy or national plan and does not need to be involved with each individual project. The planning authority only determines the limits of the projects and the financing, whereas the implementation authority is responsible for the tendering or for giving the order to design and construct the systems. In a country where there is no pipe drainage tradition and no existing "drainage industry" each element of the implementation has to be developed from scratch: information on all aspects of the systems has to be collected and crucial choices about alternative possibilities must be made. If there is a well-developed private sector in a country, the private sector will or may be involved in the development and/or implementation process. Failing this, vital decisions will need to be made as to whether the whole development and implementation process should be carried out and/or developed by and for government entities, or whether the private sector should be invited to participate and if so to what degree. The four main steps of the implementation process are discussed in the following sections.

I.1.2   Step 1: Policy preparation and decision-making

The first step in the implementation process of a drainage system is the request to a government to start the process. The request comes either directly from the future beneficiaries, most times farmers or an organisation representing them, or from the local authorities or in the form of a national or regional plan. The role of the government or an agency is crucial, since drainage usually requires a regional infrastructure that generally affects more than one landowner. Furthermore, governments (pre) finance all or part of the costs, because of the collective nature of drainage and the benefits that often go beyond the direct interest of the landowners involved. Only in rare cases, i.e. in developed West European countries, USA and Canada and on large estate farms for sugarcane or bananas in developing countries, do private landowners implement drainage systems on their own accord. Even then, the government may play a role as regulator of the quantity and quality of the drain water that may be discharged in to a river or lake. At this stage, the role of the government is threefold (Figure 7):
- Collection of basic information;
- Decision-making;
- Specification for follow-up activities.

Collection of basic information
To arrive at a decision to implement a drainage system and to ascertain the necessary financing thereof, the government needs to have information. Most of the information can be obtained from experiences elsewhere in the country or region. If there is no drainage history in the country, information can be gathered through a feasibility study, which in the case of international financing is usually a requirement anyway. A study such as this will logically provide the following information:
- *The effect of drainage*: An insight into the direct and indirect effects of drainage, i.e. physical, social and economical. To estimate the effects of drainage, an inventory is made of the existing conditions and problems, such as: groundwatertable levels, groundwater quality, soil salinity/alkalinity, irrigation water quality, rainfall and present yields. Then, based on this inventory, an assumption can be made of the conditions that can be created

once a drainage system has been implemented as well as the yields that can be expected under those conditions.

- *The cost of drainage*: A general estimate of the cost of the systems in relation to the available budgets, the expected subsidies and the financing available from the direct beneficiaries or other sources. The cost of drainage can be estimated by preparing a detailed analysis of the actions required to implement a drainage system and by estimating the cost of each action. If there is no local drainage industry (private or public) an estimate will need to be made of the investments required for equipment and facilities. In the absence of local references for prices and costs, estimates can be based on known international figures.

- *Impacts of the implementation*: These impacts refer to a positive or negative environmental impact affecting the project area and neighbouring areas. These impacts can include: pollution by the effluent necessitating additional capacity or infrastructure to discharge the effluent; need of future subsidies for operation and maintenance; need of sufficient capacity of services for implementation and/or maintenance; and existing regulations. The anticipated increase in yields and thus benefits, the operation and maintenance requirements, the institutional requirements, the supporting/accompanying measures and the cost of all these need to be estimated. Specialised studies are often required to assess the environmental impact of drainage implementation.

Resulting decision

The above-mentioned information helps the government to formulate a policy, which in most cases consists of:

- A decision to proceed (or not) and a formulation of the conditions;
- If government financing is involved, how this will be done, to what extent and to which governmental budget the costs will be allocated;
- Any accompanying measures to be taken, how and by whom.

Specification of following activities

Following a positive decision the next step is the technical, organisational and administrative preparation of the project. The government normally assigns this activity to a national or regional

Figure 7   The policy preparation and decision-making process

planning agency or to a special entity. To do this, the required outputs of the project have to be formulated and the preparation activities have to be specified.

I.1.3   Step 2: Technical, organisational and administrative preparation

I.1.3.1   Preparation process

Once the government has given the project the go-ahead and a budget is available, further planning and preparations take place in line with the defined objectives to arrive at a precise and quantified project concept. A specialised entity, here called the Planning Authority, carries out the planning including the procedural, technical and economic preparation. Such an entity is usually part of a ministry, regional government or a special authority within the national government, depending on the internal governmental organisation and the existing experience with the implementation of subsurface pipe drainage systems. The entity responsible for this step may ask for or contract specialised organisations, government departments or companies to carry out part of the tasks.

This step is crucial to making the right choices between the various alternative solutions for the subsurface drainage system, which are not only purely technical in nature but also involve elements of policy, economy, sociology, traditions, assessment of local capacity, the economic relationships in the country, existing privatisation, privatisation policies and existing or desired farmer participation.

Depending on the country's experience with the implementation of drainage, the planning and preparation can be a simple definition of where the desired system will be implemented, the

Figure 8   Information requirements and the output of planning and preparation step of the implementation process

budget involved and the authority concerned. If subsurface pipe drainage is new to a country or region, decisions will have to be made on all technical and procedural matters concerning the systems that will be implemented and the methods employed. In exceptional cases the planning can involve experiments, research or pilot areas. The necessary information for taking the appropriate decisions and the resulting output of the planning procedures (Figure 8) are elaborated in the following sections.

I.1.3.2   Required input information

Besides the order to proceed and the budget limitations imposed by the government on the planning and preparation, essential additional information on a number of aspects of the implementation process includes (Figure 8):
- Objectives of the drainage systems;
- Soil conditions and topography;
- Outlet conditions;
- Available equipment;
- Available drainage materials;
- National rules and regulations;
- Research data.

Objectives of the drainage systems
The objectives, such as reclamation of an area, the increase in yield, the reversing of soil deterioration and the control of salinity, have to be well specified because they have a bearing on the system to be installed. The objectives generally accompany the original request to the government or the national/regional plan.

Soil conditions and topography
Existing soil maps and field investigations should preferably be used: detailed soil maps (soil maps: scale 1:50 000 and 1:100 000) with observations to >2 m depth. If these are not available soil information will need to be collected during the field investigations, for instance, in single value maps giving information about soil texture, soil salinity/alkalinity and groundwater fluctuations/groundwater quality (scale between 1: 5 000 and 1: 10 000, the scales normally used to prepare the design of the field drainage system). Information will also be required on the general topography of the area, land use, existing infrastructure, buildings, hydrographical information, etc. (maps scale 1: 50 000 and 1: 100 000). What is important is information about levels preferably with 0.5 m contour lines. If such precise information is not available the areas must be surveyed during the field investigations, in which case contours every 0.2 m are recommended.

Outlet conditions
The outlet conditions for the proposed drainage system(s) must be fully known, including where the drain water can be discharged and to which topographical levels. This will require using hydrographical/topographical data from existing sources, which must be collected if not

available. Hydrographical information should include water levels at outlet and allowable water quality of effluent. The consequences of outlet conditions for the concept of the entire drainage system include:

(i)   limits to which a piped drainage system can be applied;
(ii)   the required water level of conveyance for open drains;
(iii) whether pumping is necessary;
(iv)   where the systems need to be pumped;
(v)   possibilities for continuous discharge or whether storage of effluent will be required, and
(vi)   feasibility or acceptability of pollution occurring as a result of the drainage effluent (salinity!).

Available equipment

The authority must have knowledge of the available equipment for drain installation together with the capacities and limitations thereof. If there is no specialised equipment available, alternative installation methods must be studied or possibilities to purchase or rent the equipment need to be worked out. Any specialised drainage equipment present in the country needs to be surveyed to ascertain the specifications, location and availability of the equipment. Absence of specialised drainage equipment will necessitate listing of the general specifications of the equipment and investigation of possible sources to purchase, rent or lease equipment. Depending on the mode of implementation, i.e. directly by government entities or by contractors, the future ownership and management of the equipment needs to be determined. This may involve a special feasibility study for the ownership of the equipment, and if it turns out that purchasing the equipment for the project alone is not feasible, subsidies will be needed together with/or guarantees for use in future projects. Installation equipment for subsurface drainage systems is discussed in detail in Chapter I.5.

Available drainage materials

Information about the available drainage materials must be complete, otherwise alternative solutions will need to be worked out. The materials used will influence the design of the systems and the cost and organisation of the construction as well the required installation equipment. An inventory will have to be made of the available materials together with the specifications (pipes, collector pipes, envelope, manholes, sumps, pumps). If no suitable materials are available, general specifications of the materials will have to be drawn up and potential sources to purchase them investigated. A feasibility survey of local production and a survey of potential local producers may have to be carried out. Field trials may be required if there is no knowledge about the suitable envelope materials under the soil conditions in the area and if pre-wrapped envelopes are to be used. Drainage materials are discussed in detail in Chapter I.4.

National rules and regulations

The authority must be well versed with the existing national rules and regulations governing the organisation and infrastructure of rural areas, landownership, cooperatives, water users, pollution control, and the like. This also includes the rules and regulations on financing of the implementation and the participation of beneficiaries. If the private sector is going to be involved it is essential to pay heed to the regulations for contracting to the private sector and tendering when preparing for drainage implementation. National rules and regulations can be obtained from the relevant ministries. If foreign or donor financing is involved the financiers may also have their own individual requirements. International financiers' rules should be included in the financing agreement with the national government, which can be obtained from special publications or web sites. Information about tendering and so forth is given in Part 1 Chapter 2.

Research data
Available research data of drainage pilot projects should be collected. These data will provide valuable information on local specific drainage criteria and suitable technologies for subsurface drainage. To some extent, data collected in pilot areas can also provide a base-line for economic and financial analysis for large scale subsurface drainage development.

I.1.3.3   Output of the preparation process

The output of the technical and administrative preparation process should include specifications on (Figure 8):
- Drainage criteria;
- Boundaries of the areas to be drained;
- Type of system to be installed;
- Outlet and pumping requirements;
- Layout of the system;
- Drainage materials to be used;
- Installation equipment;
- Implementation mode;
- Budget.

Drainage Criteria
Drainage criteria are tailored to the objective of the system. Developing the criteria requires considerable insight into "drainage science" as well as a large amount of basic information including crops to be grown, soil conditions and climate. It calls for professional knowledge from specialised institutes or consultants. In principle, the drainage criteria formulate the depth to which the groundwater level has to be lowered and the capacity of the drainage system, with possible variation over the seasons. If the drainage system has a (temporary) reclamation or rehabilitation function, the compromises for the criteria necessary for reclamation and for the post reclamation period need to be defined. The depth (or level) of the drainage system is calculated from the criterion "depth of groundwater".

Boundaries of the area to be drained
The boundaries of the area to be drained are partly based on the governmental decision (number of hectares to be drained), partly on the present land use, field layout, ownership and existing infrastructure (for instance: no urban area to be included), partly on the soil conditions (certain types of soil can be excluded), and on the topographic conditions (some very low or some very high areas can be excluded). For operation and maintenance purposes it is desirable that the boundaries of drainage and irrigation units coincide, although in practice this is often problematic.

Type of system
The basic information (soil, topography, property and field boundaries and present field layout) and the criteria underpin the choice of the type of system that would be the most suitable (tubewell, mole, open or pipe drainage). The advantages and disadvantages and the requirements of the various systems also need to be carefully taken into consideration when making the decision. In Chapter I.3 layout options for subsurface drainage systems are discussed. Note that in this handbook only pipe drainage systems are discussed!

Outlet and pumping requirement
The location of the outlet in relation to the area to be drained and the (water) level of the outlet location (the drain base) in relation to the level of the fields to be drained, provide an indication of the possibilities for (complete, partial or temporary) gravity flow or the need for pumping. Decision-making requires a fair amount of detailed information on the topography of the area and the hydrograph at the outlet, including levels.

Layout of the system
An early decision has to be made on the layout of the drainage system to be implemented: i.e. singular, composite, extended laterals etc. The layout will also affect the level of the subsurface drainage system. The decision also has to do with whether or not pumping will be required and at what level in the system. Other factors that play a role in this decision are soil type, micro topography, capacity of the installation equipment and available drainage materials. If manholes are needed then a decision needs to be made as to whether they need to be underground or aboveground. In Chapter 1.3 layout options for subsurface drainage systems are discussed.

Drainage materials to be used
The drainage materials needed for field and collector drain pipes, envelopes and structures need to be chosen. As far as *pipes* are concerned (collector and field drain) the choice is based on availability, quality and cost. In countries with no existing drainage industry it might be decided to start local production. This in itself is a project. For *envelopes* the available materials, both gravels and synthetic materials, should be matched with the characteristics of soils to be drained. If there is no experience with the suitability of the envelopes for the soils concerned, trials or pilot areas may be required. For *structures* such as manholes, sumps and connectors and to lesser degree pumps, local materials and designs are preferable. For more information on drainage materials, see Chapter I.4.

Installation Equipment
Selecting the type of installation equipment to be used (mainly trenchers or trenchless drainage machines) depends on the depth of the drainage system, the availability of the equipment, and of course the cost. Manual installation may be considered under a limited number of conditions, (mainly with small scale very shallow drainage systems in an area with a dry season so that installation can be carried out under dry conditions in stable soils). These conditions seldom prevail so in the majority of cases machine installation is technically the only feasible alternative. In countries with no existing drainage industry a decision to purchase the equipment will have to be made. This requires a scenario in which is specified how the equipment is financed, who will

purchase it from where and who will manage it. This in itself is also a project. For more information on drainage equipment, see Chapter I.5.

Implementation mode
Corresponding with rules, regulations and customs in the country, the implementation mode might such that the design and/or the construction is tendered on the private market. If no drainage industry or suitable contractors are available, the government entities might carry out part or all of the design and construction themselves. If international or donor financing is involved, the financiers could affix certain conditions to the financing agreement regarding the implementation mode. Implementation modes are discussed in detail in Chapter I.2.

Budget
A general budget for the implementation must be drawn up as a guideline for the implementation authority, confirming (or not) that the budget allocated by the government is adequate and specifying in broad terms items such as the budget for materials, for design and for installation. How to prepare a budget is discussed in detail in Chapter I.9.

I.1.3.4   Handing-over specifications

Once the planning and preparation has been completed, the next step is for the organisation in charge to request an implementation authority to implement the drainage systems. This request specifies the conditions that are in essence the outcome of the planning and preparation (Box 1.1)

Box 1.1	Schematised output of planning and preparation
Objectives	• Implement pipe drainage system in ... area of approx .... ha
	• Create conditions (<*if applicable:* after reclamation>) that:
	• Groundwater level is maintained at levels of <...>m below field level
	• Soil salinity at root zone (<...>m) is controlled at a maximum of <...>dS/m
Area	• Total area is <...>ha, area to be drained approx. <...>ha. Location of area (on map)
	• Define excluded areas because of: too high, too low, built area etc.
Budget	• Total budget for the implementation is <...> <*monetary unit*>
Drainage	• Groundwater level <...>m below field level during <*month*> to <*month*>
Criteria	• Groundwater level <...>m below field level during <*month*> to <*month*>
	• Capacity of pipe drainage system <.........>mm/day
	• Capacity of open drainage system to be <.........>mm/day of the pipe drainage system plus <...>mm/day of surface runoff
Outlet	• Outlet of the system is located approx.<.............>
	• Outlet level at outlet location not lower than <...........>m +/- mean sea level
	• Discharge is (*either/or make choice*):
	• Fully by gravity
	• Pumped with approx. <*number*> pumping system(s) located <*near outlet at end of main open drain/ at the end of the secondary open drains/at the end of the piped systems*>
Drainage	• The piped part of the drainage systems will be (*either/or*):
System	• Singular system with field drains with lengths between approx <...>m and <...>m
	• Composite systems with field drains with lengths between approx <...>m and <...>m and collector drains with lengths between approx <...>m and <...>m

- Field drain spacing expected to vary between <…>m and <…>m but to be designed on the basis of the detailed field investigations. Standards spacings to be used are <…>m, <…>m, <…>m etc.
- Depth of field drains will vary between <…>m and <…>m below field level but be not deeper than <…>m
- Depth of collector drains varies between <…>m and <…>m below field level but be not deeper than <…>m
- Field drain pipes will be of *PVC/PE* of<…>mm, <….>mm, <…>mm Ø
- Collector drain pipes will be of *PVC/PE* of<…>mm, <….>mm, <…>mm Ø
- Collector drain pipes with Ø larger than <…> mm will be of concrete
- *<Aboveground/Underground>* , manholes *<pre fabricated/prepared in situ>* will be installed:
- At all junctions of field drains with collector drains
- In field drains so that the distance between manholes and/or end of the drain is no more than *<300m>* and or at change of diameter of the field drain
- Connections between field drain sections will be <… … …> the end of the field drain will be blocked by <………..>
- Connections between plastic collector drain sections will be <………>
- Connection between concrete collector sections will be <…>
- Field drains will covered all around by a *<granular envelope, designed for the soil texture>* or *<a pre-enveloped synthetic envelope of …(specifications)>*

Installation
- The piped field drains will be installed with *<trenchers/trenchless machines>* equipped with laser which can install pipes up to <…>mm Ø *<with/without>* envelope at a maximum depth of <….> m
- Piped collector drains will be installed with *<trenchers/trenchless machines>* equipped with laser which can install pipes up to <…>mm Ø at a maximum depth of <…> m
- Collector drains with a Ø of more than <….>mm will be installed *<by excavator/others>*

Field Investigations
- Field investigations will be carried out according to detailed terms of reference by *<make choice>* :
- *<Institute/department>*
- Nominated consultant *<name/to be selected by…>*
- Consultant selected through *<international/national/local/tendering>*

Design
- The design is to be implemented according to detailed terms of reference by *<choose: the same entity as the field investigations/a different entity as the field investigations>*
- *<make choice>*
- *<Institute/department>*
- Nominated consultant *<name/to be selected by…>*
- Consultant selected through *<international/national/local/tendering>*

Contents of design
- The design work shall *<include/not include>* the preparation of detailed specifications including the bill of quantities and *<include or exclude>* a full set of tender documents for *<national/international/local tendering or price comparison>* of the works under *<national/international>* regulation

Construction
- The construction is to be carried out according to detailed specifications by *<choose>*
- *<Government unit … … …>*
- Nominated contractor *<name/to be selected by…>*
- Contractor selected through *<international/national/local/tendering>*

Supply of drainage materials
- The purchase of drainage materials based on detailed specifications shall be *<choose: part of the construction contract/purchased separately from the construction contract>*
- In case of separate purchase:
- The drainage materials shall be purchased through: *<choose>*
- Direct purchase from *<Government unit/supplier … … …>*
- Price comparison of at least <…> suppliers
- Tendering *<international/national/local>*

Supervision of construction
- The construction shall be supervised by*<choose>* *<The organisation/consultant that prepared the design>* , or:
- *<Government unit … … …>*
- Nominated consultant *<name/to be selected by…>*
- Consultant selected through *<international/national/local/tendering>*

I.1.4   Step 3: Actual implementation

I.1.4.1   Activities during actual implementation

Once all governmental decisions to proceed with the drainage project have been made and qualitative and quantitative details of the drainage systems have been worked out, the actual implementation process can start guided by the planning and preparation authority (as specified in Box 1.1). A government authority, hereafter called the implementation authority, is responsible for the implementation process. This authority can delegate or contract all the activities to specialised government units or consultants. Depending on the way the national government is organised it could well be that the planning and preparation authority is the same as the implementation authority. Note, that these are two distinct phases:

- Preparation phase, in which all the existing information is collected and analysed, results in principle decisions about the drainage systems and its mode of implementation and;
- Construction phase, in which the actual implementation takes place including the detailed preparation. The implementation process ends once the system is handed over to users or beneficiaries.

The actual implementation process can be divided into four clusters of activities (Figure 9):

- *Field Investigations and Design.* Field investigations and design is a specialised job best carried out by a specialised institute, department or consultancy firm who do this on a routine basis. The input for field investigations is a detailed Terms of Reference with the available basic information about the area. The output of the design is the information that will serve to construct the system, including a detailed bill of quantities for budgeting and tendering together with details for the preparation of specifications, or the specifications itself;
- *Planning and budgeting.* The physical implementation can be planned in detail and budgets can be made available based on the design. The planning and budgeting has to be carried out in close cooperation with the beneficiaries and/or land owners;
- *Tender preparation and tendering.* If construction and/or supervision are to be tendered, a specialised (governmental or private) organisation has to prepare the tender documents, which may involve a separate tender for construction, supervision and/or the procurement of drainage materials;
- *Construction.* The construction of the actual subsurface drainage system starts with handing-over the contractor the authority over the project area and ends with the handing-over of the installed subsurface drainage to the Implementation Authority. It is an activity in which three parties are involved: (i) the contractor(s) or governmental constructions unit; (ii) a supervision team either from the implementation unit or a contracted consultant (often the same consultant as the one responsible for the design and/or tendering procedures); and (iii) the drainage material suppliers.

All these four activities are required to be carried out by specialised unit(s), which may be government units, specialised (government or private) institutes or contracted consultants. These four clusters of activities are discussed in more detail in the following sections.

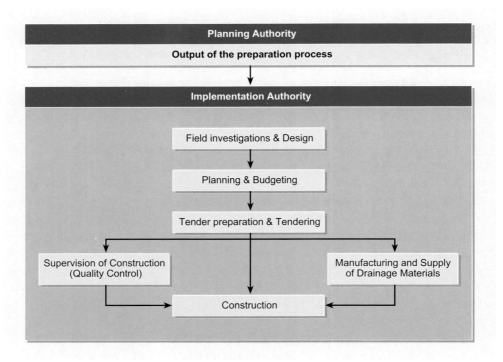

Figure 9   The actual implementation process can be divided into 4 main activities

I.1.4.2   Field investigations

The main purpose of the field investigations is to collect all the relevant information to enable a detailed design to be drawn up. Part of the collected data can also serve as baseline information for monitoring. Directions for field investigations are in the instructions or Terms of Reference stipulating:

- The objective of the drainage system, including the drainage criteria;
- Size and location of the area;
- Available soil, topographical, geological and (geo) hydrological information;
- Additional information to be collected, including the density and accuracy;
- Interpretation and presentation of the results: maps and scales of maps for topography, soil texture, salinity, hydraulic conductivity, drain spacing. Estimate of upward seepage and/or lateral inflow.

The output of the field investigations should include:

- Topographical maps with sufficient information about levels to assist the preparation of the detailed designs;
- Maps or tables with soil texture, soil salinity and hydraulic conductivity. If the information is provided in tables, it must be clear where the points referred to in the tables are located;

- Baseline information (detailed) on groundwater levels/salinity and soil salinity at different depths;
- Recommendations for making provisions for upward seepage and lateral inflow;
- Recommendation for drain spacing and the distribution over the area (presented on maps);
- Recommendations for the necessity and type of drain envelopes.

Detailed instructions or Terms of Reference for the design are derived from the output of the field investigations and the general instructions from the planning and preparation authority (Chapter I.1.3). More details about field investigations and design can be found in the publications discussed in the Bibliography.

I.1.4.3   Design

It is a common practice that the same entity that carries out the field investigations is also responsible for the design. The purpose of this phase is to design a drainage system that can be constructed and to obtain details of the budgetary requirements. The inputs required for the design are also compiled in the instructions/Terms of Reference and should stipulate:

- The general concept of the drainage system as described in the instructions of the planning and preparation authority (as discussed in Chapter I.1.3);
- All information collected and processed during the field investigations, including all detailed topographical maps;
- The drain spacing maps;
- A drainage rate (or a revised rate in case upward seepage/lateral inflow);
- A decision of the Implementation Authority about the type of envelope to use in specific areas;
- Design criteria stating at least the maximum and minimum slopes, length and depth of drainage pipes.

The output of the design should consist of:

- Maps indicating the layout of the drainage system, location of field and/or collector drains;
- Detailed list of each field and collector drain: location, starting-depth, end-depth, slope, diameter(s). These maps should have a scale of 1:5 000, for areas where important structures are to be built, e.g. around the drainage outlet or pumping station, maps at a scale of 1:2 500 may be required;
- Design of connections, manholes and drain outlets;
- Design of granular envelope (if applicable);
- Bill of quantities;
- Specifications.

A detailed cost estimate for the implementation can then be made as well as an estimate of the envisaged construction period and equipment required.

I.1.4.4 Planning and budgeting

After the design phase has been completed the final planning and budgeting can be prepared. Planning and budgeting are processes in which the implementation authority is required to play a key role.

Planning
Planning is based on an analysis of all the activities that must be carried out to implement a subsurface drainage project, whereby estimates are needed of: (i) the time required carrying out each activity; (ii) the interrelationship between the different activities; and (iii) the assignment of each activity to the different parties involved in the implementation process. The estimates can be based on experience obtained in previous projects. If there is no previous local experience, international norms can be applied. The result of planning is an optimal schedule clearly showing when the different activities need to be carried out and by whom.

Process control
Besides a clear allocation of tasks and periods during which these tasks have to be carried out, planning is also a tool for monitoring the progress of the project. The monitoring makes it possible to take corrective actions if the implementation or construction process is not carried out according to schedule (Figure 10).

In countries where drainage is not yet a matter of routine, a database of time requirements for each activity can be built up during the construction from the data collected during progress monitoring. Apart from managerial purposes, these results of progress monitoring can be used

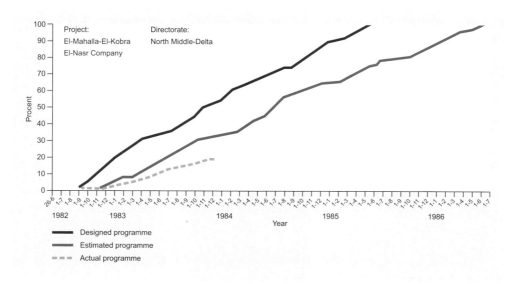

Figure 10   Progress of the actual implementation compared to the estimated and design programme (Example from the execution of a subsurface drainage project in the Nile Delta, Egypt)

to assess whether the original planning schedule was realistic or not. In this manner experience can gradually be built up with the time requirement for the different activities. The methodology for progress monitoring (operational monitoring) of the trencher installation given in Part II-A serves as an example.

Planning tools
A number of tools and techniques are available for the planning of the implementation of drainage systems. The most important ones are:
- Network planning;
- Bar charts.

Network planning
Network planning highlights the activities critical to the total progress of the project and the potential bottlenecks. Essential to network planning is the determining of the so-called "critical path". The critical path identifies the actions that are critical to be completed on time, which if not done will result in an increase of the total time required for completion of the implementation process or the need for additional equipment or staff.

Network planning requires an analytical approach of the whole implementation process in which the interrelationship of each activity is central. The interrelationship focuses on determining: which activity or activities must be completed before a next activity can start; which activity can start once an activity is completed; and which activities can be carried out simultaneously. The steps to be taken for the development of network planning are presented in Figure 11 and discussed in more detail in Part II-A.

In theory, network planning is an almost perfect planning tool. It provides a visualisation of the interrelationship of the various activities and the impact of each activity on the total progress. Network planning, however, is also a dynamic tool that is only functional for progress monitoring if it is rigorously maintained, necessitating the entering of the actual progress of each identified activity into the original planning at regular intervals. Consequently, after each interval a new critical path needs to be calculated resulting in a new expected end date. Based thereon the management can take the necessary corrective actions to assure that the activities of the (new) critical path get adequate attention. For instance, the management can reallocate staff or equipment to make up for lost time or assure that no more delays occur.

For scheduling and progress control, network planning has the following limitations:
- Preparing, maintaining and interpreting a network plan is a specialised job that requires continuous attention of qualified personnel during the progress of a project;
- Network planning is a dynamic tool, meaning that if no detailed progress monitoring is carried out the value of the network planning will be minimal;
- Network planning and progress monitoring with a network planning is labour intensive;
- Cost control is difficult to integrate into network planning.

Thus, generally speaking, network planning is only a suitable tool for very large and complicated projects, although some governments and development banks stipulate the need for network planning for all construction projects.

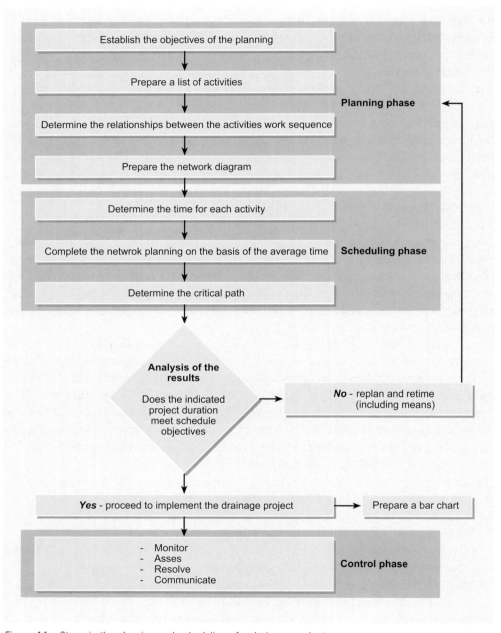

Figure 11   Steps in the planning and scheduling of a drainage project

Bar Chart

A bar chart is a simpler planning tool that visualises the timing and sequence of the various activities. The interrelationship and interdependency of these activities are less explicit compared to network planning. Bar charts are relatively easy to prepare and to update and are the most practical planning and progress control tool for smaller projects. Bar charts can be made by simple standard computer programs such as the bar chart tool of Microsoft projects or Timeline (see also Part II-A).

Planning and progress control are major tasks of project management whatever tool is used. The project's management has to review the progress on a regular basis and take the necessary measures to make corrections and reallocations of machinery or staff. In extreme cases it may need to call in extra staff or machinery either on a permanent or temporary basis. Just who bears the responsibility for which action and who bears the risks and the costs of the adjustments depends on the legal agreement between the different parties involved in the implementation process.

Budget planning

Each activity has its cost and must be paid for (cost calculations are discussed in Chapter I.9). The frequency of payment depends on the contract agreements or the customs of the country. Payments are normally made on a regular (monthly) basis and are either based on the volume of work done or on the completion of specified parts of the contract. If the construction is carried out by government entities, on a so-called *"forced account"* basis, payments are based on the input of the construction units. Determining the activities or percentage of the activities that must be completed at each payment interval is based on the planning. The payment to be made is based on the sum of the quantities of work carried during this period multiplied by the contracted or agreed unit prices. In this way budget planning is drawn up and to assure that the money is available in the right quantities at the right time. Realistic budget planning (disbursement schedule in case of loans) is essential for both governments that have to foot the bills or banks if credits are obtained for the project. Both governments and banks have to be sure that the necessary funds are available. More often than not delays in payments carry penalties, and if available money is not used (disbursed) there is almost always a loss of interest.

Budget control

Budget control has two main objectives:
- To check if the project is constructed within the limitations of the allocated total budget, and;
- To check if the previously planned payment schedule is adhered to. Obviously, budget control must go hand in hand with progress control.

If there are deviations from the planned payment schedule or budgeted amounts the management will need to take the necessary action. The paymasters must be informed that disbursements will take place at other moments to keep "idle" money to the bare minimum. If the payments requirements indicate that the total costs will exceed the budget, contingencies will have to be mobilised if available, or savings made for instance by limiting the scope of the project.

I.1.4.5   Tender preparation and tendering

To prepare tender documents for private (or state) contractors and supervisors, very clear instructions are necessary so that there is no doubt at all as to what is required and what the quality should be. These instructions are similar to the specifications required when government units carry out the construction and/or supervision tasks. Tender documents consist of: (i) the invitation; (ii) instructions for tendering; iii) the required (pre-) qualifications of the contractors; (iv) the contract and contract conditions; (v) the technical specifications; and (vi) the bills of quantities. If the tender procedure includes prequalification, the prequalification documents will also have to be prepared. Tendering involves the following activities: the advertising of the tender, the preparation of the tenders by the interested parties, the evaluation of the tenders and the tender award. A more detailed description of the tender procedure and tender preparation is given in the Chapter I.2.

I.1.4.6   Construction

The construction is a co-production under the overall responsibility of the Implementation Authority between the:
- *Contractor or construction unit.* The task of the contractor or construction unit is to construct the drainage system in accordance with the design and the specifications. Details of the construction are given in Part II of this handbook;
- *Manufacturers/suppliers of drainage materials.* The choice and specifications of drainage materials have already been made in an earlier stage (Chapter I.4);
- *Supervisors (quality control).* The supervisors have to ascertain that the construction (including the drainage materials) is in compliance with the design and specifications. They normally have the power (defined in the conditions of contract) in case of doubt, to stop the work or request corrections or replacement and/or to withhold payment. If there is severe doubt with considerable financial consequences, the supervisors will have to report back to the implementation authorities.

I.1.5   Step 4: Handing-over to beneficiaries and operation & maintenance

Once the construction is completed the system can be handed over to the users, beneficiaries or the organisation that will operate and maintain it. This handing over is mostly a task of the implementation authority. Subsurface drainage systems, of course, require operation and maintenance (Chapter I.8). The operation of subsurface drainage systems is mostly limited to the operation of pumps if pumping is done. In some cases, where controlled drainage is practiced, the operations can also involve opening and closing of gates. Maintenance of subsurface drainage systems consists mainly of removing sediment from the pipes and manholes, repairing and - if necessary - replacing these pipes, manholes and outlets.

I.2 Implementation Modes and Tender Procedures[4]

I.2.1 Implementation modes

I.2.1.1 Implementation process: activities and players

In Chapter I.1 the main activities and players in the implementation process were discussed. The various players such as government entities, consultants and contractors can implement one or more activities (Figure 12). The implementation mode defines which activities are carried out by whom and under what conditions. Basically two modes are possible to carry out activities, i.e.:

- By a (specialized) government entity;
- Contracted to a specialized company.

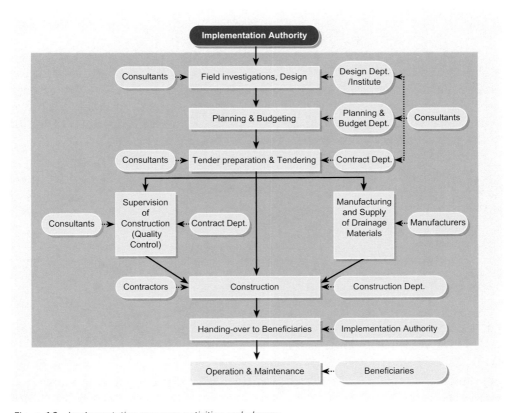

Figure 12   Implementation process: activities and players

[4] The review and upgrading of this chapter by Ir.J.P. Driessen, Senior Contract Engineer, is gratefully acknowledged.

The implementation authority has to decide the implementation mode for each activity of the implementation of the subsurface drainage system (Box 2.1). In many cases the mode is already routinely prescribed by the rules and regulations of the country and/or financers. In countries with a well-developed drainage tradition and drainage industry, contractors and/or consultants usually carry out most if not all of the implementation process. This is especially so in countries where privatisation is well established. If a country has no qualified consultants and/or contractors and/or suppliers of drainage materials, a decision must be made to either fully or partly privatise the development of the drainage technology (i.e. contractors/consultants/material supply) or request special government entities to build up the knowledge and skills and/or purchase the equipment. An alternative is to obtain all the services, equipment and materials on the international market.

Some activities like planning and budgeting and handing-over the completed system to the beneficiaries are purely governmental tasks. However, if a decision is made to contract out an activity, the implementation authority must supervise the contractor. If one or more activities are carried out by government entities, consultants may be engaged to support the entities.

In countries where contracting is common practice, the activities *"Field investigations and Design"*, *"Tender Preparation & Tendering"* and *"Supervision of Construction"* are often grouped into one contract with one consultant. If the *"Construction"* is contracted out to a private contractor, the *"Supply of Drainage Materials"* can either be directly contracted by the implementation authority, or can be part of the *"Construction"* contract.

Box 2.1   Decisions that have to be taken at government level

At the start of the implementation process, the following decisions have to be taken at government level:
- Mode of implementation completely/partly by government entities or completely/partly through contracts;
- How the activities will be contracted and how will the contracted activities be grouped;
- How and in what way will the contracts be supervised;
- If no local drainage industry exists: will the development of drainage technology be privatised or will government entities develop all or part, and if so which part of the technology;
- If government entities require routinely or temporarily support of consultants.

I.2.1.2   Contracting procedures

Every country, ministry or department has their own rules for contracting services, supplies and construction. International financers also have their own procedures. They stipulate in the financing agreement, namely, the agreement between the financier and the Government, whether the national or the financier's procedures are to be used. One of the following contracting procedures can be used:
- International tendering (International Competitive Bidding: ICB). ICB is World Bank terminology. The World Bank uses the terms "bidding" and "bidders", whereas in UK English the terms are "tendering" and "tenderers". The latter is what this book will use;

- National tendering (national (or local) competitive bidding: LCB);
- Price Consultation (Prices have to be asked from a minimum number of contractors/ consultants/suppliers, this can be either locally, national or international);
- Restricted tenders;
- Direct Award.

The method to be used is often specified in the national rules or in the financing agreement, but is also dependent on the estimated value of the contract. Price consultation is often used for small supply contracts, while international or national tendering is the prescribed method for large contracts. Loans or grants from international development banks (World Bank, Inter American Development Bank, Asian Development Bank, African Development Bank) or international donors often stipulate that ICB is to be used for all larger contracts. Each procedure has its advantages and disadvantages (Box 2.2).

Box 2.2 Advantages and disadvantages of the various contracting procedures

- **International Competitive Bidding**: The advantage of ICB is that it may result in an international competitive price setting making available the knowledge and experience developed elsewhere. The disadvantage is that if the national tenderers (contractors/consultants/suppliers) are not very well versed or experienced with the complex tendering procedures, foreign or foreign related companies tend to win the contracts. In this way local knowledge and experience will not be developed. This can be partly overcome by favouring joint ventures between national and international tenderers. Furthermore, ICB tends to be complicated and often scares off smaller contractors who prefer not to/or cannot afford to go through the complicated and costly process with no guarantee of success. Development Banks try to counter the bias in favour of national tenderers by stipulating that in the final price comparison national tenderers are given the advantage of a certain percentage. In that case, the price of the national tenderer is reduced by a percentage before the price is compared with the other international tenderers. If the reduced national tenderer's price turns out to be the lowest the contract will be awarded to him at the real price of his tender. International contractors are seldom interested in smaller contracts since the costs of transport of personnel and equipment and the risks of working in a foreign country usually outweigh the profits.
- **National Tendering**: Similar to ICB with the exception that it avoids the complication and competition of foreign contractors. LCB also tends to scare off smaller contractors.
- **Price consultations**: This is the simplest form of tendering with the least complications. A minimum number (mostly three) of companies/contractors are requested to quote prices and the one who quotes the lowest price is awarded the contract. This system is mostly used for suppliers of materials of which the specifications are well known and generally accepted. The selection process of potential suppliers is inherently biased.
- **Restricted tender**: A restricted tender is a tender where a number of well qualified contractors/consultants /suppliers are requested to prepare a tender for a certain task. This system is biased since the term "well qualified" is not necessarily well defined. The problem can be overcome if a so-called "prequalification" round is carried out. This is a procedure in which interested contractors/consultants are requested to present their professional and financial credentials for rating. Of the contractors/consultants that fulfil the predefined norms, the best are selected (mostly between 5 and 10) and these prequalified tenderers are then requested to present a full tender. The advantages are: (i) that only a limited number of tenders are to be evaluated; (ii) the chance to win the tender increases for the limited number of tenders and; (iii) less money is spend on preparing tenders. Moreover there is an increased likelihood that professional and financially capable contractors/consultants will win the contract.
- **Direct award**: Direct award of contract is when one well-known contractor/consultant is invited to prepare an offer, on the basis of which the contract price is negotiated and the contract is awarded. This system is of course biased in favour of the chosen contracting partner.

I.2.1.3   Engaging Consultants

International or national consultants can be engaged following national procedures or international procedures. The development bank or international donors such as the World Bank (WB) and the European Union (EU) may insist that (International) consultants are engaged to perform the tasks of design, tendering civil engineering construction works and construction supervision. These institutions issue Guidelines for the Procurement of Consultants in which is stipulated that international consultants must fulfil certain prequalification criteria. When invited, the first step for consultants is to submit their pre-qualification papers presenting, among other things, an overview of their expertise and experience, as well as details of their financial strength. Their prequalification papers will be either evaluated by staff of the International Donors or by the Implementation Authority.

Following their qualification the qualified consultants will be invited to submit a Proposal. This Proposal is often based on the submission of two Envelopes.
- One containing the Technical Proposal;
- One containing the Financial Proposal.

In the "Technical Proposal" the consultants will, among other things, describe in detail how they intend to perform the task of implementing the relevant project. The general rule applied when evaluating the proposals is that the financial envelope is left unopened and that first of all the Consultants Technical approach and methodology is evaluated. This is done on the basis of a scoring table so that in the end the Consultants can be ranked in accordance with their capability. Only once this has been done will the financial envelopes of the top 2 or 3 Consultants be opened to select the consultant offering the most economically attractive proposal.

I.2.1.4   Engaging contractors

The procedures for engaging Contractors are different from those to engage Consultants. Contractors can be selected through direct tendering or through tendering amongst earlier prequalified contractors. With prequalification, the likelihood is avoided of engaging an inexperienced contractor that offers a price that in the end may appear to have been too low, resulting in protracted difficulties during the execution of the construction. Prequalification procedures will normally require more time than direct tendering. To avoid this, prequalification procedures can start whilst the design and the preparation of tender documents are taking place. The procedure for tendering construction works is a rather elaborate process and is dealt with in more detail in Chapter I.2.2.2.

I.2.1.5   Tender documents

As discussed earlier most countries have in the course of time developed their own tender documents and procedures. In case there is a need to develop new documents/procedures or if a financing agreement prescribe that international or donor related procedures are to be used, the following information can be useful.

There are basically two distinct sets of "Standard Tender Documents":
- The Standard FIDIC Conditions;
- The Standard Regulations and Conditions as issued by the European Union (EU).

The FIDIC (Federation International des Ingenieurs Conseils or International Federation of Consulting Engineers) is the first international body that has introduced the application of international standards in engaging Contractors way before the existence of the European Union. Consultants and Contractors therefore accept the relevant FIDIC Conditions worldwide, as they are fully conversant with its international application. Using these standard documents is preferable and more secure than developing an entire set of Standard Conditions from scratch. To allow for national regulations, the principles of the national requirements can be stipulated under "conditions of particular application".

The Regulations and Conditions as developed by the EU contain the specific requirements that all Member States of the EU should take into account. The relevant documents have been prepared by legal experts rather than by people experienced in the international construction industry (as is the case with FIDIC). The EU documents therefore differ notably from the FIDIC documents.

The application of either FIDIC or EU documents is as follows:
- The EU documents are applied solely for projects funded by the EU;
- All other International Donors such as: the World Bank, the Asian Development Bank, the African Development Bank, and the Abu Dhabi Fund use the FIDIC documents or documents based thereon.

I.2.1.6   Advantages and disadvantages of tendering

Generally speaking, tendering has the following advantages and disadvantages:
Advantages
- Provides a fair chance to all qualified contractors/consultants to win a contract;
- Theoretically the best price/quality relationship is obtained;
- Introduces competition that in most cases promotes efficient work and innovation;
- Fulfils the conditions of most governments for spending public money;
- Fulfils the conditions of most international donors/financers.

Disadvantages
- Mostly a long procedure;
- Costly both for the tendering organisation and the tenderers. The cost made by the tenderers will be recuperated in their contract price;
- Does not necessarily result in the best contractor getting the award, especially if price is the main selection criterion;
- In most cases biased against smaller and starting contractors;

- Can result, especially if rules are not well defined or strictly applied, in lengthy procedures before a contract is signed. However, experience in countries where the FIDIC contracts were introduced has shown that after an initial period of adjustments by all parties, the number of claims and the time required to settle claims were considerably reduced;
- Changes in the design can only be made to a limited extent.

I.2.2   Tender procedures

Tendering activities to consultants/contractors can be broken down into a number of steps (Figure 13). The tender procedure can be a direct tendering or a procedure with prequalification of consultants/contractors. The management of the tender procedures is directly or indirectly carried out under the responsibility of a (governmental) contracting department. They can carry out the task themselves or they can nominate either a consultant or a tender committee. This committee can include hired professionals (consultants) that mostly act as advisers or the consultants can be asked to carry out and take full responsibility for the task.

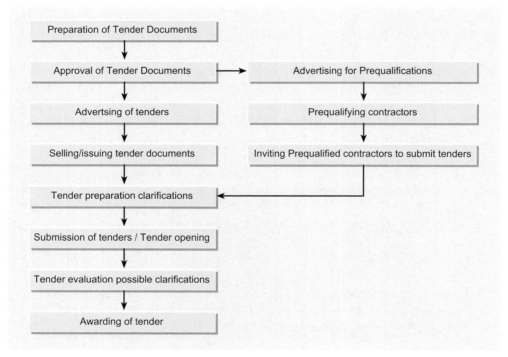

Figure 13   Activities of a tender procedure

To make the reader aware of the possibilities and complications of tender procedures, the steps are described in the following sections. Where relevant, references are given to publications that provide detailed information or can serve as models.

I.2.2.1   Preparation of tender documents

Preparation of tender documents is chiefly the task of the implementing authority. It is quite a complicated process especially for international tenders and mistakes can have costly consequences. Therefore, it is a professional job requiring specialists (quality surveyors) who are in regular employment or specially contracted. Model contracts can be used for the preparation. A widely accepted model is the standard Conditions of Contract for Works of Civil Engineering Construction (the so-called Red Book) prepared for international tendering by FIDIC. Although there are possible variations, an outline of the contents of tender documents is given in Box 2.3. Tender documents are meant to be clear and unambiguous and should provide all the requisite contractual and technical information necessary to prepare a "responsive" tender designed to carry out a quality job. Model tender documents such as the FIDIC documents are designed to be open and transparent to avoid conflicts, and to be fair towards all parties. Going into further details about contract preparation is beyond the scope of this handbook. FIDIC publications are very useful examples. Chapter I.2.2.6 contains some titles and addresses of organisations and development banks that publish model contract documents and instructions for the preparation of documents.

Box 2.3   Contents of FIDIC-based tender documents

- **Invitation to tender**. Description of who issues the tender, who finances the project, the nature and the volume of the activities/works is, time frame of the activities/works, general qualification of the tender, where, when and at what cost documents can be purchased, when and where the tender is due (the invitation gives in more detail the information provided in advertisements).
- **Instructions to tenderers**. This part contains an instruction to the tenderers and includes: who issues the tenders, the minimum qualifications of tenderers, how to prepare the tender documents including the qualifications of the tenderer, the rules and regulations of the tender procedures, the value of the tender bond, how, when and where the tender has to be submitted, the required validity of the tender, how the tender will be opened and how the tenders will be evaluated and awarded.
- **Forms of tender**. Letter to the implementation authority in which the tenderer commits himself in writing to perform the task according to the specifications for a certain amount. Tender bond (bid bond) in which the tenderer authorises his bank to pay the implementation authority a prescribed amount if he does not sign the contract in case the tender is awarded to him. In this way the companies submitting a tender guarantee that they will sign the contract if the contract is awarded to them. If they refuse or cannot sign they forfeit the tender bond and thus have to pay a penalty through this bond.
- **Qualification information of the tenderer (optional)**. Section in which the tenderer is asked for information about his company, its technical proficiency, its financial capacity his work record etc. This section is not necessary in the case of a direct tendering or prequalification.
- **Standard form of agreement**. Model of contract that has to be signed once the tender is awarded. Contract forms are rather standard, (general conditions) and have a section for "conditions of particular applications".
- **Conditions of particular application**. Section discussing the specific items valid for the contract for which the tender is issued. Most of the items have a direct reference to a section of the contract.
- **Bill of quantities**. For physical works: A detailed list of each item of the works to be carried out, the quantities, the unit costs and the total cost. The bill of quantities is used by the issuing organisation to estimate the cost of the works; the contractor uses this for preparing the cost of his offer. An example is given in Chapter I.9, Table 9.6.
- **Standard form of performance bond**. Model of performance bond that the bank of the tenderer will have to issue once the contract is awarded. The value of this bond (5-10% of the contract cost) is a guarantee that the tenderer will carry out the works as described within the time etc. In case of failure the implementation authority can request payment of the money by the bank.
- **Technical specifications**. Detailed specifications concerning all the part of the works to be carried out including the test to be performed to guarantee the quality. In case of studies, designs etc. the technical specifications are called the "Terms of Reference".

I.2.2.2   Direct tendering or prequalification?

If a decision is made to tender one or more of the task in the implementation process, a follow-up decision is to be made as to: whether the tender procedures will be direct or whether there is to be a prequalification.

Direct tendering
Direct tendering is usually a fast process. The tender is published in newspapers or magazines and interested tenderers can buy the tender documents. The charges for tender documents compensate for the production costs of the tender documents and are meant to attract only serious tenderers. If there is much interest in the tender the chances are that a large number of companies will prepare a tender. This can also be a disadvantage.
Part of the information requested in the tender documents will form a basis for determining whether the tenderer is qualified. This information focuses on the legal, professional and financial capabilities of the contractor based on which a tenderer can be qualified or disqualified. Contactors incur much expense and put a lot of effort into preparing a tender even though the chances are limited in view of the large number of tenderers. If a tenderer is disqualified all his efforts will be wasted. The cost of tender preparation will directly or indirectly always be incorporated into the final contract price. The tender evaluation in this case can also be a lengthy procedure.

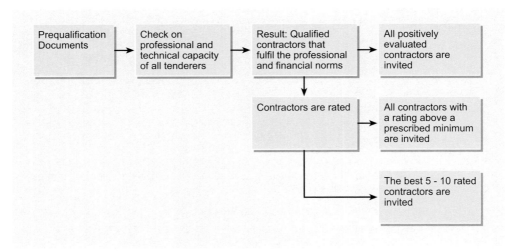

Figure 14   Schematic overview of the tender procedure with prequalification

Tendering with prequalification
The prequalification is published and interested tenderers provide the requisite information about their experience, financial and professional capacity. The prequalification applications are then evaluated to determine whether the tenderers are financially and professionally qualified to carry

out the tender (Figure 14). The selection of the contractors that are invited to prepare tenders can be done according to one of the following methods:
- Qualified contractors are invited to prepare a tender;
- The qualified contractors are rated from best to worst. (Mostly with a scoring system), and subsequently;
  - Contractors with more than a predefined number of points are then invited to prepare a tender;
  - Only the best contractors (mostly 5-10) are "short listed" and invited to prepare a tender. Both consultants and contractors prefer this system so that they do not have to go through the costly business of tender preparation with limited chances.

I.2.2.3   Advertising of tenders

Tenders are published in newspapers magazines or professional publications according to national or international rules and regulations. The text of the advertisement gives an indication of:
- The nature and the volume of the work to be carried out;
- Location of the work;
- Implementation authority (principle) and, if relevant, financer of the project;
- Timing of work;
- Summary of qualification of tenderers;
- Tender date, time and precise location of tender submission;
- Where and when to obtain tender documents and costs.

The advertisement for prequalification procedures should contain similar information. Many international financers prescribe the formulation of part of the advertising text.

I.2.2.4   Selling/issuing tender documents

A record of persons to whom documenters are sold is to be kept. Only the tenders of companies who are recorded as having bought the tender documents are accepted. For international tenders it is not unusual that tenders are sold at different locations (for instance at the office of the implementing authority and at the offices of the consultants or at major embassies).

I.2.2.5   Tender preparation by tenderers

Tender preparation is the task of the contractor. If there are aspects of the tender that are not clear, tenderers can ask for clarification in writing. The contracting department will answer the questions in writing, but to be fair to other tenderers, they will also copy the questions and answers to the other tenderers.

The preparation can include a visit to the site, either organised for all tenderers, including an explanation by the implementing authority, or individual visits by the tenderers to study the area. In case of an organised site visit, a report that records all the issues discussed and answers given is to be sent to all tenderers and will form part of the contract documents. In the case of individual visits, a register of the visits will normally be kept and/or certificates of the visits issued to the tenderers. If tenderers consider that there is not enough time for tender preparation, they may ask for an extension of the time limit. This can be granted or refused (normally if 3 or more tenderers ask for an extension, the extension is granted). The information about the extension of time is then sent to all tenderers.

I.2.2.6   Tender submission

The tenders are to be submitted at a pre indicated time (not later than.....) and a pre-indicated place. Directly after the time is passed the tenders are opened publicly. A list of the timely submitted tenders (name and address of company) and the main characteristics of the tenders (cost) is publicly read. The minutes of the public opening of tenders have a legal status and must be signed by the "tender committee" (and often those present at the tender opening) in order to maintain an official record of the tender opening proceedings. These minutes will serve as documentary evidence in case of legal challenges.

I.2.2.7   Tender evaluation

The "tender committee" may evaluate the tenders or engage consultants to do this. The objective of the evaluation is to select the most responsive tender, meaning the best quality at a reasonable price. During the evaluation the evaluators check whether the:
*   Tenders are complete;
*   Tenderers qualify (fulfil the norms);
*   Tender is technically sound and fulfils the norms;
*   Cost calculation is correct (the cost calculation can be corrected for arithmetic errors during the evaluation).

The rules and regulations for evaluation are all prescribed in the tender documents. In some cases the tender committee can ask the tenderer for clarification. These are to be securely documented because they are part of the potential contract. The tenderers are not allowed to make changes after opening their offer, or give clarifications on their own initiative. If they do so, they break the rules and this is reason for disqualification. The contract is eventually awarded to the tenderer who is qualified, has made a technically sound offer and has the lowest evaluated price. Generally, in public tendering procedures the price as given in the tender is the final contract price, which means that there will be no more price negotiations once the tenders have been submitted.

I.2.2.8   Background information

A considerable amount of literature, guidelines, handbooks and the like are available on tendering and tendering procedures. As mentioned before most countries have their own customs and regulations that may or may not conform to the generally applicable internationally accepted rules and regulations. International banks and donors have often their own rules, which in most cases are very similar to the internationally accepted rules. The fore-mentioned FIDIC systems of contracting and tendering are still the most widely used. The publication Construction Contract (1999) is the most important one. A prevision edition "Construction of Civil Works" can be informative. For smaller contracts, the publication "short form of contract" can be useful. A model Services Agreement is available for contracts for services (consultants). Provision of a detailed guideline for tendering and preparation of tender documents is not the objective of this handbook. For more detailed (practical) information and guidelines reference is made to the literature below. This selection should not be considered to be complete but provides a guide for further study.

FIDIC
(Federation International des Ingenieurs Conseils or International Federation of Consulting Engineers)
Address: P.O. Box 86, 1000 Lausanne 12 - Chailly, Switzerland. Website: http:/www/FIDIC.org, email: *fidic.pub@pobox.com*
Documents:
- Tendering Procedure. Procedure for obtaining and evaluating tenders for civil engineering contracts;
- Conditions of Contract for Works of Civil Engineering and Construction (the Red Book);
- Conditions of Contract for Electrical and Mechanical Works (the Yellow Book);
- Conditions of Contract for Design - Build and Turnkey (the Orange Book).

World Bank
Address: 1818 H Street N.W. Washington DC-20433 USA.
The World Bank has introduced its own set of Standard Documents. These are generally based on the FIDIC Standard Documents. The relevant WB documents are:
- Sample Bidding Documents. Procurement of Works;
- Sample Bidding Documents. Procurement of Small Works;
- Sample Bidding Documents. Procurement of Goods (also adopted by the Asian Development Bank and the Inter-American Development Bank);
- Standard Prequalification Documents. Procurement of Works. Major Equipment and Industrial Installations.
For ordering publications: P.O. Box 960, Herndon VA 20172-960 USA Fax: 001 7636611501 or by e-mail: *books@worldbank.org*

Asian Development Bank
Address: P.O. Box 789, 0980 Manila, Philippines, email: *adbhq@mail.asiandevbank.org*
Documents:
- Guide to Prequalification of Civil Works Contractors.

European Union

Address: Rue de la Loi 200, B-1049 Bruxelles, Belgium.

Documents:

- Information Note. How to participate in contracts financed by the European Economic Community in the Developing Countries;
- General Conditions for Works Contracts financed by the European Development Fund;
- General Conditions for Supply Contracts financed by the European Development Fund;
- General Conditions for Service Contracts financed by the European Development Fund;
- General Provisions. Contracts for the Supervision of Works.

I.3   Layout Options for Subsurface Drainage Systems

I.3.1   Layout considerations during the various steps of the implementation process

Although the detailed layout of the field drainage system will only be designed during step 3 of the implementation process (*Actual implementation - Field investigation and design* (Chapter I.1.4)), the selection of the general layout of the field drainage system must already be made during the planning (Step 2 Technical preparation), often as part of the feasibility study (Box 3.1).

Box 3.1   Choice of the layout of the field drainage system: decisions to be made during the planning phase of the implementation process

Considerations that play an important part in the decision-making process are:
- Configuration of existing infrastructure;
- Farming practices (mechanisation now or in the future);
- Slope of the area;
- Water levels at discharge point;
- Available drainage materials;
- Available installation equipment;
- If pumping is required: the place in the system where pumping will be done, i.e. at field level, at the discharge point or in between;
- Initial investments.

Early selection is necessary because the general layout affects the drainage materials needed, additional infrastructure, pumping and the initial investments, as well as the configuration and required water depth of the open drainage system to which the subsurface drainage systems will eventually discharge. The choice is likely to be automatic in countries with a well-developed drainage tradition and/or industry, however, if a country has no drainage tradition this could require considerable effort.

This chapter discusses the different layouts of subsurface drainage systems and the consequences of the selection of a particular layout. A general description of the alternative layouts was already presented in the preamble.

I.3.2   Elements of a drainage system

A drainage system consists of the following elements (Figure 15):
- *Field drains.* Field drains (in this handbook we only consider subsurface pipe drains) control the watertable and collect the excess water in the soil or from the groundwater and convey this drainage effluent towards the collector drain;
- *Collector drains.* Collector drains can be either open or piped. Open drains convey rain and groundwater towards the main drainage system and piped collectors only convey the drainage water from the field drains towards the main drainage system;
- *Sub main and main drains.* The main drainage system, which consist of several sub mains (if applicable) and a main drain, conveys the drainage water from the collectors towards

the discharge site. Main drains are normally open drains, although theoretically these main drains can be pipes, the required diameters are generally very large and therefore prohibitively expensive;

- *Discharge site.* The discharge site or outlet is the terminal point of the entire drainage system from where the discharging is done into a river, lake or sea. The outlet can be a gravity outlet structure or a pumping station. A gravity outlet structure is a drainage structure in an area with variable outer water levels where drainage can take place by gravity when outside water levels are low. In delta areas, drainage by gravity is often restricted to a few hours per day during low tide. In the upstream regions of a river, drainage by gravity can be restricted for several weeks during periods of high river discharges. A pumping station will be needed in areas where the required water levels in the drainage system are lower than the water level of the river, lake or sea.

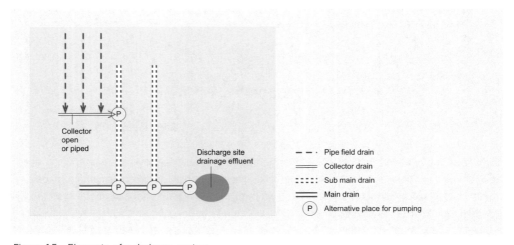

Figure 15   Elements of a drainage system

I.3.3   Considerations for the selection of a layout

Considerations for the selection of a layout are as follows:

- *Matching of layout of (subsurface drainage) with irrigation and road layout.* For new (reclamation) areas without existing agricultural development the layout of the drainage system has to match with the designed layout of irrigation, roads and possibly electrification. It is the most practical to design the irrigation, drainage and road systems at the same time, even if the drainage system is to be constructed at a later date;
- *The layout has to "fit" into the layout of the existing infrastructure.* In areas with an existing agricultural infrastructure, the configuration of the subsurface drainage system and accompanying open drainage system has to "fit" into the configuration of the existing fields in terms of lengths, direction of slope etc. (field drain length is approximately the same as field lengths). This will limit "damage" during the construction and thus additional costs to the existing infrastructure;

- *The level of the outlet of the subsurface drainage system* (determined by the drain depth, lengths and slopes) has to be at or above the highest water level in the main drain system. Depending on the natural slope of the area, the longer the subsurface system the greater the difference between the highest and the lowest point of the system and, normally, the lower the water level at the outlet needs to be. The minimum slope of piped drains is steeper than the minimum slope of open drains;
- *Pumping of the system.* In most cases (drainage is mainly necessary in relatively flat areas) pumping will be required somewhere in the system. If so, the location of the pump or the pumps will have a considerable influence on the layout, design and cost of the system. Alternative options are elaborated in the next section;
- *Available drainage materials.* In countries with a well-developed drainage industry, most of the drainage materials (field drain pipes in various diameters, collector pipes in various diameters, envelopes etc.) are readily available. The cost of the materials is chiefly related to well-balanced market prices. In countries where the drainage industry is not yet (fully) developed, available materials are either limited or the production of drainage materials has still to be set up. These limitations have to be taken into account and if the production has to be set up, each additional pipe diameter that will need to be produced will result in (considerable) additional investments;
- *Installation equipment.* The choice of layout is directly related to the depth of installation. The desired depth of the drains is determined by the drainage criteria, while the actual installation depth is determined by the drainage criteria and the slopes required in the system. The depth to which the installation equipment can install drains is limited so this must be taken into account when choosing the layout;
- *Subsoil conditions.* Unstable subsoils (in extreme cases quicksand) can limit the installation. Under these conditions installation is possible in most cases if plastic drain pipes are used. The installation, however, requires special techniques and skills, also for the installation of manholes and pipe connections. The installation of concrete collectors requires the use of special, expensive, techniques like vertical or horizontal well pointing systems.

I.3.4   Pumping

Most drainage systems require pumping somewhere in the system (Figure 15), especially in relatively flat areas. When pumping is required a crucial decision has to be made as to where in the system the pumping is to be done. This choice has its repercussions on the drainage layout, drainage materials, operation of the system and the total infrastructure of the area. The water level in an open drain or river determines the reference level for discharge; the bottom level of the drain is not relevant. Theoretically, one can pump at the end of each field drain and lift the drainage effluent above the water level of the open collector drain. At the other extreme one can pump at the outlet point of the total drainage system at the location where the system discharges the drain effluent into an evaporation pond, river, lake or sea. Locating the pumps farther away from the field drains and closer to the discharge site will result in a decreasing number of pumping points and an increase in the required capacity of the pumps.

Considerations in the choice of the location of the pumps are:

- *The relative cost of pumps and pumping stations.* Large pumping stations require elaborate civil engineering works and can therefore be a very costly. The cost of the pumps and engines is often a minor part of the cost of the whole pumping station. Small underwater pumps with automatic switch on/off functions are produced in series. These pumps are cheap and require very little and simple civil engineering works like sumps. The total cost of a great number of very small pumping stations is to be compared with the total cost of one or a few larger stations (including power supply, structures and operation & maintenance costs);
- *Power supply.* If electricity (of acceptable quality and continuity) is available, a cost comparison should be made between the possibilities to supply a large number of small pumps or a limited number of larger stations (or one) (including the cost of transformers!). If no electricity is available and diesel power is required, the stations become more complicated to build and operate. This often limits the choice to only a few (or one) larger pumping stations. The costs of road construction for supplying diesel to the stations must be included in the comparison;
- *Operational complications.* Small automatic pumping stations require very little attention, certainly no pump houses, guard houses etc. Larger stations and especially the diesel driven stations require virtually continuous attendance with all the added facilities. Small stations serve a limited area and can provide tailor-made water level control for that area. Large stations that serve a large area can only realise an average water level control for the whole area;
- *Water level in and depth of open drainage system.* Pump stations can discharge at any required level at practically the same cost. This means that if pumping is practiced, the water level in the open drainage system, or disposal area into which the system discharges, can be very close to field level. If there are a large number of small pumping stations the open drainage system can be shallow resulting in less construction and maintenance costs. Shallow open drains are especially advantageous in areas with unstable subsoils. If pumping is done at the downstream end of the system with one large pumping station, open drains will have to be constructed and maintained at considerable depths (especially in salinity control areas) of often up to 3-4 meters. These deep drains require an expensive complicated maintenance system (especially in areas with unstable subsoils).

I.3.5   Layout options of subsurface field drainage systems

I.3.5.1   Singular drainage system

Description of a singular drainage system
A singular system consists of field drains that discharge directly by gravity into an open collector drain. There are two variants of the singular systems (Figure 16):
- The one-sided singular system (in areas with a slope);
- The two-sided singular system (in flat areas).

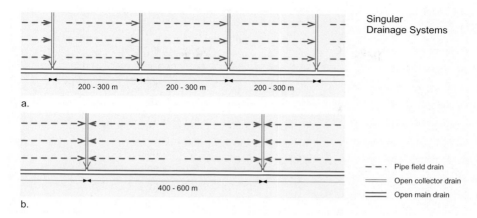

Figure 16   Singular drainage systems: one-sided (a) and two-sided (b) field drains

The length of the field drain is 300 m at the most, being the maximum length of cleaning devices. Field drains need to slope towards the open collector drain. The water level in the open collector drain has to be below the outlet level of the lowest drain. If pumping is required this can only be done from the open collector drain in the main drainage system. The difference in level between the desired drain depth (at the upstream end of the field drains) and the end of the subsurface system (the outlet) is between 0.15 and 0.20 m in flat areas with 300 m of drain pipes (Figure 17).

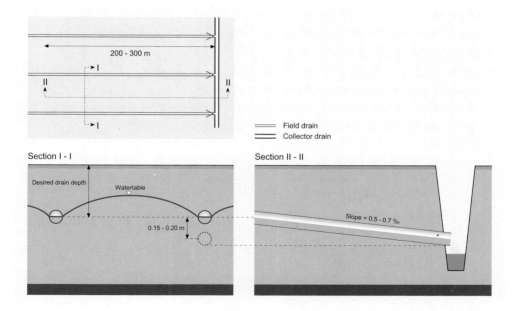

Figure 17   Relation between the desired minimum drain depth and the acceptable water level at the outlet of a field drain

Advantages of a singular drainage system
- Singular systems are simple to design and to install. The levels of the field drains do not have to be related to each other as long as the outlet of each field drain is above the highest water level in the open collector drain and the drains are within the prescribed depth range;
- Generally speaking, only one diameter of drain pipe is required;
- Once installed the functioning of singular systems is simple to check by visual observation at the outlet;
- Cleaning of the pipes is relatively easy and can be done directly from the outlet;
- Little level difference between the end of the field drain and the water level of the open system (only the slope requirement of the field drain).

Disadvantages of a singular drainage system
- Open collector drains spaced at every 300 or 600 m at the maximum require (expensive) crossings (culverts/bridges) and are an obstruction for mechanised farming even if there are crossings;
- Higher maintenance costs. Maintenance of open collector drains is often more expensive than maintenance of piped collector drains;
- Multitude of outlets, one per field drain. These outlets are susceptible to damage especially during maintenance of open drains.

I.3.5.2   Composite drainage system

Description of a composite drainage system
A composite system consists of field drains that discharge into a piped collector drain (Figure 18). Like the singular systems, there are two variants of the composite system:
- The one-sided composite system (in areas with a slope);
- The two-sided composite system (in flat areas).

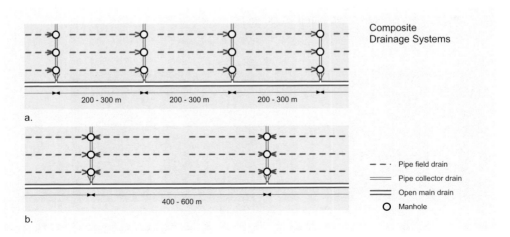

Figure 18   Composite drainage: (a) one-sided and (b) two-sided systems

A device is required at the junction of the field drain and the collector drain so that the field drains can be cleaned, this is normally a manhole. The length of the field drain is approximately 300 m at the most (the maximum length of cleaning devices). For hydraulic reasons a minimum slope is needed in both the field drains and the piped collector drain of 0.7-0.5 ‰. This result in considerable level differences, for example the level difference between the upstream end of the field drain and the outlet of the collector would vary between 0.90 and 0.65 m for field drains with a length of 300 m and a collector that is 1000 m long. To this must be added the desired drain depth to determine the acceptable highest water level in the open main drain at the discharge point (for flat areas). If the water level in the main drain is too high, a (small sump) pump can be placed at the end of the collector system. This pump can then discharge into a shallow open main drain system. Alternatively the open drain can be pumped to obtain an acceptable water level (Figure 15).

Advantages of a composite drainage system
- Composite systems require a lower density of open drains and consequently fewer crossings. The system forms only a limited or no obstruction to agricultural activities;
- Maintenance of a composite system is in most cases simpler and cheaper, because there is less length of open drain per area unit;
- If pumping is required this can be done cheaply and simply at the discharge point of the collector system;
- There is only one outlet per system.

Disadvantages of a composite drainage system
- During the design and construction phase the levels of field and collector drains have to match up well;
- Checking the functioning of composite systems is more complicated than checking singular systems;
- Maintenance (flushing) of the field drains requires special devices so that the flusher can enter into the field drain;
- The outlet of the system is deeper than the outlets of a singular system because of the slope requirement for the piped collector;
- Different pipe diameters are needed for both field drain pipes (mostly of one diameter) and collector pipes;
- Field and collector pipes cannot always be installed using the same installation equipment for all cases;
- Checking the functioning of each field drain is complicated.

I.3.5.3   Extended field drain system

Description of an extended field drain system
Extended field drain (lateral) systems are a variant of the singular and composite systems described above. The basic difference is that the field drains are much longer (up to some 1000 m) than the field drains of the systems described above that are approximately 300 m at the

maximum. The following variants of extended field drain systems are possible (Figure 19):
- Extended field drain singular one-sided;
- Extended field drain singular two-sided (not shown);
- Extended field drain composite one-sided;
- Extended field drain composite two-sided (not shown).

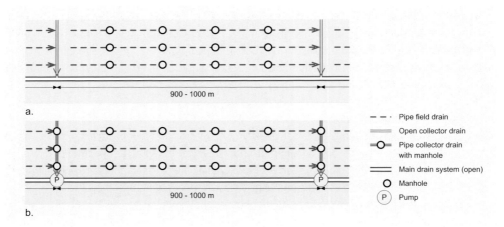

Figure 19   Extended field drain in a singular (a) and composite (b) drainage system

To clean these long field drains provisions (mostly manholes) have to be constructed every 300 m, in extreme cases up to a maximum of 350 m, provided that there are special flushers for the purpose. Because the long field drains serve larger areas than the regular ones, the capacity and thus the diameter of the pipes has to be greater. This raises the cost somewhat. Increasing the diameter of the field drain progressively in a downstream direction would be an economising measure. The changes in diameter can be made at a manhole. In the case of a singular system with a 1000 m long field drain, the head difference between the top end of the field drain and the downstream end would be between 0.5 and 0.7 m. In composite systems also with a collector of 1000 m in length, the head difference will be between 1.2 and 1.6 m. The downstream end of the extended drainage systems is therefore at a greater depth than for singular and com-posite systems.

Advantages of an extended field drain system
- Extended lateral systems require far fewer open drains and consequently fewer crossings than the other systems and consequently form much less obstructions to agricultural activities;
- Maintenance of a composite system is in most cases simpler and cheaper, because there is less length of open drain per unit area;
- If pumping is required this can be done relatively cheaply and simply at the end of the collector pipe (only for the composite variants). Fewer pumping points per ha will be needed than for the regular composite collector systems;

- The system has fewer outlets per unit compared with the regular singular and composite systems.

Disadvantages of an extended field drain system
- In the composite system, the design of the levels of the field and collector drains has to match up well;
- The downstream end of the system (thus field drains for the singular systems and collector drain for composite systems) is deeper than in the regular systems because of the slope requirement and the length of the field drains. Consequently, the whole system (including collector pipes) is deeper so this can make installation somewhat more complicated;
- The entrance for cleaning device (manholes if above ground) can form obstructions for agricultural operations;
- For economic reasons the diameters of field drains are sometimes required to be larger. Thus, the diameters of the collector drain (for composite variants) are also required to be larger than the regular composite system;
- The functioning of each drain in the system is difficult to check.

I.3.6 Quantitative comparison of different layout systems

An example of the calculation of the required infrastructure for different layouts of drainage systems is presented in Table 3.1. Note, Table 3.1 is an example only and has no universal applicability. The calculations refer to an area of 1000 m x 1000 m = 100 ha (one sided) or 2000 m x 1000 m = 200 ha (two sides). Drain spacing is taken as 50 m (thus 200 m field drain/ha) and the length of field drains for singular and composite drainage systems are 250 m. The extended field drains are 1000 m in length. A similar table can be made to suit any and every situation. Such a table can also help in the preparation of a cost comparison of the system if local unit prices are known.

For this example it can be concluded that:
- The length of field drains per ha is the same for all layout options;
- Field drains tend to have a larger diameter in the extended systems and more diameters tend to be used;
- In the case of composite systems, the length of collector pipe is considerably less in the extended systems than in the regular systems;
- The length of open drain is considerably less in the composite systems than in the singular systems. Of all the systems, the extended systems require the least density of open drains. Fewer open drains generally results in less maintenance cost (and problems);
- As can be seen the number of outlets is vastly reduced in the case of composite systems and is the smallest in the extended composite system;
- Extended systems normally have more manholes, which has a cost repercussion. The composite one-sided system has the most manholes;

- Extended systems have the least the number of crossings. In this example the norm of one crossing per 500 m of open drain has been arbitrarily taken, which is likely to be insufficient for small fields;
- The extended systems end at lower levels than the regular systems, which may make installation more complicated;
- In the composite systems pumping can be done at the end/outlet of the subsurface systems. Considerably fewer pumps are needed for the extended composite systems than the regular systems. If pumping is done the open collector drains and (sub)main drains can be shallow;
- The main drains have to be deep in the singular systems; the water level has to be lower than the level of the outlets. This may pose complications for the maintenance of these open drains. If no pumping is done the same is true for the composite systems.

Table 3.1 Example of calculation of required infrastructure for different layouts of drainage systems for areas of 1000 m x 1000 m (100 ha) and 1000 m x 2000 m for two sided systems. Based on spacing of field drains of 50 m, length of field drains in singular and composite systems of 250 m, extended systems 1000 m. Minimum slopes of pipes (collector and field drain) 0.5-0.7 ‰, and collector pipe Ø =200 mm.

| Type of system | Pipe Drains | | | | Open Drains | | | | Structures | | | Head | In case of Pumping | |
| | Field Drains | | Collector Drains | | Collector drain [a] | | Main drain | | Outlets | Manholes | Crossings | top to outlet | Pumping Possible | Number pumps |
	Length (m/ha)	Ø (No.)	Length (m/ha)	Ø (No.)	Length (m/ha)	(S)hallow or (D)eep	(S)hallow or (D)eep		(No./ha)	(No./ha)	(No./ha)	(m)	(Yes or No)	(No./ha)
Regular systems														
Singular one sided	200	1	0	0	40	D	D		0.8	0	0.08	0.12-0.15	No	0.8
Singular two sided	200	1	0	0	20	D	D		0.8	0	0.04	0.12-0.15	No	0.8
Composite one sided	200	1	40	<1	10 (5[b])	S/D	S/D		0.04	0.8	0.04	0.72-1.05	Yes	0.04
Composite two sided	200	1	20	<1	7.5 (3.7[b])	S/D	S/D		0.02	0.4	0.02	0.72-1.05	Yes	0.02
Extended field drains														
Singular one sided	200	>1	0	<1	10	D	D		0.2	0.4	0.02	0.5-0.7	No	0.2
Singular two sided	200	>1	0	<1	5	D	D		0.2	0.4	0.01	0.5-0.7	No	0.2
Composite one sided	200	>1	10	<1	<1	S/D	S/D		0.01	0.6	0	1.2-1.6	Yes	0.01
Composite two sided	200	>1	5	<1	<1	S/D	S/D		0.005	0.5	0	1.2-1.6	Yes	0.005

[a] or sub main drain in case of composite systems

[b] in case of two sided use of the sub main drain

I.4 Materials for Subsurface Drainage Systems

I.4.1 Considerations on material selection during the various steps of the implementation process

Selection of the drainage materials to be used has to be done at an early stage of the implementation process, because the choice of specific drainage materials can have far-reaching, long-term consequences that may require additional investments (Box 4.1).

Box 4.1 Drainage materials: Major decisions to be taken during the planning phase

- What type of pipe should be selected for the field and collector drains?
  If the preferred type is not readily available:
  - Will the pipes be imported or produced locally?
  If the pipes are going to be produced locally:
  - In which way will the production process be started (by private parties or by the government)?
  - How will the production facilities be financed?
  - Who will be responsible for the establishment and running of the local production facilities?

- What type of drain envelope should be selected?
  If there is no experience with envelopes in the soils to be drained:
  - How will a suitable type of envelope be selected?
  If field trials have to be done:
  - Who will carry out and who will finance the field trials?
  If the selected envelope is not available in the country:
  - From where will the envelope be purchased (imported or local manufacturing)?
  If the envelope is going to be produced locally:
  - How will the production process be started (by private parties or by the government)?
  - How will the production facilities be financed?

Some of the materials used for drainage are also used for other civil engineering constructions. Materials specific to subsurface pipe drainage systems are:
- Field drain pipes and fittings;
- Collector drain pipes and fittings;
- Drain envelopes;
- Drainage structures.

This chapter provides an overview of these specific drainage materials from which, during the design and planning stage of the implementation process, a final choice has to be made. The materials are described insofar as their nature and characteristics have an impact on the choice. For more detailed and background information please refer to the FAO Irrigation and Drainage Paper no. 60 and ILRI Publication 16 (see Bibliography).

I.4.2 Pipes for field drains

I.4.2.1 Function of a field drain

The function of a field drain is to collect excess groundwater and to convey it to a collector or open drain. The pipes have to be permeable (perforated) or require openings at the joints of pipe sections so that water can enter them. The perforations or openings of the pipes should be (Figure 20):
- As large as possible to limit the entry resistance of the water;
- As small as possible to prevent the soil particles surrounding the pipes entering the pipe as a result of mobilisation by the water flow. If soil particles enter the pipe they will sediment in the pipe and obstruct the flow.

These are contradictory and incompatible requirements. In most soils, especially in soils with little cohesion (sandy or loamy soils and even some clay soils), the perforations or openings cannot be made so small that the soil particles cannot enter the pipes. This is why in most soils an envelope has to be placed around the pipe.

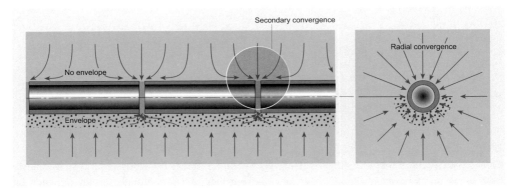

Figure 20 *The perforations in a drain pipe should be large enough to let the water in and small enough to prevent soil particles to pass*

I.4.2.2 Types of pipes for field drain

Pipes for field drain can be made of:
- Perforated plastic (PVC or HDPE);
- Concrete;
- Clay (tile)[5].

---

[5] The terminology used for clay pipes varies. With clay pipes is meant ceramic pipes made of clay that is fired at high temperatures. English literature often refers to tiles (tile drainage).

Plastic drain pipes (either PVC or HDPE) are currently the most common and the easiest and most secure types of pipes for machine installation. The plastic material is inert and is not affected by soil chemicals. The production of plastic pipes is a specialised process requiring high cost equipment.

Concrete pipes can be used if plastic pipes are unavailable or if only small quantities of pipes are required. They can be made relatively simply, onsite. The installation of drains with concrete pipes is more cumbersome and much more susceptible to misalignment than the installation of plastic pipes. Under unstable soil conditions it is almost impossible to properly install concrete pipes. Some soil chemicals attack concrete pipes. When making cost comparisons the risks of breakage and possible high transport costs have to be taken into account.

The quality of clay pipes or tiles is comparable to concrete pipes. They are somewhat lighter than concrete pipe and are chemically resistant to soil chemicals (see below). The production of clay pipes is a specialised process requiring expensive equipment. The use of clay pipes/tiles used to be standard in Europe in the first half of the 20th Century. However, since the 1960s clay pipes have been completely replaced by corrugated plastic pipes.

I.4.2.3   Plastic field drains

General
Corrugated (perforated) plastic drain pipes are standard at present, especially for field drains. Most of the installation equipment is geared to the installation of these flexible corrugated plastic pipes.

Base materials
Plastic pipes can be made of polyvinyl chloride (PVC[6]), high density polyethylene (HDPE), and to a minor extent, polypropylene (PP). The choice from these three materials largely depends on the availability and price of the parent material. All plastic pipes are resistant to all chemicals that may be found in agricultural soils. The major differences between the base materials are:
- All plastic materials are sensitive to ultra violet (UV) radiation and should not be exposed to direct sunlight therefore. UV filters can be included in the base material that can give some, but not complete, protection;
- HDPE is sensitive to deformation at high temperatures;
- PVC becomes brittle at low temperatures (near freezing point), HDPE also becomes brittle, but at somewhat lower temperatures and may thus be installed at lower temperatures. Once installed neither PVC nor HDPE are affected by low temperatures;
- HDPE requires approximately 20% more base material in weight per meter than PVC to attain the same strength.

---

[6] Sometimes more specifically called *Unplastified* PVC or U PVC.

Types of plastic pipes
Plastic pipes can be:
- Rigid smooth pipes;
- Corrugated pipes;
- Double walled pipes (corrugated outer pipe and smooth inner pipe).

Rigid pipes are less easy to install and are considerably more expensive than corrugated pipes. To achieve the same strength and resistance to outside pressure a rigid pipe requires 3 x the amount of base material and, consequently, is about 3 times more expensive. The slightly rougher wall of the smaller diameter corrugated plastic pipes will require marginally larger diameters. The extra costs thereof are negligible compared to the extra cost of either rigid or double walled pipes. The double-walled pipes were originally developed specifically for irrigation and can withstand higher than necessary internal pressures. They have the same disadvantages as the rigid pipes but are slightly lighter. The use of these expensive pipes is only justified for larger diameters required for special conditions.

Available pipe diameters
Corrugated plastic pipes are available in diameters ranging from 40 to 600 mm. The smaller diameter pipes can be produced in coils in lengths of up to 300 m weighing between 30 and 50 kg. The larger the diameter, the smaller the length that can be coiled, e.g., 200 mm PVC pipes can be coiled up to a length of 50 m and the largest diameter pipes are seldom delivered on coils but as straight lengths of 6 or 9 m.
- *PVC drain pipe sizes* are standardised and refer to the *outside* diameter (in mm). Standard outside diameters are 40, 50, 65, 80, 100, 125, 160 and 200 mm, but larger diameters are also available;
- *HDPE drain pipe sizes* are standardised to the *inside* diameter in inches. Standard diameters are 2, 3, 4, 5, 6, 8, 10, 12, 15, 18, and 24 inches.

Production of corrugated plastic pipes
The production of corrugated plastic pipes is a specialised job. It requires expensive production lines consisting of: extruders, corrugators, perforators and coilers (Figure 21). During the production process a constant quality control is required. The production capacity of a modern line is about 500 kg/per hour, for an Ø 100 mm pipe it amounts to approximately 1000 m/hour. The extruder can also be used for the production of rigid pipes. The corrugator and the perforator are parts of the production line that are specifically made the production of corrugated drain pipes.

The corrugator gives the pipe its form; the form of the corrugation determines the strength of the pipe. Sophisticated corrugation forms can give the pipe the required strength at minimal wall thickness. The smaller the required wall thickness, the less the base material needed and thus the cheaper the pipe.

The perforator has to provide perfect holes in the pipe for water entry at the indicated place (in the valley of the corrugation) so that the perforation does not influence the strength of the pipe. The perforator should make holes and not slits or cuts. This means that the cut-out material has to be removed from the pipe. Slits and cuts tend to bend back and close the perforation over time.

There are production lines for roughly Ø 40 - 100 mm and for Ø 100 - 200 mm. For each diameter to be produced on a production line, special tooling is required on the extruder, corrugator and perforator. These special tools are expensive. So, if a drainage industry is to be developed, there is an interest to limit the number of pipe diameters to be used and thus produced.

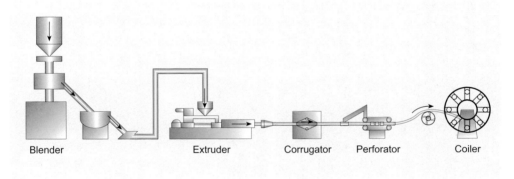

Blender   Extruder   Corrugator   Perforator   Coiler

Figure 21   A production line for plastic pipes consists of a blender, extruder, corrugator, perforator and coiler

Transport of plastic pipes

Transport of corrugated pipes over long distances is rather expensive, because of the high volume/weight ratio (it boils down to the expensive transport of air). To counteract these pipes ought to be produced as close as possible to the site of installation. Mobile factories have even been produced in the past, but these proved to be expensive and complicated because of necessary power supply and cooling. They are hardly used any more: transferring the production line from one factory hall to another is far simpler to do. Comparative studies indicate that transporting the production facilities to a location close to the construction site is economical if the distances are more than 300 - 500 km. The importing of large quantities of plastic drain pipes is therefore not considered to be a rational option.

Quality Control

The quality of corrugated plastic pipes is documented in national and international norms and standards. Quality control of the production is a specialised job, which is beyond the scope of work of drainage engineers and should be left to specialised institutes. The staff in charge of installation should ascertain that pipes are produced according to a national or international standard as indicated in the specifications. Some examples of the most commonly used international norms and standards are given in Table 1.

Visual checks that can be done before installation are to assess: form, resistance, size regularity and quantity of perforations and brittleness. Although experienced drainage engineers may do these checks they cannot match up with specialised quality checks. If a proper factory test has been carried out on the pipes, the quality control during the installation process can be confined by checking whether the pipes:

- Have been produced, transported and stored according to norms and/or contract specifications;
- Have not been produced longer than 3 months before delivery;
- Have been stored in the shade;
- Have not been damaged during transport;
- Are stored on the site outside the direct influence of sun shine;
- Have not been damaged during the installation process.

Table 1   Standards for corrugated plastic drain pipes [a,b]

Country	Standard No.	Type of pipe	Source
Europe	CEN/TC155/WG18 (1995)	Plastic piping system for agri. land drainage U-PVC	CEN Draft
Germany	DIN 1187	U PVC pipes	RAL
ISO	1985 Draft	Pipes and fittings of UPVC for sub soil drainage	ISO
USA	ASTM F-405, F-449	Corrugated PE Ø75-150 mm and fittings	American Society for Testing and Materials
	F-667, F-800, F-892	Corrugated PE Ø200-300 mm and fittings	

[a] Only one of these standards should be applied, combining parts of different standards does not necessarily result in well-balanced effective standards.

[b] The draft European standards are given in the Annex to the FAO Irr. & Dr. Paper No. 60. Thus far, these standards are (2003) the most complete ones available.

I.4.2.4   Concrete field drains

Types of concrete pipes for field drains
Concrete pipes for field drains generally come in a cylindrical form in lengths of about 0.30 m. The ends are either straight or in some rare cases have a spigot and groove (Figure 22). Water entry is through the joints between pipe sections. Pipe diameters are as desired; 60-100 mm is common for the (internal) diameters of concrete pipes for field drains. Like clay pipes, however, they virtually became obsolete when plastic pipes were introduced.

a.

b.

Figure 22   Concrete (a) and clay (b) drain pipes generally come in a cylindrical form in lengths of about 0.30 m

Base material
Concrete pipes are produced from cement and sand. If concrete pipes are used in acid or sulphuric soils, sulphate resistant cement must be used, in which case the density of the concrete has to be high so that it absorbs little or no water.

Production
Concrete pipes can be produced either in a factory or on site. The pipe production in a factory usually has a better and more homogeneous quality. It is up to the manufacturer to prove that the quality standards (often national standards) are met and that they are checked by an independent entity. If the pipes are produced in a factory, the pipes have to be transported to the site. During transport some breakage normally occurs.

Moulds, preferably vibration tables, weighing units, hoppers and curing basins are required for on site production of pipes. Quality production requires considerable supervision and quality control needs constant attention. The advantage is that no transport to the site is required and part of the breakage risk is eliminated.

Transport
Transport of concrete drain pipes over long distances is hardly economical as the weight of a Ø 100 mm is about 18 kg/m and, in addition, there is the breakage (5%) to consider. One of the redeeming features of concrete pipes is that they can be produced near the installation site. Importing of concrete pipes is not considered to be a feasible option.

Quality control
The required quality of concrete pipes is documented in national and international norms and standards. Quality control during the production is a rather specialised job that is the responsibility of the manufacturer. Quality control concentrates on: form, dosage of cement, concrete and water, quality of the cement, quality of the water (no saline or muddy water), cleanliness of the sand, compaction, curing period and regular wetting during curing. The staff in charge of installation should ascertain that pipes are produced according to a national or

international standard as prescribed in the specifications (Table 2). These standards focus on (see also FAO Irr. & Dr. Paper no. 60):
- Roundness and curvature;
- Verticality at end of pipes;
- Resistance to weathering and deterioration in the soil;
- Resistance to freezing and thawing cycles;
- Density;
- Water adsorption;
- Crushing strength;
- Sulphate resistance (if required);
- Acid resistance (if required).

Visual quality control in the field before installation focuses on checking that the pipes:
- Have been produced according to the prescribed norms and/or contract specifications;
- Are regular in roundness and thickness;
- Are not damaged;
- Have straight ends (are vertical at end planes;
- Are not chipped.

Table 2 *Standards for concrete drain pipes*

Country	Standard No.	Type of pipe	Source
USA	ASTM C412M-99	Concrete drain tile	American Society for Testing and Materials (ASTM)
	ASTM C44-95	Concrete pipe Perforated	ASTM
	ASTM C118M-00	Concrete pipe for Irrigation and Drainage	ASTM

I.4.2.4   Clay field drains

General
In the past, clay pipes were standard usage in most European and some (South) American countries. They have gradually been phased out since corrugated plastic drain pipes became available. They are rarely used nowadays. High quality clay pipes are resistant to weathering and aggressive chemicals in the soils.

Types of clay pipes
Clay pipes are cylindrical in form and about 0.30 m in length. Ends are either straight or sometimes have *"collars"* (effective but expensive) (Figure 23). Water entry is through the joints

between pipes. The most common pipe diameters are 50, 65, 75, 80 and 100 mm. Diameters of 130 and 160 have been known to be used at times. The wall thickness varies between 12 and 24 mm.

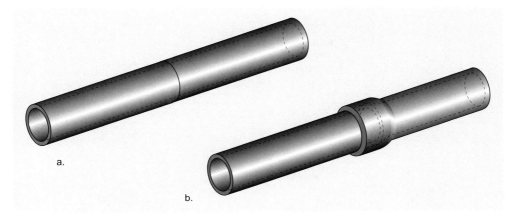

Figure 23   Clay pipes have either straight joints (a) or collar (b)

Base material
Clay pipes are produced from clay through vitrification in an oven at a high temperature (>900 °C). For the production of high quality pipes the clay should have no or limited content of montmorrilonite.

Production
Clay pipes have to be produced in a specialised plant. The mixing and wetting of the clay, the pressing through the mould, the cutting, the storing and the baking in the oven are all specialised jobs requiring specialised equipment. The baking process is highly sensitive, since the vitrification of the clay minerals only takes places at specific high temperatures that are to be maintained during a number of days. It also demands a considerable amount of energy. The pipes have eventually to be transported to the site carrying a risk of breakage.

Transport
Transport of clay pipes over long distances is not considered to be economical. The weight of a Ø 100 mm pipe is about 12 kg/m and there is also the added breakage risk of 5% to consider. Importing of clay pipes is not feasible.

Quality control
The required quality of clay pipes is documented in national and international norms and standards. Quality control during the production process is a rather specialised job and is the responsibility of the manufacturer. The staff in charge of drain installation should ascertain that pipes are produced according to a national or international standard as prescribed in the specifications (Table 3). These standards focus on the same aspects as concrete pipes (see

previous section). The quality control in the field before installation focuses also on the same aspects as concrete pipes.

Table 3   Standards for clay drain pipes

Country	Standard No.	Type of pipe	Source
Germany	DIN 1180	Clay pipes	RAL
USA	ASTM C4-99	Clay drain tiles and perforated drain tile	American Society for Testing and Materials ASTM
	ASTM C498-95	Clay drain tile, perforated	ASTM
	ASTM C700-99	Clay drain tile, vitrified perforated	ASTM

I.4.2.5   Pipe fittings

Couplers
For concrete pipes plastic rings with grooves were used to restrict inflow of sediments in case of damaged pipe ends (Figure 24a). For plastic pipes, so-called couplers (connectors) are used to connect two sections of drain pipes (Figure 24b). Sophisticated click couplers are the most practical in use. If couplers are not available, connections can be made by hand using iron wire, knives and small parts of drain pipe (See Part II). The larger the diameter of the drain pipes the more difficult it will be to make coupling by hand.

End caps
End caps are used at the upstream end of a plastic field drain to prevent soil and water flow into the drain. End caps that click onto the pipe are also produced in a special production facility. If these are not available the pipe ends can be closed of by first heating the end of the pipe (on the exhaust of the drainage machine) and then by closing it by folding over.

T-joints
T-joints are used to connect plastic field drains to a collector drain (Figure 24b) and also require a special production process. They can be manufactured by welding two parts of rigid PVC pipe or by blow moulding. The T-joint can be extended to allow for easy access for the flushing of the field drains.

Y-joints
Y-joints are similar to T-joints.

Couplers for concrete pipes
In rare instances plastic couplers are used for concrete pipes (Figure 24c). They provide a secure joint of the pipe sections and avoid dislocation and inflow of sediment material.

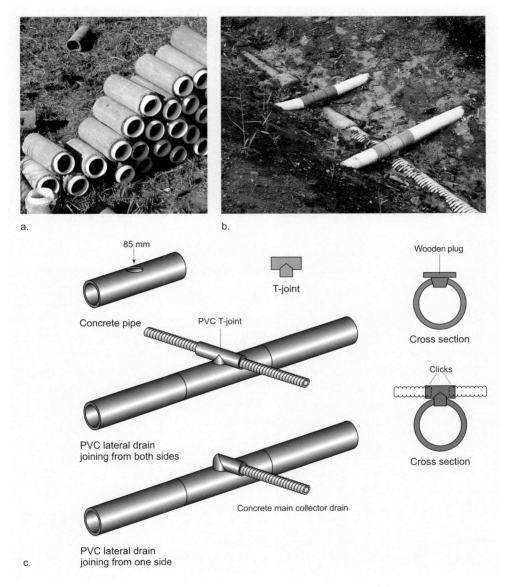

Figure 24   Pipe connectors between (a) field drains and (b) field and collector drains

Outlet pipes
Outlet pipes for singular drainage system are mostly rigid PVC pipes that can be coupled to the drain pipe.

Transport
Since the quantity of fittings is rather limited and neither the weight nor volume considerable, transporting over long distances and/or importing can be considered.

Standards
The standards for fittings are often included in the standards for the drain pipes (Table 1) Additional standards are:
- ISO norm 2507, 2507-1 and 2507-2 for thermo plastic pipes and fittings;
- ISO norm 4493 for PVC-U pipes and fittings;
- CEN/TC 155 WI 127 for joint strength.

I.4.3   Pipes for collector drains

I.4.3.1   Function of collector drains

Collector drain pipes are usually only for the purposes of conveying the excess water to an outlet. These pipes are closed, the joints are sealed and there are no perforations, thus the groundwater only enters through the junctions with the field drains. Under specific conditions it may be useful for collector drains to also have a draining function, in which case the pipes will need to be perforated.

Cost comparisons of installed subsurface drainage systems reveal that total costs (both material and installation costs) for plastic collectors with diameters of 300 mm or less are considerably cheaper than for concrete collectors. Concrete collectors are cheaper for diameters over 300 mm. This price balance may vary with the cost of base materials. Furthermore, concrete collectors are more cumbersome to install than plastic ones and there is a higher risk of displacement occurring especially in unstable subsoils resulting in leakage and damage. Therefore, if there is a choice, plastic collectors are preferable.

I.4.3.2   Types of pipes for collector drains

Collector pipes are generally similar to field drain pipes, only the diameters tend to be larger. Collector pipes are normally made of plastic (PVC or HDPE) or concrete. The production of clay collector pipes of larger diameters is complicated and expensive. Therefore clay pipes are seldom used for collector drains.

I.4.3.3   Plastic collector drains

The characteristics of plastic collectors are similar to field drain pipes, with the exception that they are usually not perforated. Plastic collectors can be produced in pipes on coils, but especially for the larger diameter, they are often produced in lengths of 6 or 9 m. The norms and standards for the production of plastic collector pipes are the same as those for field drain pipes (Table 1).

I.4.3.4   Concrete collector drains

For many years, the use of concrete for collector drains was standard practice. Over the past twenty years plastic pipes have gradually been replacing the smaller diameter concrete collector drains. Concrete pipes are still in use for larger diameter collector drains, but may very well be slowly phased out. There is practically no limit to the diameter of concrete pipes, although the concrete must be reinforced for large diameters (> 400 mm). Wall thickness varies between 25 and 50 mm. Pipe ends are straight or have a collar, or a spigot and groove.

The length of the individual pipe sections varies between 0.75 and 1.0 m, depending on local custom and diameter. A limitation is the weight per section. The sections have to be installed and transported. The quality production and quality control for collector concrete collector pipes is similar to those of concrete field drain pipes.

I.4.4   Envelopes

I.4.4.1   Function of envelopes

A drain envelope is a porous material placed around a perforated drain pipe to perform the following functions:
- Filter function: to prevent or restrict soil particles from entering the drain pipe where they may settle and eventually clog the pipe;
- Hydraulic function: to provide a porous medium of relatively high permeability around the pipe to reduce entrance resistance.

I.4.4.2   Envelope Materials

Drain envelopes (or filters) can be made of granular (or mineral), organic and synthetic materials (Figure 25).

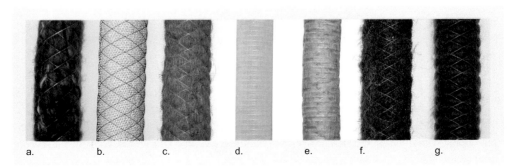

Figure 25   Envelopes can be made of wrapped polypropylene fibres (a, f & g), polystyrene granules (b) and coconut fibres (c), non-woven nylon (d) and woven typar (e)

Granular envelopes

Granular envelopes are made of sand, gravel (both natural and crushed), slag (often industrial waste products) or fired clay granules. They have been tried world wide and have been proven to be functional in almost all soil types, provided the grading of the envelope is designed in relation to the soil texture, although granular envelopes cannot be used with trenchless drainage.

The application of granular envelopes requires a logistically perfect organisation and special equipment (gravel trailers and front loaders). Imperfections in the supply line tend to hold up the whole installation process. Generally, the use of granular envelopes is considered to be cumbersome. Large volumes of heavy, well-graded envelope material (for example 4 m³/100 m of field drain Ø 80 mm weighing some 8 tons) have to be transported to the site and in the field towards the drain. Because of its weight alone, transport and application costs can be high, especially when the base material has to come from far away.

Correct placing of the granular envelope around the pipe can be done using modern drainage trenchers that can be equipped with hoppers and gravel gates. In the case of liquid subsoils, special hydraulic provisions can be attached to the drainage trencher to place the gravel around the pipes.

Although well-designed and applied granular envelopes have proven to be technically functional, they are less desirable for practical reasons. In new areas without drainage experience where no field tests on synthetic envelopes have been conducted, a granular envelope is still the first most secure choice.

Organic envelopes

In North and West Europe peat, coconut fibres, (flax) straw, chaff, heather, wood chips and sawdust have been used, but have been phased out. They tend to decompose over time; decomposition materials of some organic envelopes tend to block the water entry to the pipes. The coconut fibre envelopes used in Western Europe, have been totally replaced by PP fibre envelopes (see below). Furthermore, in warmer climates the decomposition process is speeded up and the organic materials tend to last less than one or two seasons. Generally speaking, organic materials are not a feasible proposition for drain envelopes.

Synthetic envelopes

Synthetic envelopes that are normally used in combination with corrugated plastic pipes are made of:
- Loose voluminous synthetic envelopes of polymeric fibres (polyamide (PA), polyethylene (PE), polyester (PETP = polyethylene terephtalate) and polypropylene (PP). Polystyrene (PS) granules in netting around the pipe also belong to this category;
- Geo-textiles are woven, knitted or non-woven (thin) sheets. The fibres used for the production of the geo-textiles are the same as those used for the voluminous synthetic envelopes.

Voluminous envelopes combine the filter and hydraulic functions of an envelope. The geo-textiles mainly serve as envelope and tend to clog earlier. Synthetic materials are inert and are not affected by soil chemicals.

As yet there are no common standards and norms for the functionality of synthetic envelopes in keeping with the soil characteristics in which they are placed. Positive results of synthetic envelopes in laboratory tests do not necessarily translate into positive results in the soil. In areas where there is no experience with synthetic envelopes, field tests are the only known method to determine whether a certain envelope is functional. In some countries some envelopes (often geo-textiles) have given positive results when used as filters for wells. The hydraulic conditions (pressures) around wells are different than around drain pipes. These experiences cannot be extrapolated simply. The production of envelopes of synthetic materials requires a specialised industry, both for the production of the fibres and for the wrapping around the pipe. For further information see the bibliography.

Conclusion

Pre-wrapped synthetic envelopes are the most practical for the installation of subsurface drainage systems. If suitable, well-tested and proven synthetic envelopes are available, the use thereof being most desirable. If this is not the case, the most logical approach would be to start with the technically secure graded gravel with a view to replacing it as soon as possible with a well- tested and proven synthetic envelope.

I.4.4.3   Granular envelopes

Production

The required particle size distribution of granular (gravel) envelopes is dependent on the particle size distribution of the soil in which the drain will be installed. In other words, the envelopes have to be designed and later mixed or sieved on the basis of the prevailing soil texture at drain depth in the project area. If there are important variations in soil texture in the project area, the "average" granular envelope must be checked to see if it is functional under all conditions. If this is not the case, the necessary adjustments need to be made to suit the specific area.

Preparation of these types of envelopes is done by sieving out particles of an undesirable size from natural or crushed base material, or by mixing particles of specific size ranges. Vibration during transport can cause a de-mixing of the particles, if this occurs the gravel has to be mixed again at the site.

Standards

The first criterion for granular envelopes is that the particles are stable (stone or sand) and will not deteriorate over time, e.g. by soil chemicals, or dissolve in water. Selection of the required particle size analyses has to be done during the design phase of the project. The results must be documented in the specifications. Detailed information is presented in FAO Irr. & Dr. Paper 60 (see Bibliography).

I.4.4.4   Synthetic envelopes

Synthetic envelopes are commonly pre-wrapped, meaning that the envelope is wrapped around the pipe before delivery to the site. Consequently, they can only be used in combination with corrugated plastic pipes.

Production
Production of the synthetic material is a very specialised job mostly carried out by the chemical or artificial fibre industry. Since the volume and the weight of the synthetic material are limited, transport over longer distances and import is not prohibitively expensive.

a.

b.

Figure 26   Pre-wrapping drain pipes can be done manually (a) or mechanically (b)

Pre-wrapping

Geo-textiles can be manually wrapped around the pipes, although it requires a considerable amount of labour and a large (long) workplace (Figure 26a). Pre-wrapping of the loose voluminous materials can only be done with wrapping machines. Wrapping machines require conscientious management and high-quality machinery to assure that an even layer (even in thickness and even in density) is wrapped around the pipe (26b). Very strong nylon thread is required to fix the envelope around the pipe. The exact type depends on the wrapping machine.

Since the envelope has to be wrapped around the pipe, carrying out the process of pipe production and wrapping in one location would be preferable and save on transport costs. If this is not possible it would be logical to do the wrapping as close as possible to either the pipe factory or the installation site.

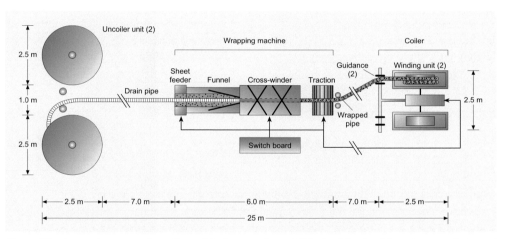

Figure 27 An envelope wrapping-unit consist of an uncoiler unit (2), sheet feeder & funnel, cross-winder and winding unit (2)

Depending on the type of envelope (loose fibres or sheets) two basic technologies are used to wrap drain pipes:

- Sheet-wrapping machines. This type of machine can handle both voluminous envelope materials like PP450 or PP700 or thin geo-textiles. The production process is rather simple: needle-punched envelope sheet purchased from specialised factories are wrapped around the pipe and fixed with strong nylon thread;
- Loose fibre-wrapping machines. This type of machine is used to wrap envelopes made from loose fibres, either organic or synthetic. The loose fibres are loosened (they are often compacted during transport), mixed, fed into the wrapping machine and fixed. The necessary technology here is more complex than in the sheet-wrapping machines as the quality of the envelope material depends on the production process (mix, feed and wrapping strength all influence the final quality of the envelope).

A wrapping unit consists of four components (Figure 27). It covers a net area of approximately 25 x 6 m and should be placed on a level and preferably a concrete floor. The equipment can be moved from one place to another relatively simply.

Standards

Pre-wrapped synthetic envelopes are a recent development in drainage technique. No common standards and norms have been developed for determining which envelope is to be used in which soils. There are a multitude of synthetic envelopes that are used or are still under experimentation. Quality standards for pre-enveloped synthetic material as such (thus not the relationship envelope/soil) focus on: material tensile strength, fibre length and density, or unit weight per unit length and pore size opening. European norms (EN) and ISO norms for testing several aspects of the synthetic envelopes have been prepared (see Bibliography).

Quality control

Quality control must be carried out by specialists before the pre-wrapped pipes are transported to the site. The best procedure is for the factory to deliver a quality certificate with the pre-wrapped pipes issued by an independent organisation.

I.4.5 Structures and pumps

I.4.5.1 Considerations on the selection of structures and pumps during the various steps of the implementation process

Many structures used for subsurface drainage systems are made of concrete or brick and, in most circumstances, can be produced in a conventional way. A number of decisions have to be made before the design phase by either the planning or implementation authority (Box 4.2). If pumping is necessary the decisions "where to pump in the system" and "what pumps to use" can be crucial for management and maintenance of the system.

Box 4.2 Structures and pumps: decisions to be made

- Are the structures, where possible, going to be prefabricated or "cast in place"?
- If they are prefabricated: will this be done by a specialised industry or prefabricated onsite?
- If manholes are used: are they to be aboveground or underground?
- If pumping is required: what energy source is to be used, what type of pump and what automation?

The decisions depend very much on the local situation, customs and existing building practices:
- Casting of concrete structures onsite or building them from bricks (manholes sumps etc.) can be troublesome in situations with a high groundwater level and/or unstable soils;
- The quality of prefabricated structures in specialised industries is often higher and more uniform than "prefabrication onsite". Quality control is also less complicated;

- Aboveground manholes are easier to open; cleaning and inspection of subsurface drainage systems is easier. Aboveground manholes, however, are obstacles to agricultural activities that can be easily damaged and vandalised or used as an outlet for excess irrigation water;
- Underground manholes do not have the disadvantage of being an obstruction, but are cumbersome to dig up and difficult to locate once installed. The techniques to locate them with metal detectors are not always successful in practice;
- Pumps can be either driven by electric motors or diesel engines. Electric motors are by far the most economical, convenient and reliable. They can be automated relatively simply. They require, however, a connection to the electric grid;
- A choice has to be made between underwater pumps (pumps where the electric motor and the pump are combined, suction pumps (electrically or diesel driven) or long axel pumps (also electrically or diesel driven).

I.4.5.2   Manholes

Manholes can be used for connecting field drains to collector drains, for creating access to (long) field drains. The manhole can be either aboveground or underground (buried) (Figure 28) and can be made of pre-cast segments, cast in place concrete or masonry.

I.4.5.3   Sumps

The term sump is used for the last manhole in a composite drainage system. Here all the water is collected and discharged either by gravity or by pumping into the discharge area (open drain). Sumps are in effect similar to manholes, and have either a concrete pipe as gravity outlet or serve as reservoir from where the water is pumped. The dimensions should tally with the pumps. Sumps have the functions to:
- Provide storage capacity in the subsurface drainage system, so that pumps do not have to operate continuously;
- Act as pump house;
- Act as silt trap.

Sumps can be made of pre-cast concrete rings or brickwork (Figure 29). The diameter depends on the required storage capacity. Calculation of the required storage capacity is dependent on the capacity of the pump, the design drainage rate, the over-dimensioning of the drainage system for safety, the maximum number of switching per hour and the storage capacity in the collector drainage system. Furthermore, the diameter depends on the type of pumps, e.g. under water pumps, suction pumps and to a lesser extend the required storage capacity. In practice the collector system itself provides the major part of this storage, the sump itself contributes hardly to it. Installation of sumps is often problematical because of the required depth (needed to create silt trap capacity below the invert level of the collector drains) combined with the frequently high groundwater levels, especially in areas with unstable subsoil.

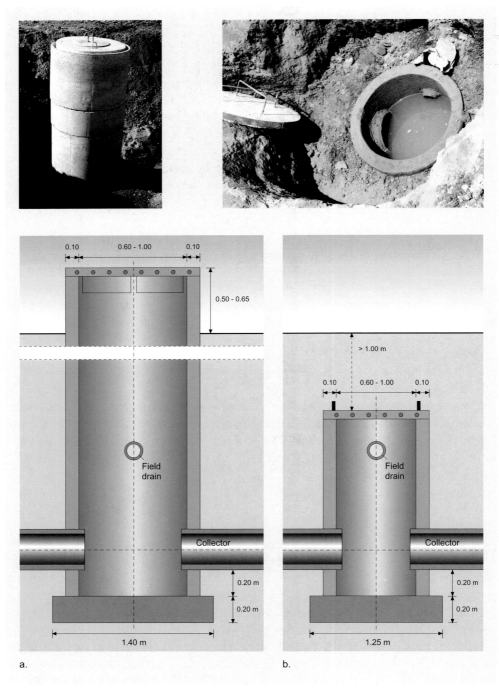

Figure 28   Manholes with a cover above (a) and below (b) the soil surface

a.   b.

*Figure 29   Sumps are made of brickwork (a) or pre-cast concrete rings (b), examples from Drainage Pilot
Areas in Rajasthan, India*

I.4.5.4   Outlets

A singular drainage system has a large number of field drain outlets, so they should not be too
expensive. Furthermore, because all outlets of a singular system can easily get damaged,
regular inspection and repair is necessary. The outlets are mostly drain pipes of plastic or concrete that protrude from the slope of the open collector drain (Figure 30a) or minor structures
built in the slope with the necessary protection devices against erosion.

The outlets of a composite drainage system are similar to the outlets of singular system, their
construction is more permanent and robust since there are fewer outlets and the area served is
larger than that of a singular system (Figure 30b).

a.   b.   c.

Figure 30   Outlet of a field drain (a), collector drain (b) and sump (c) in an open main drain

I.4.5.5   Pumps

Diesel driven pumps

If there are no electrical connections available or if a connection to the electric grid is considered too expensive, diesel driven pumps can be selected for the drainage system. For diesel powered pumping one larger station serving a large area usually be a more logical choice than a number of smaller pumping stations. This is because of the logistics of fuel supply and the need for the stations to be almost continuously attended. Automation (automatic switch on and of) is possible but rather complicated. Larger stations pump from open watercourses, consequently the diesel pumps are best placed at the end of an open drainage system into which the subsurface drainage systems discharge.

Electrically driven pumps

Electrically driven pumps are mostly smaller and can be combined with the motor. They are relatively simple to automate (switch on and off in relation with water levels). These pumps are available for a large range of capacities sizes and can efficiently pump water directly from subsurface system without any special housing. Electrically driven underwater pumps require hardly any specialised housing and can easily be installed in sumps (Figure 31). The only infrastructure required is a connection to the electric grid (240-380V). With electrically driven underwater pumps, a number of small pumps can be installed at the end of the subsurface systems, instead of pumping the water from the main drainage system by installing larger pumping stations at the outlet. Once properly installed the maintenance of electrical pumps is minimal.

If pumps are used in a saline environment, the pump, pipes, etc should be made of salt resistant components.

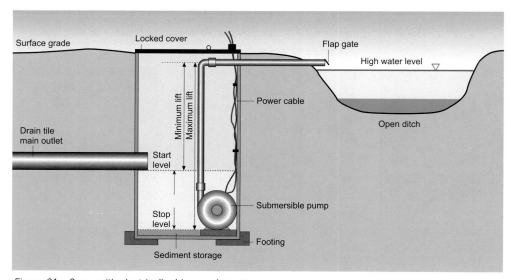

Figure 31   Sump with electrically driven underwater pump

I.5 Installation Equipment for Subsurface Drainage Systems

I.5.1 Introduction

I.5.1.1 Installation equipment: decisions to be made during the planning phase

The selection of installation equipment has far-reaching consequences for the implementation process as it affects the degree of freedom of choosing the depth and the layout of drainage system and the pertinent drainage materials. If there is an existing drainage industry and tradition, the characteristics of the available installation equipment will be well known, and consequently are a readily available input for the planning and design process. In countries where drainage is just starting, suitable and cost effective drainage installation equipment will need to be selected. The characteristics of the equipment will be a basis for estimating the required investments in case the equipment has to be purchased, and they are an essential input for the planners of the implementation authority. Information about installation equipment can also be found in ILRI Publication 16 or publications of the manufacturers. This chapter will be confined to the information required to making a cost effective choice of installation equipment under the prevailing conditions.

Box 5.1 Installation equipment: major decisions during the planning phase

1) What would be the most cost effective type of installation equipment under the given conditions?
2) How much equipment will be required to carry out the installation within the foreseen time frame?
3) Is the equipment available in the country?
   If not:
   a) Does the quantity of the work warrant the purchase of equipment or should leasing, renting, temporary import or other installation methods be considered?
   b) Will the desired equipment have to be rented or purchased and by whom?
   c) Is the government involved in the specification and/or purchase or is this left to contractors?
   d) Is there enough work for the equipment to make the purchase commercially viable?
   e) Can the equipment be properly maintained in the country, if not how and by whom is this going to be organised?

I.5.1.2 Equipment requirements resulting from the chosen drainage method

The equipment requirement follows from the selected installation methods of which there are three to choose from:
- Full manual installation;
- Combined mechanical and manual installation;
- Mechanical Installation.

The conditions and preferred and appropriate type of drainage installation method is discussed in Chapter I.6. Generally speaking, for large areas mechanical installation is the most appropriate methodology. Manual installation and/or a combination of mechanical and manual installation is used only for draining small areas and/or if machines have no access to the site. Each of these methods requires specific equipment:

- Special hand tools have been developed for manual installation consisting of specially designed spades and hooks for placing the clay pipes in position (see Figure 49 and Part II);
- Hydraulic excavators are mostly used for digging the trenches in the combined mechanical & manual installation method. Hydraulic excavators are well-known machines that are available in most countries;
- Mechanical installation necessitates the use of specialised drainage machines, often in combination with excavators, bulldozers and tractors.

This Chapter focuses on mechanical installation while the methodology for manual and combined installation will be described in Part II.

I.5.2   General considerations on the selection of installation equipment

I.5.2.1   Installation equipment

A complete set of equipment is necessary for the installation of drainage systems. The constitution of the set largely depends on the characteristics of the drainage systems and drainage material to be used. A list of the required equipment for an installation unit can be found in Chapter I.6 and I.9 and in Part II. Most of the equipment is support equipment that can also be used for other purposes (tractors, trailers, hydraulic excavators, front loaders etc.) and is not specific to drainage. Since this is equipment that is mostly well known and available in most countries no further comments are needed. Equipment specific to subsurface drainage installation is confined to: drainage machines and to a lesser extent the gravel trailers and backfill equipment. This chapter focuses on the drainage machines.

I.5.2.2   Required characteristics of drainage machines

A drainage machine must be capable of installing a drain pipe at the desired depth with the desired grade with minimal deviations under the prevailing soil conditions. Allowable deviations are plus or minus 25% of the drain diameter. In practice the drainage machines have to install the pipe at the required depth and grade either:
- In a trench (trencher) that is later backfilled, or;
- At the desired location by pulling the pipe in a gallery formed by a knife like device (trenchless machine).

Both methods require near perfect grade control.

Although drainage trenchers and pipe layers or cable laying machines (used for Public Utilities like electricity, drinking water pipes and gas pipes) are very similar at first glance, there are some essential differences. Pipe and cable laying machines dig a trench in which a cable or later a pipe is placed directly. Since within relatively large ranges only depth below field level is important for pipes and cables, these machines are not constructed for precise grade and depth control. For subsurface drainage, however, it is essential to have the capacity to install pipes at the desired depth at a near perfect grade. In general, pipe & cable laying machines do not have the capacity to install agricultural drainage pipes in flat areas with the required precision of grades and depth. In hilly or sloping areas where drains are installed with the slopes, grade control is less of a sensitive issue. On the other hand, drainage trenchers are perfectly suitable for making trenches for pipes or cables.

I.5.2.3 Maintenance requirements for drainage machines

Drainage machines need maintenance, spare and wear parts. Since a considerable amount of hydraulic drives and hydraulic commands is integrated into modern drainage machines, it is essential for maintenance facilities for hydraulic systems to be either available or created. The wear parts consumption, such as the digging knives and chains belonging to drainage trenchers machines is relatively high. These parts are made of highly specialised steel. To permit a continuous and smooth operation it is vital that the supply of these spare parts (including financing and import facilities) is available or organised.

I.5.2.4 Depth and grade control with laser

In order to facilitate the essential depth and grade control and to limit operator errors the facilities for automatic depth/grade control with laser have become standard on all agricultural drainage machines. Laser can directly command the hydraulic valves of the depth regulation (see Part II). Depth and grade control have since the introduction of laser vastly improved. The cost of laser equipment in comparison with the cost of drainage machines is limited (<10%). (The visual depth control as used up to the seventies of last century, although theoretically still possible, is in practices completely superseded by laser depth and grade control. (see ILRI Publication 16, Chapter 21.4.1).

I.5.3   Hydraulic excavator/backhoe

As discussed in Chapter 5.1.2, drain installation with a hydraulic excavator that digs trenches in which drain pipes are placed by hand is an option if:
- No specialised drain installation equipment is available, and/or;
- Only small (trial) areas are to be installed with subsurface drains, and/or;
- It concerns areas where the access of drainage machines is problematical.

The excavation of a uniform graded trench bottom on which the pipe can be laid with the proper grade is difficult and often results in a slow working speed (Figure 32). The depth and grade control under these conditions has to be done with the aid of levelling instruments; the precision is very dependent on the skill of the operator. A laser system can also be used, but this will not automatically regulate the digging depth of the excavator. Proper installation can only be done if there is no water in the trench and the soils are stable. Under unstable soil conditions, installation using an excavator can prove to be an impossible task and/or dangerous for the labourers. Since the hydraulic excavator is a multiple purpose piece of equipment it is often readily available. The cost effectiveness, however, is dependent on the speed of installation and consequently the cost per meter of installed drain.

Figure 32
Hydraulic excavator digging a drain
trench

The advantages and limitations of installation of drain pipes by hand in trenches dug by excavators are:

Advantages:
- Excavators are well known and normally readily available;
- Excavators can be used for other jobs if there is no drain installation.

Limitations:
- Proper installation is only possible in stable soils (no caving in of trench) and during periods that there is no water in the trench;
- No automatic depth/grade control is possible and the skill of operators is essential;
- Progress is slow;
- Depth limited because of danger to labourers of trench collapse.

I.5.4   Trencher drainage machines

I.5.4.1   General

The vast majority of drainage machines used worldwide are so-called drainage trenchers or short "trenchers" (Figure 33). Trenchers dig a trench with its bottom at the required depth and the required grade and place the drain pipe on the bottom of the trench. After the pipe has been placed, the trench has to be backfilled either by hand or with motorised equipment (Chapter I.6.8.8). Trenchers are produced in various sizes in a wide range of capacities and depending on the type, can:

- Install pipes to a depth about 3 m (deeper installation is possible but requires specialised equipment);
- Make trenches up to 0.50 - 0.60 m in width;
- Install drain pipes in hard or stony soil with special components (knives, chains) for the trencher (see Chapter I.5.7);
- Work in soils with hard layers using machines that are specially designed for the purpose (see Chapter I.5.7);
- Install drains in unstable subsoils and/or under the groundwater level (in extreme cases special attachments have to be used).

Figure 33 Trencher drainage machine

I.5.4.2 Composition of drainage trenchers

A trencher is basically composed of the following elements (Figure 34):

- Machine frame with the engine;
- Crawler tracks;
- Intermediate frame from where the depth/grade regulation takes place;
- Digging mechanism, consisting of a digging boom and continuous digging chain with digging knives;
- Trench box.

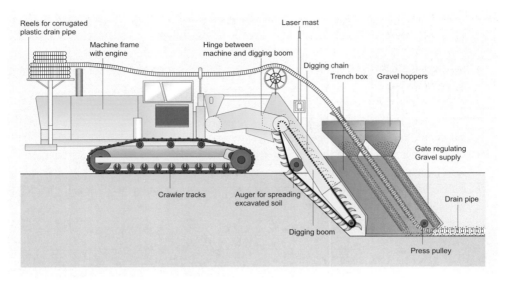

Figure 34   Schematic layout of a trencher showing the main elements

The following attachments/variations are available (Figure 35):
- Two gravel hoppers can be mounted on the trench box (Figure 35a). Chutes from the hoppers guide the granular envelope downwards and subsequently place it under (hopper 1) and above (hopper 2) the drain pipe. These hoppers and guides are only required if a granular envelope is used;
- If a granular envelope is used at the end of the trench box a valve can be installed to regulate the thickness of the granular envelope;
- The trench box dimensions can vary according to the desired depth of the drain installation and the width of the trench. The required width of the trench can be determined as: the diameter of the largest pipe to be installed+ the thickness of the envelope + the thickness of the trench box sides (2 x 25 mm). The thickness of a granular envelope is often taken as 2 x 75 mm. The trench width should not be not too large since most of the energy for the installation is used up in the digging exercise and the more soil volume is dug out the more energy is required. If the trenchers are used for installation at a variable depth, a change of trench box and length of digging boom can be advantageous, for instance, when collector trenchers are used for field drain installation;
- The knives on the digging chain and the distance between the knives can vary in accordance with the soil conditions;
- Part of the digging mechanism is an auger to transport the excavated soil to both sides of the trench. In the case of deeper and wider trenches, the amount of soil may be too much to handle by an auger and so a conveyor belt is used (Figure 35b);
- The commands of the hydraulic valves of the intermediate frame can be connected to the electronics of the laser equipment for automatic manipulation by the laser (this is practically standard);

*Figure 35   Attachments to trenchers: (a) gravel hoppers; (b) conveyor belt; (c) water tank; (d) water sprayer
            alongside the trench box; (e) blinding device; (f) reel for corrugated plastic pipe, and (g) platform
            for pipes*

- A water tank can be installed on top of the engine to feed a water spraying installation that lets water flow along the outside of the trench box (Figure 35c&d). This prevents the clay from sticking to the trench box in heavy clay soils;
- For corrugated plastic drain pipes delivered on rolls, reels can be mounted on the trencher with hydraulically operated hinges (Figure 35f). The rolls can be loaded on these reels and guiding devices guide the drain pipes towards the trench box. The pipe feeding and guiding devices have to be designed to accommodate the largest diameter drain pipe;
- In the rare instances when clay or concrete pipes are used, a platform can be built on the machine to store pallets of drain pipes (Figure 35g). A crane can also be built on the trencher to lift the pipe pallets onto the platform;
- A so-called blinding device can be attached to the trench box for scraping some of the topsoil off the trench behind the trencher (Figure 35e). This soil covers and stabilises the just installed drain pipe. This device can only be used on stable homogeneous soils. In other soils it can disturb the depth regulation of the trencher;
- If, for the installation, a trencher has to work in liquid soils with a granular envelope, a gravel extruder can be mounted to extrude under the pressure the granular envelope surrounding the pipe;
- Trenchers can be equipped with retractable crawlers. The width of the crawler can be increased for more stability. The crawlers can be retracted for transport;
- The cabin and the control panel of the trencher can be either mounted on the chassis or on the digging boom. If the trencher is not equipped with laser the cabin needs to be positioned on the digging boom to make visual grade control possible. In case of grade control by laser the cabin can be positioned in either place. Mounting of the cabin on the chassis is generally more comfortable and gives less disturbance of the installation depth caused by staff moving in and out of the cabin.

I.5.4.3   Sizes of trenchers

The engine power of the most commonly used trenchers ranges between 100 and 400 HP (70 -300 KW). Lighter types have an engine power of up to 200 HP (150 KW) and weigh about 8-10 tons. This type is mostly used for shallow drainage (routine < 1 m maximum 1.5 m), often in parks, for sporting facilities or in horticulture. The medium-sized drainage trenchers have an engine power of around 300 HP (225 KW) and can install pipe drains up to a maximum depth of 2- 2.5 m and trench width of around 0.30 m. They weigh around 20 tons and are mostly used for field drain installation. The heavy drainage trenchers have an engine power of around 400 HP (300 KW) and can install pipe drains up to a maximum depth of 3 m with a trench width of around 0.40 - 0.50 m. They weigh around 23-25 tons and in extreme cases up to 40 tons and can be used for larger diameter collectors. Larger drainage trenchers with more power are used for special conditions like in rocky soil.

I.5.4.4   Types of trenchers

Among the several principles and models have been tried out and used over the years, the major developments were as follows:
- The initial trenchers were fitted with a bucket wheel type digging mechanism (Figure 36a). Although they are still used in some parts of the world they are outmoded and cannot deliver the required exactness of depth and grade control;
- Trenchers mounted on and behind wheel tractors (36b). These are sometimes used on sloping areas for shallow drains. For flat areas they lack adequate depth and grade control;
- Trenchers with a so-called "flat digging chain" have been used in the past in softer soils for shallow drain installation. Machines with flat digging chains have no intermediate frame and the digging mechanism is attached to the frame of the machine. The variation of depth is obtained by varying the vertical angle of the digging boom;
- Trenchers consisting of a separate digging mechanism and trench box that is pulled by a crawler tractor and activated by the power take off (PTO) are used for shallow drain installation in some parts of the world. The depth/grade control is not adequate;
- Trenchers mounted on tracked machinery with trench boxes and a so-called vertical digging boom that are attached to intermediate frames (parallelogram construction) are currently the most common and universally applied (Figure 33).

a.   b.

Figure 36   Bucket-wheel type trencher on tracks (a) and mounted behind a wheel tractor (b)

I.5.4.5   Advantages and limitations of installation of drain pipes with a trencher

Advantages
- High speed of installation: 2000 m/hr at the maximum with an overall installation output of 1.5-2.5 km per day, depending on the logistics supporting the machine. The installation speed per hour is of limited significance, since it does not take into account the preparation time, time required for starting the drain at the correct level, the time to drive

back to the next drain after completion etc. Thus, the actual installation speed per day that takes these factors in to account is of more practical value during the planning phase;
- Next to perfect depth and grade control is possible;
- All currently known envelopes can be applied;
- Trenchers are available/adjustable for a wide range of depths and trench width and soil conditions;
- Trenchers can be easily coupled to depth/grade control devices based on laser technology;
- The backfilled trench generally has a limited flow resistance and can improve drainability of the soil.

Limitations
- Practically speaking, trenchers can only be used for drain installation;
- Digging knives/chains wear out continuously and must be replaced with parts made from specially hardened steel;
- Well-trained handling and maintenance is needed;
- The full potential and depth control of trenchers can only be used for installing either corrugated (flexible pipes) or small clay or concrete pipes with a maximum length of 1 m. The trencher can prepare the trench for installing rigid pipes of greater lengths. The pipe has to be deposited in the trench later after the machine has completed the trench.

I.5.5   Trenchless drainage machines

I.5.5.1   General

The technique of trenchless drain pipe installation has been developing since the late 1960s/early 1970s. 'Ploughing-in' of drains became possible with the introduction of the flexible corrugated plastic drain pipes delivered on coils. These pipes can make the rather sharp curves at the spot where the pipe leaves the machine. With the trenchless installation technique a blade is pulled through the ground to break and lift up the soil to make room for the pipe, which is guided into position through the hollow part of the blade, or through a pipe guide trailed behind the blade.

Trenchless drainage machines can work faster than trenchers and suffer less wear and tear. However, they require more power for the same installation depth than the trenchers. A daily installation output of 4 km/day is not uncommon in a logistically well-organised environment.

These machines can install only corrugated plastic pipes of limited dimensions (Ø 100 - 25 mm). If envelopes are required only pre-wrapped envelopes can be used; no granular envelope can be installed. The maximum depth of installation is 1.8 m, however an average depth range of 1.4 m - 1.5 m is a more realistic figure.

Trenchless drain installation is quite common at present in Western Europe and North America. The main reason is that under the economic conditions in these countries with high labour costs and relatively shallow drain installation, trenchless installation is faster and cheaper. The application of trenchless drainage in irrigated areas in arid and semi-arid zones is rather limited because the limitation in depth. Up to now very limited experience has been obtained in these areas, the only well documented experiences are: the use of a plough-type trenchless drainage machine in the Mardan SCARP project in Pakistan and the RAJAD project in India (both projects are discussed in Part III) and the testing of a V-plough in Egypt (see Bibliography).

I.5.5.2 Composition of trenchless machine

A trenchless machine consists of a machine frame with the engine mounted on crawler tracks and an installation blade hinged to the machine frame. The hinges can be operated hydraulically to regulate the depth of the installation (Figure 37).

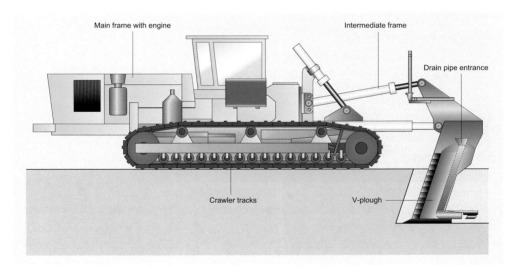

Figure 37   The hinges of a trenchless drainage machine can be operated hydraulically to regulate the depth of the installation

Tracks
A trenchless drainage machine has a much higher traction requirement than a trencher. The engine power is almost completely transferred to the tracks, whereas with a trencher the power is mostly transferred to the digging chain. The tracks used for trenchless drainage machines are therefore different than the tracks for trenchers. Trenchers are equipped with "Triple Grouser" plates. These tracks function well under dry conditions but do tend to slip, especially on wet soils. If the field conditions are too wet vertical plates or so-called cleats can be mounted on the Triple Grouser plate for extra traction (Figure 38a). The mounting process is a time-consuming job. Moreover, cleats cause more vibration and wear and tear on the machines. A second best

alternative is to use "APEX" plates with delta shaped enlargements (Figure 38b). Tracks with these types of plates can also be used on dry fields with minimal vibrations and give sufficient traction on wet fields.

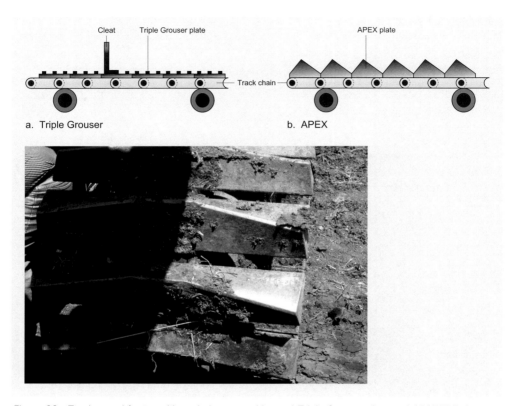

Figure 38   Tracks used for trenchless drainage machines: a) Triple Grouser plate and; b) "APEX" plates

Engine and engine power
Trenchless machines require higher engine power than trenchers, because these machines are heavier and because ploughing the soils at high speed requires more energy than digging. The power is almost exclusively used for traction. The power requirement increases with the square of the installation depth.
Generally speaking for installation to 1.8 m (maximum) the power requirement is in the range of 400 HP (300 KW) and weights of the trenchless machines are around 30 tons.

Installation blades
Two main types of trenchless drainage machines are presently used:
- *Subsoiler type blade*. The vertical plough acts as a subsoiler (Figure 39). In some soil types and under specific moisture conditions, the soil is lifted up to a limited depth and large fissures and cracks are formed. If these extend down to the drain depth, the increased

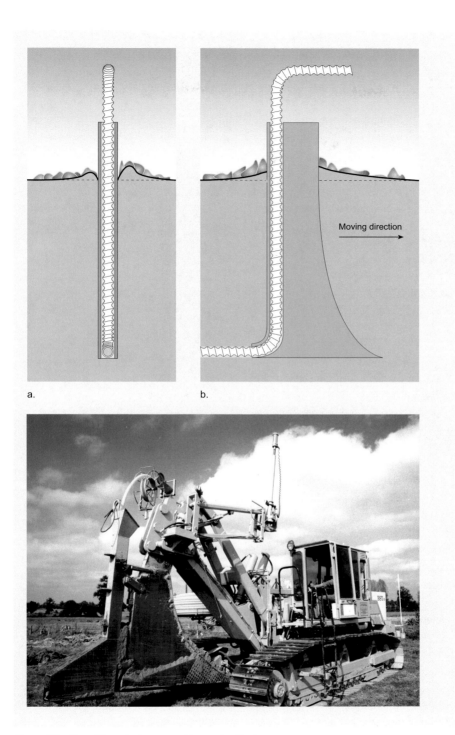

Figure 39   Trenchless drainage machine: subsoiler type

permeability leads to a low entrance resistance and an enhanced inflow of water into the pipe. Beyond a certain critical depth, however, the soil is pushed aside by the plough blade instead of being lifted and fissured. This results in smearing, compaction, and destruction of macro pores, reducing the permeability and increasing the entrance resistance. The critical depth depends mainly on the soil texture and water content during pipe installation. Soil resistance is higher in fine-textured soils than in coarse-textured ones;

- *V-plough type blade.* The V-plough lifts a triangular "beam" of soil while the drain is being installed (Figure 40). The corrugated drain pipe is conveyed through one "leg" of the V-plough. With this type of blade the problem of soil compaction does not arise and the required traction is also somewhat less than with the subsoiler type. The V-plough in Figure 40 can be equipped with a roller that runs over the uplifted soil when the machine drives back to the next drain to install to compact it. A drain can only be installed from the outlet in an upstream direction.

I.5.5.3 Advantages and limitations of installing drain pipes with a trenchless drainage machine

Advantages
- High installation speed (net installation speed up to 4 km/hr, daily installation of 4-5 km);
- Less wear of the pipe laying implement as there are no revolving part;
- Lower drain installation costs in western countries;
- Less damage to soil surface and crops;
- No need to backfill trenches.

Disadvantages/limitations
- Only suitable for flexible corrugated plastic pipes delivered on coils;
- Limited to smaller diameter pipes;
- Only suitable for pre-wrapped envelopes;
- Maximum attainable depth approximately 1.8 m;
- Trenchless machines are heavy and require large tracks;
- High traction required which can cause smearing of topsoil;
- Difficult to install under wet conditions. The grip of the tracks on the land surface is more critical;
- Installation cost increases with depth more than in case a trencher is used (Chapter I.5.6.1);
- Depth and grade control: only possible by laser. Manual depth regulation not possible;
- No possibility of visual inspection of correct positioning of drain pipe or correction;
- Possible compaction of soil around the pipe;
- Cannot be used in unripe soils in reclamation areas, as the drains only begin to function when soil has ripened around the drain and this may take many years.

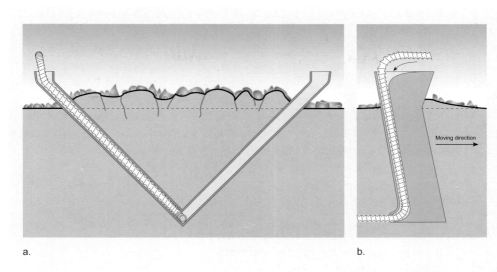

a.   b.

Figure 40   Trenchless drainage machine: V-plough type

I.5.6 Comparison of capacities and cost of drainage installation machinery

I.5.6.1 Cost comparison of trenchers and trenchless installation

The cost of trencher installation and trenchless installation is dependent on many local factors. A study in the Netherlands in 1990 revealed that at shallower depths trenchless installation is cheaper than trenching (Figure 41). The cost of trenchless drain installation, however, increases disproportionately with depth compared to the higher cost of trenchers.

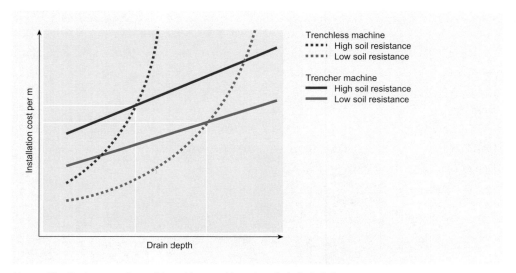

Figure 41   Cost comparison of trenchless and trencher drain installation

I.5.6.2 Capacity of drainage machinery and supporting equipment

The technical capacity of drainage machinery can be obtained from the manufacturer. An indication the average capacity of the main types of machines is presented in Table 5.1.

The actual implementation capacity depends on the organisation of the logistics, maintenance, skills of operators, etc., and consequently largely on the local conditions. The capacities of the drainage machines and the supporting equipment are decisive factors for the implementation of drainage projects. Time estimates with respect to the drain pipe laying activities (collector drain/ lateral drain) can only be made if these data are available. The actual production of a drainage machine is influenced by a number of factors, such as:
- Operator capability;
- Age of the drainage machine;
- Type of drainage machine;
- Weather conditions;

- Soil conditions;
- Drain depth;
- Net operating time (effective time);
- Type drain pipe (PVC/PE or concrete pipes);
- Application of granular or pre-wrapped envelope.

Table 5.1   Drainage machines and their technical capabilities

Machine type	Excavator	Trencher			Trenchless	
		Light	Medium	Heavy	Subsoiler	V-plough
Power (HP)	100-200	200	250-350	350-450	325-525	325-525
Power (KW)	75-150	150	185-260	260-340	245-400	245-400
Weight (tons)	15-25	8-10	18-20	20-30	30-35	30-35
Average installation speed [a] (m/hr)	150	800	800	450	2500	2500
Installation depth (m)	2.0 m	1.5	2.0 m	3.9m	< 2.0m	< 2.0m
Trench width (m)	0.60 and up	0.20-0.30	0.20-0.45	0.20-0.65	No trench	No trench
Drain pipes (type)	All types (including rigid pipes)	Clay, concrete, corrugated plastic			Only corrugated plastic pipes	
Drain diameter (mm)	Not specified	< 200	<200	<400-500	Up to 200	Up to 125
Envelope material	All types	All types	All types	All types	Pre-wrapped	Pre-wrapped
Depth control	Manual	Manual + laser	Manual + laser	Manual + laser	Only Laser	Only Laser
Stony soil	+	-	-	-	+	+/-
Damage to crop and soil surface	Yes	Yes	Yes	Yes	Little	Very little
Visual quality control	Yes	Yes	Yes	Yes	No	No
Unstable soil	No	Yes	Yes	Yes	No	No
Wear parts	Less significant		Significant		Less significant	
Comparative Investment cost (general indication only)	80%		100%		140%	

[a] Installation speed of a trencher depends on soil type, digging depth, trench width and machine power. Under normal soil conditions. the installation speed can be calculated by using the formula: $I = HP/E$, where I = installation speed (m/hr), HP = horse power of the trencher and $E = m^3$ of soil excavated per m' drain (= drain depth x trench width). For hard rock conditions $I = HP/3E$.

Taking all these factors into consideration, it is seldom that more than 50% of the theoretical capacity is actually realised. Part II (A.2) discusses how standards and norms for the capacity of drainage machines and support equipment can be obtained through operational research or monitoring during implementation. Based on operational research the capacity and efficiency of lateral and collector laying drainage machines (trenchers) can be calculated. An example for Egypt is presented in Part III.

Operational research data can be used to determine the number of new machines required to implement the annual plan of a drainage organisation or department. Not only can the duration of the pipe laying activities be estimated, it is also possible to calculate the total capacity of all drainage machines operational in a certain country or region, or the capacities of individual contractors, and so forth. The data can also be used for awarding drainage contracts. Contractor estimates can be checked more easily when installation figures are sufficiently known. Furthermore, the figures can be used for monitoring individual projects. If there is a fixed period during which the drainage project has to be implemented the number of machines required can be calculated.

Data can also be used by mechanical sections in organisations for decision-making on the procurement of new equipment. The capacity and efficiency and performance of different kinds of drainage machines can be compared as well as the assessment of the performance of different machine under various field conditions.

Capacity of supporting equipment
The capacity of supporting machinery, like bulldozers, excavators, etc., is generally well known by local construction units or contractors. Work norms for the *bulldozers* to clear the surface of the drain line or to backfill the drain trench have to be assessed so that the duration of these activities can be estimated. The duration of transport of materials to the site by *trailers* and tractors or *trucks*, and the amount transported to the site are also important data for planning.

I.5.7   Specialised drain installation machinery

Besides the drain installation machinery described above, the machinery designed for special conditions includes:
  • Hard rock trenchers;
  • Trenchers for orchards;
  • Dewatering equipment.

I.5.7.1   Rock trenchers

Installation of drains in soils with hard layers requires a great power source and special cutting knives or bits at the digging chain of the trencher. There are machines that have been specially designed for very hard soils that have been used in desert reclamations areas (Figure 42).

a.   b.   c.

Figure 42   Rock trencher (a) with special knives at the digging chain (b,c)

I.5.7.2   Drain installation machines for orchards

Proper drainage is also vitally important for orchards to obtain good quality fruits and high production. Drains have to be installed in between the row of the fruit trees. Because the space between the rows is rather narrow the design of the drainage machine is such that it enables the drains to be installed without damaging the trees. As can be seen in Figure 43: the reel accommodating the coils of the drain pipe are placed high above the operator and can be lowered in front of the machine to put a new coil of drain pipes on the reel. Another feature is that the machines have narrow tracks.

Figure 43
Drainage machine operating in orchards

I.5.7.3   Dewatering equipment

Horizontal well pointing machines
The dewatering equipment has been developed to install concrete collector drains in unstable/liquid subsoils. Essentially, it consists of installing a drain at a great depth (4-5 m). This drain is connected to a pump. By pumping the watertable is lowered, so that the collector drain can be installed in a stable environment. After installation, the pumping is stopped and ground

water rises again (Figure 44). The pipe is installed by a machine that resembles a trencher (Figure 5.14), but with a vertical digging chain and no trench box. The trench usually collapses immediately behind the machine. Depths of more than 6 m are feasible with a horizontal dewatering machine.

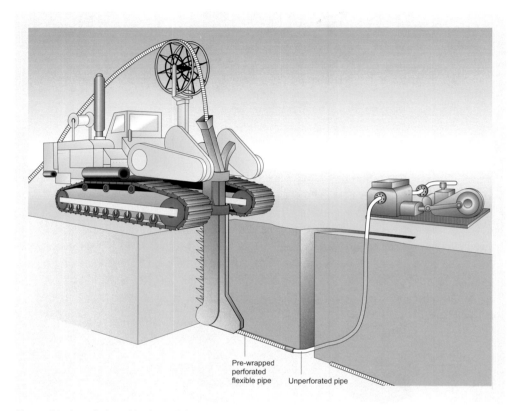

Pre-wrapped
perforated
flexible pipe   Unperforated pipe

Figure 44   Installation of horizontal dewatering pipe

Figure 45
Horizontal dewatering machine

I.5.8   Specialised drain installation support equipment

The specialised support equipment can be confined to:
- Gravel trailers;
- Backfilling equipment;
- Transport equipment.

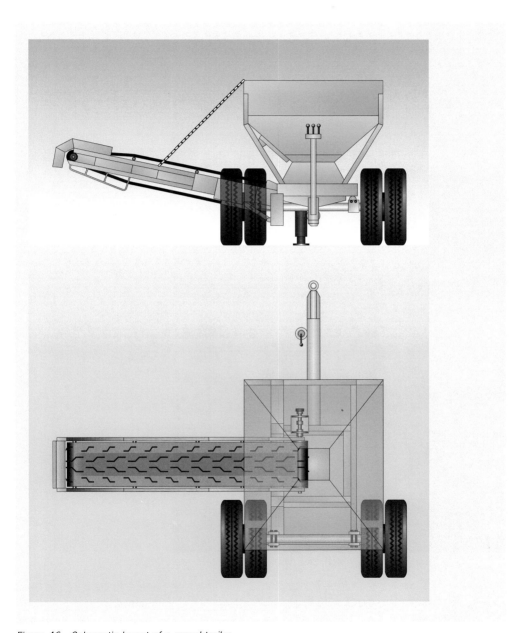

Figure 46   Schematic layout of a gravel trailer

Gravel trailers

A gravel trailer consists of a wheel-mounted hopper with a conveyor belt (Figure 46) and is pulled by a tractor. The tractor is driven parallel with the trencher, while the conveyor belt unloads the granular envelope into the gravel hoppers on the trencher. The conveyor belt is either mechanically activated by PTO (power take off) of the tractor or hydraulically by the hydraulic pump of the tractor. A gravel trailer has a load capacity of some 4 m³ (approximately 8 tons!), which is adequate for some 100 m of field drain of Ø 80 mm. Efficient uninterrupted operation of each trencher requires three gravel trailers (one unloading, one loading, one travelling). The construction of a gravel trailer must be sturdy enough to bear the weight of the gravel trailer.

a.

b.

Figure 47   Backfill equipment: tractor with dozer blade (a) and V-shaped disc-blade mounted at the rear end of a subsoiler type trenchless drainage machine (b)

Backfilling equipment

Numerous motorised solutions are used for backfilling including (Figure 47):

- Bulldozer driven perpendicular to the trench;
- Angle dozer driven parallel with the trench;
- V-shaped disc-blade mounted on bulldozer or tractor;
- Grader;
- Levelling blade on tractor.

The most appropriate system depends on the available machinery and soil type. The dryness of the soil to be backfilled can be a determinant for the choice of the equipment.

Transport equipment

Transport over longer distances of drain installation machines that are track mounted has to be done with low loaders (Figure 48) as track mounted equipment is not designed for road transport and will damage the roads and the tracks.

Figure 48   Transport of drainage machine using a deep loader

I.6 Installation of Subsurface Drainage Systems

I.6.1 Introduction

The implementation authority has to be instructed on how to install the pipe drainage systems. The installation method has far-reaching consequences for the speed of installation, the required equipment, the total cost and total investments to be made. The following installation methods can be considered:

- Manual installation;
- Combined mechanical and manual installation, (installation of pipes by hand in trenches dug by excavators);
- Mechanical installation.

Mechanical installation is the most common method for large-scale installation, using trenchers, excavators, bulldozers tractors, gravel trailers, laser equipment and pumps. It is the best cost and quality effective method. Special circumstances calling for other installation methods include:

- Non-availability of specialised drain installation equipment;
- Only small (trial) areas require to be installed with subsurface drains;
- Areas where the access of drainage machines is problematical.

This Chapter places the emphasis on the mechanical installation of subsurface drains. Manual and the combination of mechanical and manual installation will only briefly be touched on in Part I, but guidelines for manual installation are included in Part II for the sake of completeness.

Box 6.1 Installation methods: major decisions during the planning phase

During the planning phase, the authorities concerned have to decide on:
- The most cost effective and functional installation method to use under the given conditions;
- The equipment, personnel, organisational set up and investments needed for the chosen installation method.

I.6.2 Installation methods

I.6.2.1 Manual installation

Digging trenches by hand and placing the pipes in the trenches by hand was common practice in the past and is still practiced sporadically. Special tools have even been developed for manual installation (Figure 49). Manual installation is a possible alternative:

(i) If the groundwater is not high (placing a pipe at a desired grade under water is practically impossible);

(ii) If the depth is limited (<1 m, greater depth is only feasible under certain conditions with stable soils and seasonal watertables below drain depth).

Figure 49 Special tools have been developed to install drains by hand

The process of manual installation is slow and very labour intensive. For example, in the relatively light soils in the Netherlands the standard was around 25 m'/person/day at a depth of 0.8 m and 13 m'/person/day at a depth of 1.5 m (Case The Netherlands in Part III). Grade control also requires particular skill and care of the installation crew. Manual installation in unstable soils with high watertables and installation at greater depths is perhaps theoretically possible, but is not recommended. The economics of manual installation depends entirely on the cost and availability of labour. In general, manual installation is more expensive than machine installation. For example, in 1986 and 1987, the contractor rate for the manual installation of pipe drains in India was about € 1.10 per meter compare to € 0.35 per meter of machine installation in The Netherlands (Bibliography: Ochs and Bishay 1992). See for installation instructions Part II, Chapter C.32.

I.6.2.2   Combined mechanical and manual installation

The combination of mechanical and manual installation consists of digging trenches with hydraulic excavators and placing the drain pipes into the trench by hand (Figure 50). The excavation of a uniform graded trench bottom on which the pipe can be laid with the proper grade is difficult and the progress of the work is often slow. The depth and grade control under those conditions has to be done with the aid of levelling instruments; consequently the precision is very much dependent in the skill of the operator. A laser system can also be used, but this will not automatically regulate the digging depth of the excavator. Proper installation can only be done if there is no water in the trench and the soils are stable. Under unstable soil conditions installation with an excavator is practically impossible and/or can be dangerous for the labourers.

Figure 50   The combination of mechanical and manual installation consists of digging the drain trench with a hydraulic excavator and placing the drain pipes into the trench by hand (Example Segwa Drainage Pilot Area, Navsari, Gujarat, India, for more details see Part III)

Since a hydraulic excavator is a "multipurpose" piece of equipment it is often readily available. The cost effectiveness, however, depends on the speed of installation and consequently the cost per m of installed drain. See for installation instructions Part II, Chapter C.33 and the example in India in Part III.

It can be concluded that manual installation of drains in trenches dug by excavators has the following advantages and limitations:
Advantages
- Excavators are widely known and normally readily available;
- Excavators can be used for other jobs if there is no drain installation.

Limitations
- Proper installation is only possible in stable soils (no caving in of trench) and when there is no water in the trench;
- No automatic depth/grade control is possible and the skill of operators is essential;
- Progress is slow;
- Depth is limited because of risk to labourers of trench collapse.

I.6.2.3   Mechanical Installation

Mechanical installation consists of installing the drains either with a trencher or a trenchless drainage machine. With this method drains can be installed in most conditions with an automatic depth and grade control, either above or under the water level. The organisational requirements for the full mechanical installation methods, which are to be taken into account during the planning phase, are discussed below.

Drainage machines are expensive pieces of equipment that cost a few hundred thousand euros. The technical lifespan of these machines is at least 10,000 hours or some 10 years. The purchase of a drainage machine may not be economically justified if only small areas are to be drained and no extensive areas are to be equipped with subsurface drainage systems in the near future. Besides renting, temporary import, and so forth, other installation methods can also be considered, although these are not always optimal.

I.6.3   Machinery and equipment requirements for mechanical installation

The machinery and equipment required for installing drains depends on the selected:
- Drainage method;
- Layout of drainage system;
- Drainage materials.

Table 6.1 presents a list of suggested machinery and equipment for the mechanical installation of composite and singular drainage systems with either granular envelopes or with pre-wrapped envelopes. The list is based on the assumption that two trenchers are set to work in the same installation unit. Not included is the equipment required for the transport of the gravel and drain pipes to the field, nor the requirements for making electrical connections for the sump pumps, if applicable. It is assumed that these tasks will be carried out under contract by the relevant organisations. Included are the general and infield transport facilities for personnel, which of course will be locally determined. Efficient installation, including prevention of waiting times, requires adequate transport both to and in the field. The rapid development of the use of mobile phones (cell phones) and walky-talkies as infield communication between the different units has proven to improve efficiency by reducing waiting times. The extent to which this can be realised depends on local conditions. Investment costs of the machinery and equip-ment are discussed in Chapter I.9.

Table 6.1   Suggested list of machinery and equipment require for pipe drain installation for a composite and singular system with and without granular envelope, respectively (requirements for granular envelopes given in italics)

Item	Quantity		Remarks
	Composite	Singular	
Field drain installation machine with laser	1	2	If gravel is used trencher to be equipped with gravel hoppers
Collector installation machine with laser	1		Machine to be adjustable for field drain installation, equipped with gravel hoppers if gravel is used
Laser transmitter	2	2	Matching laser receivers on installation machines
Battery charger for laser	1	1	Not required for modern laser
Hydraulic Excavator	2	1	For making start holes and manhole/sump installation. Not required for singular system in case of start from open ditch.
Gravel trailer	*6*	*6*	
Tractors for gravel trailers	*6*	*6*	*> 75 HP*
Bulldozer	1 - 2	1 - 2	Field preparation/trench closing/support
Front loader	*1*	*1*	*For loading of gravel into gravel trailers*
Agri. tractor & trailer	2	2	Infield transport op pipes etc.
Dewatering pump	1 - 2		Facilitation manhole placement
Fuel tanker & tractor	1	1	Infield fuel supply possibly contracted to fuel supplier
Servicing/maintenance truck (or pickup)	1	1	
Topographic equipment	2	2	Mainly levelling instruments
Cars	1 - 2	1 - 2	For fast transport to field
Motor cycles	1 - 2	1 - 2	Mainly in field transport
Bus for personnel transport	1	1	If necessary
Communication equipment			Depends on local conditions

I.6.4   Organisation and staff requirements for mechanical installation

I.6.4.1   Organisational set-up for mechanical installation

Mechanical installation requires a well-defined organisational set-up. There are no hard and fast rules for the organisation, but it must be geared to the available equipment, the drainage system, the drainage materials to be used and the local customs. The set-up presented in Figure 51 has proved to be effective for the implementation of various drainage projects.

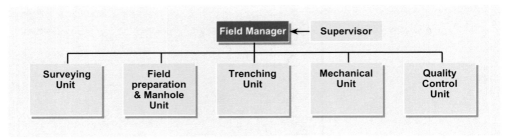

Figure 51   Example of an organisational setup of a drain pipe installation unit

I.6.4.2   Task requirements for mechanical installation

The Staff needed for the construction of subsurface drainage systems vary from project to project. The Staff requirements, including their tasks, for a typical project are presented below. Depending on the situation, the allocation of tasks can vary. The Field Staff of the contractor is normally checked by supervisors representing the implementation authority and/or the beneficiaries.

Field manager
The task of the field manager is the overall management of the installation process. Furthermore, he can be responsible for the coordination of the supply of drainage materials (pipes, gravel, manholes, sumps) and the transport thereof to the site. Whether or not the job can be combined with the supervision of other aspects of the implementation of drainage systems depends on the volume of work.

Surveying Unit
The surveying unit is responsible for:
- Setting out the drainage system (with pegs in the field indicating where the drainage system will come, where the manholes are to come etc.);
- Giving reference levels for the installation of the drainage system (for adjustment of the laser);
- Managing the laser: transporting, charging and setting up the emitter and adjusting the slope;
- Giving levels for installation of manholes and checking the levels during installation.

The survey group may be linked to the quality control group.

Field preparation and manhole unit
The field preparation and manhole group will be responsible for:
- Physically preparing the field, including clearing and smoothing the alignment of the field and collector drains (closing ditchers, removing banks, trees etc., restoring the drains and irrigation canals after installation);
- Making start holes for the trenchers with an excavator, if required;

- Installing manholes and sumps (if relevant);
- Providing all required construction assistance (for instance making of drain bridges);
- Closing drain trenches after installation.

Trenching unit

The trenching unit will have the task of:
- Preparing the pipes for installation (check on the quality) and, if required, laying them out in the field;
- Installing the pipes;
- Managing and applying the granular envelope;
- Carrying out daily maintenance on the machinery (in cooperation with the Mechanical O&M group).

Mechanical O&M unit

The mechanical O&M unit will:
- Carry out with the operators the daily maintenance on all equipment, including oil changes minor repairs, routine inspections etc.;
- Organise the fuel supply fuel to the machinery in the field;
- Advise the field manager on stoppage of the machines if required for technical reasons;
- Prepare major maintenance.

Quality control unit

The tasks of the quality control unit are:
- Checking the quality of the installation (mainly levels of drains installed) (This task can be combined with the surveying group).

Supervisor

The supervisor or supervising unit, as representatives of the implementing authority, has to check and verify if the works are carried out according to the standards and specifications. Supervision can be done in a passive or active way. In the latter case, the supervisor has taken over the tasks of the Quality Control unit. The detailed tasks, rights and duties of the supervisor are described in the conditions of the contract and its specifications. Some more details are discussed in Chapter I.7.

I.6.4.3   Staffing requirements for mechanical installation

The staff requirement for mechanical installation will depend on the selected layout of the subsurface drainage system and the materials that will be used. Local customs and practices can also play an important role. In Table 6.2, "model" staffing requirements are given for installation units working with two drainage machines to install a composite drainage system and a singular system both with and without granular envelope. The total number of staff required to install 3 to 5 km of drains per day varies from between 23 and 25 persons for a singular drainage system without granular envelope and between 36 and 48 persons for a composite drainage systems with granular envelope. The cost of the staffing is discussed in Chapter I.9.

Table 6.2 *Staffing requirement for installation unit working with two drainage machines for installing a composite and singular drainage systems with and without granular envelop, respectively (requirements for granular envelopes given in italics)*

Unit	Staff	Requirements (Qty)	
		Composite system	Singular system
Field management	Field manager	1	1
	Driver	1	1
	Bus driver	0 - 1	0 - 1
	Tractor driver [a]	1	1
Subtotal Field Management Unit		3 - 4	3 - 4
Surveying Unit	Surveyors [b]	2	2
	Assistant surveyors [b]	4	4
Subtotal Surveying Unit		6	6
Field preparation Unit	Manager	0 - 1	0 - 1
	Excavator operator	2	1
	Bulldozer operators	1 - 2	1 - 2
	Assistants	3 - 4	1 - 2
	Masons etc.	2	
Subtotal Field Preparation Unit		8 - 11	3 - 6
Trenching Unit	Trencher operators	2 - 4	2 - 4
	Tractor drivers (gravel trailers)	*6*	*6*
	Loader drivers	*1*	*1*
	Gravel manager	*1*	*1*
	Operator assistants	2-4	2 - 4
Subtotal Trenching Unit		4 - 8 *(12 - 16)*	4 - 8 *(12 - 16)*
Mechanical Unit	Mechanics	1	1
	Fuel tractor driver	1	1
	Assistants	2	2
	Driver	1	1
	Subtotal Mechanical Unit	5	5
Quality Control Unit	Surveyors [b]	2	2
	Surveyor assistant [b]	2	2
	Labourers	2	2
Subtotal Quality Control Unit		2 - 6	2 - 6
Grand Total		**28 - 40 *(36 - 48)***	**23 - 25 *(31 - 43)***

[a] For infield transport, if required.

[b] Combination with quality control and survey group possible.

I.6.5   Planning and Preparatory Aspects for Subsurface Drainage Installation

I.6.5.1   General

The installation process of pipe drainage systems should fulfil a number of conditions to assure that the installation is cost effective and results in systems that are functional. Besides the actual installation techniques and methodologies, as treated in Part II of this handbook, a number of aspects are of relevance during the planning and preparation stage. A summary of these aspects is given in the following sections.

I.6.5.2   Installation season

Drains should be installed under favourable working conditions, meaning dry soil conditions and a relatively deep watertable. Under most climates, drains cannot be installed all year round. Determining the dates and the length of the installation season is an essential input for the planning. There are, so-called, favourable seasons for installation and unfavourable seasons during which installation should preferably be avoided. For optimal results drains should be installed under working conditions that are as favourable as possible. Less favourable or un-favourable periods are:
- Wet seasons when both ground water levels tend to be high and field surfaces wet;
- Wet soils during the rainy season or just after irrigation, when the heavy machinery could easily slip and damage the soil structure;
- Winter season during frost (hard frozen soils are difficult to dig, moreover, plastic drain pipes become brittle);
- Cropping periods: Although installation can technically continue if a crop is in the field, the crops on top of the drain line have to be removed before installation or they will be destroyed by the machinery (a line of minimal 5 m wide when no gravel is applied and minimal 12 m wide when gravel is applied). Such crop damage is usually not acceptable. (In Egypt in the past, installation continued when crops were in the fields and farmers were financially compensated for the crop loss).

I.6.5.3   Logistics

The drainage machines are the highest single cost factor in the installation process (this will be elaborated in Chapter I.9). To reduce costs of the total process the drainage machines have to be used continuously and as effectively and efficiently as possible. Thus waiting times, for whatever reason, have to be avoided. Experience has taught that the bottleneck for the speed of pipe installation is usually not the capacity of the drainage machine, but the organisation and logistics connected with keeping the machine going. This is why it is of utmost importance to organise the logistics around the machine in an optimal way. This is also true for the field preparation, so that the machines can start working immediately and uninterrupted when they arrive at the site. It also applies to the organisation of fuel supply and maintenance of the machines to minimise breakdowns and waiting times and ensure the timely supply of drainage materials (pipes, envelope, gravel etc.). Generally speaking, money spent on logistics and preparation is soon earned back in more efficient operation.

I.6.6   Steps in pipe drain installation

The process of drain installation starts with the handing over of the area to the contractor or installation unit and ends with the final reception of the works by the implementing authority or the beneficiaries. For planning and preparation it has to be kept in mind that drainage systems have to be installed starting from the downstream side towards the upstream side. There are two reasons for this: (1) for the purposes of level control, and (2) because drainage systems often start to discharge directly after or even during installation. If there is no opportunity for downstream discharge of water, undesirable muddy and wet working conditions will be created. Thus:

- The open main drainage system has to be ready and functional before the installation of pipe drains can start;
- The outlet of a composite system, with or without pumps, has to be ready and functional before the collectors are installed. If the pumps are not available or ready, temporary pumps can be used like dewatering pumps, for instance;
- Collector pipes have to be installed before the field drains are installed (starting downstream!);
- Connecting manholes (if any) have to be installed before the field drains are installed;
- The field drains are installed (from downstream to upstream) as the last element of the system;
- After the installation of each drain pipe, the trench box is lifted out of the soil and the drainage machine drives (without installation) to the downstream staring point of the next drain.

The construction of the subsurface drainage system consists of the following steps:
1. Outlet construction;
2. Setting out alignments and levels;
3. Grade Control;
4. Excavating the trenches;
5. Placing the drain pipes;
6. Placing the envelopes;
7. Installation of the junctions/manholes;
8. Backfill of the trenches.

In case of mechanised installation the steps 3 to 6 are a one-time operation. The steps are briefly discussed in the following section. Detailed descriptions of the process are presented in Part II of this handbook (Chapter II.C.19-C.38).

I.6.6.1   Outlet construction

Gravity outlets

If gravity outlets are used, the side slopes of the open drains must be protected from erosion by the out flowing drainage water. Samples of possible protections are presented in Figure 52 and details are given in Part II C.27.

a.

b.

c.

Figure 52   Construction of the outlet of a field drain (a) collector drain (b) and sump (c)

Pumped outlets (sumps)

In flat or gently sloping areas, the land gradients are generally not sufficient for free fall and gravity disposal of drainage water into surface drains. Pumped outlets are established by constructing a sump at the point of disposal of the drainage system and by installing a pumping system to pump water and maintain gravity flow within the system. The size of the sump depends on the area drained by the collector unit and the operating time of the pump (pumping capacity). Small-size sumps can be installed in the same way as manholes (see Part II C.28).

In case larger brick-built sumps are constructed under high watertable conditions or in unstable subsoils it may be necessary to use *vertical well-pointing* techniques to lower the watertable during the construction. This requires special skills and equipment. The *vertical well-pointing* technique consists of forcing well points, i.e. pipes with a perforated bottom part and a filter, into the soil around the building pit. The well points are connected to a suction pump. By pumping, the watertable around the building pit is temporarily lowered and construction can be carried out under dry conditions. Details on *well-pointing* techniques can be found in literature of the building industry and are not discussed in this handbook.

In case large brick or large pre-cast concrete rings are used, *well-sinking* techniques may be used. For this technique also special skills and equipment are required. The *well-sinking* technique consists of placing a concrete ring on the soil surface and by removing the soil from within the ring (in wet conditions the soil can be bailed out) the ring is lowered in the soil. After the ring has been lowered a new ring is place on top and the excavation is continued, till the sump has reached its design depth. The same technique can be used for lowering a brick structure. Details on *well-sinking* techniques can be found in literature on well construction and are not discussed in this handbook.

I.6.6.2   Setting out alignments and levels

The location and alignment of the drain lines must be set out before the actual digging can begin, (Figure 53). First, the downstream location of the drain is marked off by placing a row of pegs along the collector drain at the design drain spacing. Next, the centre line of each drain is set out by placing another row of pegs at the upstream end. Stakes are placed in the soil at both ends of the drain line with the top of the stakes at a fixed height above the future trench bed using a levelling instrument. This very clearly indicates the drain line. The direction of the field drains is assessed standing at the starting point at the collector line, thereafter marking off the location of the field drains with pegs.

I.6.6.3   Grade control

Grade control during the installation of the drain pipes can be done by:
- Automatic grade control by laser on drainage machines, both trenchers and trenchless machines (Figure 54);

- Grade control for manual installation;
- Driver controlled depth regulation on trenchers.

A laser must be used for grade control for mechanical installation of subsurface drains because it contributes to a better quality of drain installation.

Figure 53   Setting out alignments and levels

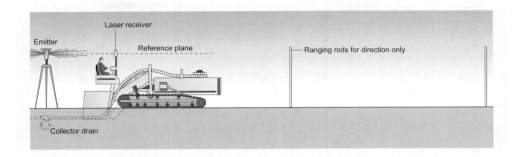

Figure 54   Grade control by laser

I.6.6.4   Excavating the trenches

As discussed in Chapter 5, there are three methods of mechanical installation (Figure 55):

- *Excavator.* All steps in the implementation process are separate steps, implemented one after the other. The trench is dug by the excavator to about 5 cm above the required drain depth and up to the last few centimetres, when the levelling and placing the drain pipes is done by manual labour;
- *Trencher.* Digging the trench, placing the drain pipes and (if applicable) the envelope, is done in a one-time operation. The pit from where the laying of the pipe will start is either dug by the trencher itself or an excavator;
- *Trenchless.* Just like the trencher method, it is a one-time operation, but instead of digging a trench the pipe is directly ploughed into the soil.

Figure 55   Excavating the trench

I.6.6.5 Placing the pipes

Several methods can be used to place the drain pipes, depending on the type of pipe (Figure 56):

- *Concrete/clay drain pipe.* The drain pipes are loaded to a platform on the machine and then put along the chute in the trench box to the bottom of the trench. This requires one labour on the platform to put the pipe in the chute and one labour in the trench box to put cloth or other sealing around the joints;

a.

b.

c.

Figure 56   Placing the pipes: (a) concrete/clay pipes (b) flexible corrugated pipes and (c) large diameter plastic pipes

- *Flexible corrugated drain pipe.* The field drain pipes are delivered in coils and the coils are put on reels attached to the machine. The drain pipe is guided over rollers into the trench box. A press pulley puts the pipe at the bottom of the trench;
- *Plastic collector pipes are larger in diameter and cannot be coiled.* The pipes are delivered in sections of 6-12 m. These larger diameter pipes are usually laid out on the field beforehand. The pipe sections need to be connected in the field over the full length of the collector drain before the pipe laying starts and then guided through the machine.

I.6.6.6   Placing envelope

Synthetic and organic envelope
Synthetic and organic envelope material can be pre-wrapped around the pipe, this is usually done in the pipe factory. Envelopes are either applied in voluminous layers (> 10 mm) completely surrounding the drain pipe in bulk or as a pre-wrapped mat, or as thin sheets. Special (band) wrapping machines are available for pre-wrapping of pipes in factories. In case the wrapping has to be done in the field, special labour and provisions have to be made available. The installation of pre-wrapped drain pipes can de done by hand (e.g. in pilot areas) or by a trencher or trenchless drainage machine.

Installation of granular envelope
A granular envelope requires a considerable fleet of extra equipment to ensure a continuous supply to the machine. How to organise the gravel supply to the site is discussed in Part II. Installation by hand is not recommended as the drain pipe can easily get dislocated (Figure 57a), the only proper solution is to use the gravel box, as shown, which results in the correct positioning of the granular envelope (Figure 57b). Installation of granular envelopes with trenchless drainage machines is a cumbersome procedure. The gravel easily gets stuck in the narrow funnel through which the gravel has to be transported, resulting in part of the drain pipe not being covered with gravel and is therefore not recommended.

I.6.6.7   Installation of junctions or manholes

Field drain - collector connection
The field drains are connected to the collectors by means of standard drain pipe fittings (cross-pieces, T-joints, Y-joints) or through junction boxes or manholes (Figure 58). If no manholes or junction boxes have been installed, an access pipe for cleaning of the field drains needs to be installed at the junction. Installation of the manhole or field-collector pipe connection is done at the start of the installation of the field drain pipes, after the collector has been installed. This should be done preferably under dry conditions, thus a pump should be at hand to pump dry the excavated pit at the field-collector junction.

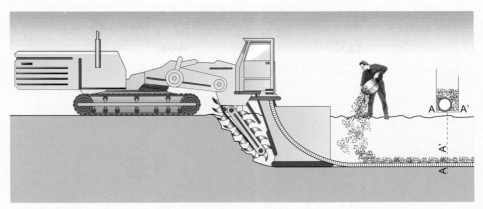

a.

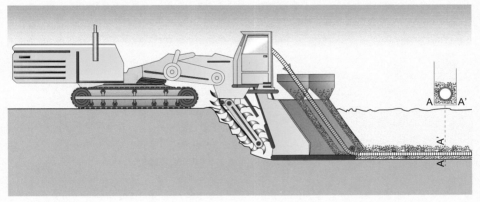

b.

Figure 57 *When the gravel is placed manually, the drain pipe easily gets dislocated (a), when gravel is applied through a gravel box mounted on the trench box of the trencher the drain is not dislocated (b)*

Soil surface

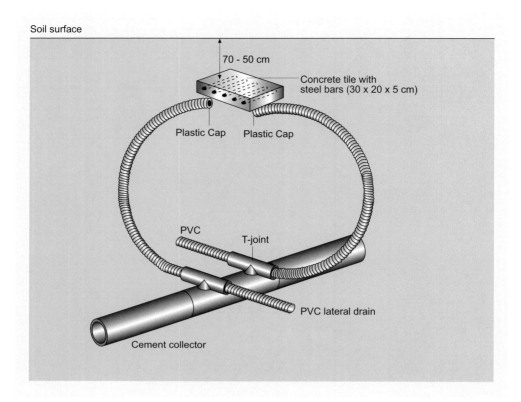

Figure 58   Example of field drain - collector connection and flushing joints

Flushing provisions
In a composite drainage system the field drains have no outlets into an open drain. In this case provisions should be installed at the junction of the field and collector drain for easy access of maintenance equipment. The T-joint should be extended with an access pipe. The end of the access pipe should be closed by a plastic cap and covered by a reinforced concrete tile 0.5 - 0.7 m below the soil surface. The access tube can be traced using a metal detector and a pit dug so that flushing of the drains can be done whenever required.

I.6.6.8   Backfilling of trenches

Backfill of the drain trench is a three-step operation (Figure 59):
- *Blinding*. Careful placing of an initial backfill of 0.15 to 0.30 m of soil around and over the drain is referred to as blinding. This is done to ensure that the drain will remain in line when the remaining excavated material is placed in the trench. Blinding the drain may be done by shaving off the topsoil at the top of the trench with a spade or with an attachment (scraping knife) to the trench box. Care should be taken that the alignment of the drain is not changed;

- *Backfill*. The fill should be firm but not compacted too much so that it prevents the passage of water to the pipe. All trenches should be filled to a sufficient level above the surface of the ground to allow for settlement. Trenches are preferably backfilled the same day they are dug to avoid a possible destabilisation of soil under wet conditions, such as irrigation, rain or high watertable. Only in unripe soil is it advisable to leave the trenches open for some time to initiate ripening;
- *Compaction*. Compacting is required to avoid serious problems arising in irrigated areas when water moves rapidly through the unconsolidated trench fill causing severe erosion (piping).

Trench backfilling is done by the following methods:
- Hand with shovels;
- Bulldozer;
- Grader;
- Tractor equipped with a dozer blade;
- Screw augers mounted on the trenching machine.

Figure 59   Backfilling of the drain trench: using a dozer and grader

I.6.7   Site clean-up

Surplus soil that is not injurious in nature should be spread over the surrounding field. Material such as large stones and roots that are likely to damage implements or livestock, or of a size and character abnormal to material found on the surface of the field, should be removed. The contractor should arrange to remove surplus pipe material, bands and ties, wood, glass, metal cans, and containers and other rubbish from the work area. Finally, all temporary passages, breaches in canals etc. should be repaired and fencing and other farm property should be repaired or replaced.

I.7   Quality Control in Drainage Construction

I.7.1   Quality control process

After installation, the subsurface drainage system would seem to have almost completely "disappeared" beneath the soil. Should malfunctioning occur, pinpointing its origin would be difficult and repairs often an elaborate, laborious and expensive procedure. Thus, the functioning of a subsurface drainage system depends almost entirely on the quality of the drainage materials used and the quality of installation. Small defects can have enormous consequences and can result in malfunctioning of the system. A properly integrated and functioning quality control system requires that the quality of each step in the construction process is checked and that possible imperfections are corrected before the next step is carried out, a so-called total quality system (Box 7.1). This means that quality control is not a stand-alone activity to be carried out at specific points in the construction process, but a process that is fully integrated into the construction process and concerns all parties involved. The implementation authority will have the final responsibility for the quality of the system, but normally nominates supervisor(s) to take responsibility for the actual quality control. The implementation authority has to decide how the quality control will be carried out during the planning stage (Box 7.2).

Box 7.1 Total Quality System

A Total Quality System is a modern system of quality control into which the contractor/manufacturer is fully integrated. Every person in the implementation process, from the planning up to the operation and maintenance, is responsible for the quality of their own work and for carrying out a quality control on the output of the previous persons. Basically, if one step is not carried out properly, the persons responsible for the next step should refuse to continue with the process until the previous step has been rectified (Figure 60).

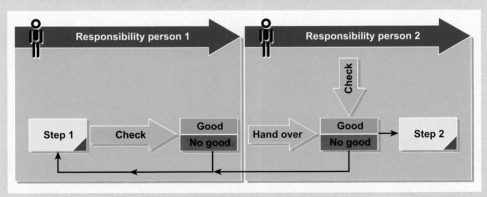

Figure 60   Principles of the total quality control system

Box 7.2 Quality Control: Major decisions during the planning phase

- Who is responsible for the day-to-day quality control and what is his mandate?
- Is the active or passive system of quality control method to be used?
- To what degree is the national/international standard quality control systems integrated?

Quality control can only be correctly carried out if:
- The quality of the work and the individual components is clearly and unambiguously formulated in the specifications and, where applicable, in the conditions of contract (see Chapter I.1);
- Quality control methods and procedures are clear and transparent and fully described in the conditions of contract and/or specifications;
- The persons responsible (supervisors) are equipped with the means and authority to carry out quality control and can impose the requirements of good quality work (in effect this means that there should be sanctions for not delivering according to the quality standards);
- All persons involved in the construction process have an understanding of the quality requirements;
- All parties involved are fully aware of the quality control system to be used and its consequences.

Quality control can be active or passive:
- *Active:* the supervisors or inspectors carry out very regular quality checks at all points of the installation process;
- *Passive:* The contractor/installation unit/manufacturer carries out the quality checks according to prescribed procedures and/or on order of the supervisor. If discrepancies are noted, these should be corrected immediately and verified with a follow-up check. The results of the checks are recorded and handed over to the supervisors who can carry out spot checks for verification or request double checks in his presence.

The passive system is the least complicated, provided that contractors have the adequate motivation and capacity to carry this out. If the construction works are contracted, it is very helpful if it is obvious from the contract that there is an interest for the contractor to deliver quality work. This can be reflected in the payment conditions, such as bonuses for good or above standard quality work and/or penalties for below standard quality work. This creates quality awareness by the construction team and avoids a mentality of "*let us cover it up before it is checked*". In the passive quality control approach, the implementation authority has to make sure that:
- Specifications and conditions in the contract are transparent and unambiguous;
- Stipulations in the specifications are clear, such as: (i) what needs to be checked; (ii) when must it be done; (iii) how should it be done; (iv) in the presence of the supervisor or not; (iv) how it has to be recorded; and (v) what to do in case of discrepancies;
- Supervisors who are capable and active and can carry out frequent spot checks and/or are present at the moment of control;

- There is a written statement from the contractor agreeing with the design;
- There is a written statement from the supervisor (preferably the design organisation) agreeing with the design modifications in the field, otherwise flaws in the design may result in malfunctioning of the systems for which the contractor may be held responsible.

The quality control in the implementation process includes the following aspects:
- Quality control of drainage materials: before and during installation;
- Quality control of installation: during and directly after installation is completed;
- Control of functioning of the system after installation: control of both the design and construction processes.

The following sections give an outline of what, when and how the quality control can be carried out. In Part II-D the details of quality control at field level are worked out.

I.7.2   Quality control of drainage materials

The drainage materials that have to be checked are (i) drain and collector pipes, (ii) envelopes, and (iii) structures. If these materials are supplied by independent suppliers or specialised units it is important that the quality is well defined in the supply contracts.

The quality of drainage materials can best be checked in three to four steps:

1st Quality Check
The materials produced by the manufacturers are expected to comply with the specifications and/or national or international norms. All materials should be satisfactory for the intended use and should meet the requirements as stated in the contract. The standards for testing are normally stipulated in the contract or standards (Chapter I.2) for which methods are used: certification and control. By certification, the manufacturer has to present a certificate that the products indeed fulfil the requirements of these norms (Box 7.3). In many countries there are nationally recognised independent authorities that verify that the products leaving the factory comply with these norms. Control means that the supervisor or the contractor (if the contract stipulates that the contractor provides the drainage materials) checks the quality and the quantity before it leaves the factory/before transport (Figure 61). This is to prevent products that are below standard from being transported. Ideally, the quality check should be confined to checking the quality certificates and the completeness of the order.

Box 7.3   Certification

Certification implies that the quality control is the responsibility of the manufacturer who must guarantee that his products meet the required certification standards. The certification is issued and checked by an independent organisation. Control is normally done by random checking during the production process. Part III of this handbook presents an example of how certification works in the Netherlands.

Figure 61
Testing the strength of a plastic drain pipe at a factory
in Egypt: elongation test

2 nd Quality Check
A second quality check can best be carried out on the site upon arrival of the drainage materials
to verify if the materials rejected in the factory are excluded from the shipment and to assure
that the supply of the materials is according to the ordered list of supplies and that no transport
damages have occurred. Any surplus or rejected materials must be removed immediately by the
supplier/contractor from the site to prevent confusion.

3 rd, 4 th Quality Check
A third and in some cases a fourth quality check takes place just before or at the moment of
installation and after installation.

I.7.3   Quality control of installation

The quality checks are carried out at different moments of the installation process as described
below. Which checks have to be carried out depend on the system to be installed and the
materials used. The checks are:

1 st Quality Check: before installation starts on drainage materials
The first quality check is the same as the last check of the quality of the materials, namely, a
check in the field depots to see if the quality (and quantity) of the materials tallies with the
standards.

2 nd Quality Check: before installation starts on alignments and levels
A second quality check is done after the contractor/construction unit has staked out the field and determined/verified the levels according to the design. The alignment and levels have to be checked. At this stage, discrepancies between the field conditions and the design can be detected that are mostly caused by imprecise topographical information. These discrepancies have to be solved immediately and preferably in cooperation with the designers.

3 rd Quality Check: before installation starts on equipment
The third quality check just before installation is to determine whether all the equipment to be used complies with the specifications and can be expected to install the system correctly.

4 th Quality Check: during installation
The fourth quality check is done during installation and focuses on: grades of the pipes, horizontal straightness, levels, joints of pipes, connection pipes and manholes and covering of pipes with granular envelope (if applicable) or the damage to pre-wrapped envelope. The quality standards are extensively described in the specifications (Figure 62).

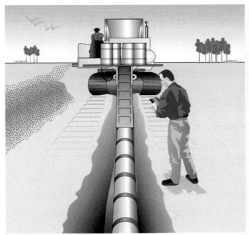 

a.   b.

Figure 62   Traditionally used quality control: visual inspection (a) and checking the drain level (b)

5 th Quality Check: after installation
The fifth quality check is right after installation before the trenches are closed. It focuses on visual inspection of the pipes, envelops, connections, joints and structures as well as floating of pipes and other distortions. It serves as a double check and, in case of doubt, the levels can be (re)checked and corrections made by the contractor can be verified.

6 th Quality Check: after backfill
The sixth quality check is after the trenches have been backfilled. It focuses on the backfill of the trenches, the compaction, covering of manholes and sumps, and the installation of end pipes.

I.7.4   Checking of the functioning of the drainage system

The performance of the system has to be checked once the construction has been completed and before handing over the drainage system to the beneficiaries or organisation that will take over the responsibility. Rules and procedures for acceptance are normally specified in the contract. This check should be done immediately after a drainage system has been installed. The check focuses on verifying that all elements of the system are functioning properly, such as field drains, collector drains, manholes, sumps, outlets and, if applicable, pumps. For example, checks are done as to whether the field drains are discharges after rain or irrigation and whether there is water is flowing in the manholes and collector drains. Note, if the groundwatertable is below drain level there will usually be no flow. This can be verified from the ground water observations. If this is the case, the check should be done during the following irrigation or rain event.

I.7.5   Post installation quality checks

The post-installation quality checks mentioned above are used to check the actual hydraulic performance of the drains to find out whether the drains discharge after irrigation or rainfall, or if water is flowing in the manholes, collectors and so forth. Of course it is a whole different story to check whether the drainage system functions according to the design objectives (Chapter I.1.3.4), namely, whether the groundwater level is maintained at the specified level or whether the soil salinity in the root zone is controlled at the specified level, and the like. This type of quality check has to be done by specialised research organisations and is beyond the scope of this handbook. For more information see the bibliography. Only if there are discrepancies and the system or part of the system is not functioning properly, or if there are doubts about the proper installation, a post-installation quality check should be carried out. Post installation checks are also rather complicated because the trenches are already backfilled and, thus, no visual inspection and use of surveyor staffs is possible anymore. The checking method focuses on determining which parts of the system are not functioning properly. The check starts with a visual inspection at the outlet and in the manholes, for instance, and subsequently more sophisticated methods are used to examine the suspected pipe sections. These checking methods require sophisticated equipment that often requires specialised personnel. Furthermore, the checks are rather complicated and time-consuming and are more suited for research and pilot projects than for routine operations. The following methods are available:

Rodding
Rodding is a technique to check whether there are abrupt disturbances in the drain line, like broken pipes, loose couplings and sharp changes in the slope. In this method, a glass fibre rod is pushed manually through the pipe outlet into the drain pipe over its entire length. In this method a solid steel rod with a torpedo-shaped go-gauge and possibly a transmitter is mounted on a glass fibre rod (Figure 63a). If the drain has been correctly installed, the rod can pass unhindered. The required pushing force increases slightly with the length of the drain. However, if the drain spirals, the required pushing force increases with the length of the drain. The required

force should not exceed a pre-set limit. If the rod cannot pass a particular point in the drain, there is a fault in the installation and the drain has to be excavated at this point. Drains up to a length of 400 m can be checked by rodding. In principle, every single drain can be tested but this will prove to be rather expensive (see Part III, Case Study in the Netherlands). It is therefore recommended to randomly test only a limited number of drains, for instance, 10% of the drains. Testing can be increased if more than a prescribed percentage of drains fail the test. The number of drains to be tested, the method and whether or not the contractor has to replace malfunctioning drains must be specified in the contract. Rodding is also a useful means of making sure that the drain will be accessible for flushing. Although rodding is a useful tool to check whether there are disturbances in the drain line, the method cannot be used to check the slope of the drain line. To do this continuous depth recording is required.

Continuous depth recording

Vertical alignment and grade can be checked using the Collins apparatus, a method based on the ancient water-level gauge, which was developed by Collins at the Leichtweiss Institute of the University of Brunswick, Germany. One end of a hose is connected to a special open container, the water surface of which serves as a reference level. A pressure transducer, fitted to the other end of the hose, slides into the drain (Figure 63b). This transducer transforms the hydrostatic pressure into an electric signal, which is proportional to the hydrostatic pressure over the reference level. The transducer can be inserted into the drain to a maximum length of 200 m. Measuring takes place while the hose is being withdrawn from the pipe. The hydrostatic pressure can be measured with an accuracy of less than 2 mm. The data can be recorded in digital form and plotted graphically. This method is quite costly: in the Netherlands the cost per metre amounts to about half the total costs of pipe drainage. Thus, a routine check of all installed drains is too expensive, so a system of random checking and certification has to be adopted.

The methods above are described in more detail in Part II, Chapter D.5.

Video inspection

Visual inspection of the drain pipe itself is also possible by using a video camera, whereby damage to pipes, siltation in pipes and the exact location can be determined. The camera is pushed through the inside of the pipe manually. As the camera has its own lighting, the inspector can directly check the interior of the pipe on the video display and can freeze the camera and make a print if he observes disturbances like sedimentation, ochre, roots, collapsed pipe section or loose couplings (Figure 63c). He can enter his remarks on the computer. Thus, apart from the video record a printed report can be made of the irregularities in a drain line. Inspection of a 150 m long drain line takes around ¾ hour. If the pipe is damaged to such an extent that excavation is required, the location can be deducted from the distance the camera has been pushed in to the drain or with a tracking device coupled to the camera. The disadvantage is that it is not possible to record the exact slope and the method is rather costly. An example is presented in Part III Case Egypt.

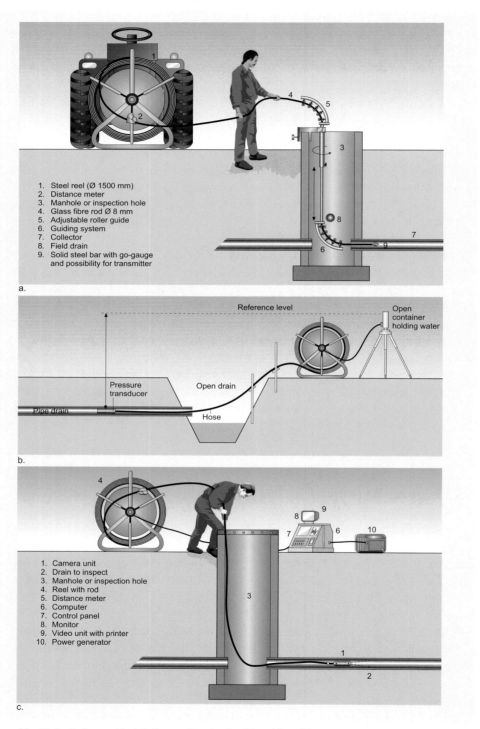

1. Steel reel (Ø 1500 mm)
2. Distance meter
3. Manhole or inspection hole
4. Glass fibre rod Ø 8 mm
5. Adjustable roller guide
6. Guiding system
7. Collector
8. Field drain
9. Solid steel bar with go-gauge and possibility for transmitter

a.

Reference level

Open container holding water

Pressure transducer

Open drain

Pipe drain

Hose

b.

1. Camera unit
2. Drain to inspect
3. Manhole or inspection hole
4. Reel with rod
5. Distance meter
6. Computer
7. Control panel
8. Monitor
9. Video unit with printer
10. Power generator

c.

Figure 63   Methods for post-installation quality checks: (a) rodding, (b) continuous depth recording and (c) video inspection

Tracking
The exact location of an obstruction of any kind can be determined by using a small transmitter fixed to the jet head of the flusher. The location of the jet head can be determined with a corresponding receiver and if the jet head gets stuck the exact location of the obstruction is known.

I.7.6   Post construction performance assessment

Once the drainage system has been operational for a number of years the performance of the system can be assessed to determine if the system is still functional and if not which measures have to be taken to correct the situation. The performance assessment can be done periodically (monitoring) or ad hoc if there are indications that the system is not functional.

The following periodic assessments are often carried out:
- *A periodic assessment of the functionality of the system* can be carried out to determine whether the system is functioning in accordance with the design. The assessment can give indications on the need of maintenance or rehabilitation and over time a knowledge base for the frequency and nature of maintenance can be built up. The methodology for checking the functionality of the system is given in Part II-D;
- *A periodic assessment of the effect of the system.* The rational behind this assessment is to determine if the system functions according to the design criteria, i.e. if the design groundwatertables and discharges are realized with the installed system, i.e. are the drain spacing, drain depth, drain envelope and dimensions of the drainage system correct. This assessment basically consists of the periodic, and according to pre-determined protocols, measuring of groundwater levels in between the drains and where relevant soil salinity levels;
- *A periodic assessment of the impact of the drainage system.* This assessment is to check if the expected benefits of the drainage system are realized. This assessment will focus on increases of yields, farmer income and possibly effects on the environment.

Next to these periodic assessments, the following ad hoc assessments are often made:
- *Complaint based ad hoc assessment.* These assessments can be carried out if there are substantial complaints made by the beneficiaries of the system about the functionality of the system. These assessments will focus on those parts of the system that are subject of the complaints;
- *Assessment to determine the need for rehabilitation.* During this assessment the main indicators studied are the frequency and cost of maintenance and repairs and the impact of the malfunctioning of the system on yields and income. It may be rational if these costs and loss of incomes surpass a certain threshold to replace the system.

A performance assessment is based on a comprehensive list of indicators. An indicator is defined as a value derived from two or more parameters that describe conditions and changes in time and space. These changes cannot usually be explained by a single indicator but only in relationship with other indicators. Ideally, the monitoring programme should contain a minimum of activities at the lowest possible cost, but resulting in a maximum insight in the performance of the system. Depending on the objectives of the monitoring programme, one or more of the following performance indicators should be measured:

- Crop yield;
- Water ponding in the fields after heavy rainfall or irrigation;
- Depth of the groundwater midway between the drains;
- Discharge at the outlet;
- Discharges in some selected manholes;
- Water levels in manholes;
- Sedimentation in manholes.

A periodic assessment program or monitoring can be contracted to a specialized agency or research organization. Once the program has been set up the actual monitoring activities are straightforward and can if so required be done by the organization in charge of the management of the system or for the impact assessments by the agricultural authorities.

I.8 Operation and Maintenance of Drainage Systems

I.8.1 Introduction

Like everything else in a country's infrastructure, subsurface drainage systems require operation and maintenance. The operation of subsurface drainage systems is mostly limited to the operation of pumps if pumping is done. In some cases, where controlled drainage is practiced, the operations can also involve opening and closing of gates. Maintenance of subsurface drainage systems consists mainly of removing sediment from the pipes and manholes, repairing and - if necessary - replacing these pipes, manholes and outlets. Maintenance of the open (main) drains is chiefly confined to removing sediment and weeds. Maintenance of the pipe (subsurface) drainage system is not entirely separate from maintenance of the downstream open (main) drains and/or outlets. If the downstream open drainage system is not properly maintained, it will influence the functioning and maintenance of the pipe drainage systems. Generally speaking, the objective of the maintenance of an open drainage system is to keep the water level below the outlet level of the pipe drainage system(s) at all times. Maintenance of open drainage systems is not discussed in this handbook and only the maintenance of pipe drainage systems will be further elaborated. When and how much maintenance is needed depends on the functioning of the subsurface drainage system, the monitoring of which has been discussed in Chapter I.7. This chapter discusses the general principles of operation and maintenance, while detailed guidelines for operation and maintenance activities are given Part II-D and E.

I.8.2 Decisions during the planning stage of the implementation process

During the planning stage of a subsurface drainage project, a number of decisions will have to be made on the future operation and maintenance of the system as well as on the allocation of responsibilities, institutional set-up and the techniques that will be used (Box 8.1). This is to ensure that:
- Designs can be harmonised with the proposed operation and maintenance methodologies;
- Support activities for operation and maintenance can be developed;
- Skills and institutions for the specialised operation and maintenance techniques can be assessed and developed;
- The maximum length of drains can be determined based on the available cleaning equipment;
- The capacity of local farmers for carrying out part or all of the maintenance can be assessed;
- Maintenance norms, supervision methods and institutions and so forth can be developed;
- A realistic division of tasks and cost allocation for the future maintenance can be decided upon;
- A fair cost estimate required for budgetary provisions can be made;
- Farmers can be informed in an early stage about the maintenance requirements and costs.

Box 8.1   Operation & Maintenance: Major decisions during the planning phase

During the planning stage clear ideas must be developed and decisions need to be made on:
- The maintenance activities for the proposed drainage system required;
- Whether the required maintenance activities can be carried out by the farmers and/or the existing organisations or support industry and if not what the missing elements are;
- Which maintenance activities can realistically be carried out by the farmers and which have to be carried out by specialised entities;
- If special facilities have to be created, how this can be done and what the costs are;
- If farmers have to be trained and/or equipped how can this be done and what the costs are;
- What investments costs will be required for creating the missing elements and how these will be financed;
- What the expected intensity (frequency) of the maintenance will be;
- What the annual operation and maintenance costs could amount to, based on the required maintenance activities and frequency;
- The part of the annual maintenance that will be financed and how (by farmers, local government or national government etc.);
- Whether timely availability of the annual maintenance budgets can be made at all levels;
- The entity that will have the overall responsibility for the maintenance and how and by whom the control/supervision methods are going to be implemented.

I.8.3   Operation of subsurface drainage systems

The operation of drainage systems is primarily confined to the operating of the pumps or pumping stations if the systems require pumping. The total operational cost of pumping is a sum of the cost of energy (electricity or diesel fuel), oil, grease and staff costs. The energy requirement can be estimated from the annual amount of drain water to be pumped, the required lift of the water and the characteristics of the pumps. For diesel pumps, the cost of oil and grease can be calculated as percentage of the fuel consumption. For electrically driven pumps, grease and oil expenses are marginal expenses that can be included in the contingencies. Modern small electric pumps are often equipped with automatic switches that switch on and off automatically at predetermined water levels. This reduces staff costs and human error. Diesel powered pumps require more supervision and thus more man-hours need to be taken into account. They can also be equipped with automatic switches if desired to reduce these higher staff costs. Depending on the organisational set up, the repairs, overhauls, annual technical service, replacement etc. of the pumps can be listed as operational cost or as a part of the maintenance cost of the drainage system. If it is considered to be an operational cost, the total annual cost of pumping can be calculated from the models given in Chapter I.9. Personnel costs for the operations are based on the number of man-days or man-hours required per year.

I.8.4   Maintenance of subsurface drainage systems

I.8.4.1   Objectives of maintenance

The objective of maintenance is to keep the drainage system functioning at its design capacity. Malfunctioning of a drainage system can be directly or indirectly noticed, for instance:

- If there is little or water no flowing out of the pipes/outlets directly indicating that the system is not functioning as required, whereas there should be a drainage flow (mainly some time after an irrigation or rainstorm);
- If the groundwater level has not dropped or remains above the desired depth, which is an indirect indication of malfunctioning.

The impact of a non-functioning system is water logging and/or that soil salinity is not decreasing or even increasing. Unfortunately these phenomena can only be noticed after some time usually when most of the damage has already been done. The ultimate result of a non-functioning drainage system is that crop growth is hampered.

I.8.4.2   Maintenance process

The maintenance process consists of the following activities:
- Regular checking of the functioning of the different elements of the system;
- Regular routine minor cleaning/maintenance;
- Periodic integral check of the functionality of the system;
- Periodic general cleaning (flushing) of the system;
- Repairing broken or obstructed parts of the system, when needed;
- Carrying out preventive maintenance and repairs of pumps (if relevant).

Maintenance should be based on accurate as-built drawings of the drainage system that have been checked and approved by both the implementing authority and the beneficiaries. Records of the construction process also need to be handed over to the maintenance units. This will facilitate the maintenance activities, especially when obstructions in the drains have to be located.

I.8.4.3   Frequency of maintenance

The cost of maintenance of pipe drainage systems is proportional to the frequency/intensity of this maintenance. There are examples of well-installed drainage systems that did not require any maintenance for 25 years. In other systems the sedimentation was so high that annual maintenance was required. It is not uncommon for fairly frequent maintenance to be necessary at first, gradually reducing over the years as conditions stabilise. The frequency/intensity of maintenance depends on:
- *Site-specific conditions:*
  - If soils consist of unstable aggregates, the systems tend to sediment relatively quickly and will thus require fairly frequent cleaning. The sedimentation will be substantially less in areas with stable soil aggregates;
  - In climates and/or under irrigation regimes where there is year-round flow in the drains, sedimentation is less likely to occur than under conditions with only seasonal drain flows.

- *Drainage materials used:*
  - If clay or concrete field drains are used, there will be three joints per metre length. The likelihood that the pipes might not be perfectly aligned and that sediment can enter at least through several of the joints are considerably higher than if a plastic corrugated pipe is used. Hence, a greater frequency of maintenance can be expected for systems made of concrete/clay pipes;
  - If a completely functional envelope is installed there will be little or no sediment flow into the system, thus little maintenance will be required.
- *Quality of installation:*
  - Little or no sedimentation will collect in drain pipes that are correctly installed (even grade and horizontally straight). If pipes are less perfectly installed more sedimentation will occur (because of minor flow obstructions in the pipes);
  - If during installation the joints are not tightly installed or the pipes become dislodged (especially in case of use of clay or concrete pipes) sediment can enter through the joints requiring frequent maintenance.

Consequently, as such a large number of parameters determine the required frequency of maintenance, no general rule can be given. An important conclusion, however, is that a well planned and next to perfect subsurface pipe drainage system installation will require considerably less maintenance than a system installed with less care and less suitable materials. The extra cost of high quality installation will be recuperated in the form of less maintenance costs and better functionality of the drainage system.

I.8.4.4   Estimating the frequency of maintenance

An estimate of the required frequencies of the maintenance activities is required for planning and budgeting. This can be done by:
- Extrapolation of any local experience gained with maintenance of pipe drainage systems;
- If there is no local experience, a not uncommon maintenance frequency of cleaning the systems once every three to five years. Whether or not budget estimates have to be based on a frequency of once every 3, 4 or 5 years will depend on the site-specific conditions and installation conditions as given above;
- Monitoring the actual maintenance intensities to eventually provide a firm basis for budgeting once the system is fully established.

I.8.4.5   Routine checking of the functioning of the system and minor maintenance

The functioning of the drainage system needs to be checked on a regular basis, almost daily. The checking consists of verifying whether the drains flow normally, that there is no built-up of water levels in the manholes (Figure 64), no leakage from the system and no accumulation of sediment in parts of the system (manholes!). During the checking process minor routine maintenance activities, like removing sediment from manholes and replacing covers on manholes, can be carried out. For practical reasons, these activities can best be done by the farmers who, for various other reasons are often in the field anyway. Moreover, by involving the farmers no additional costs will be involved. If irregularities are noticed that cannot be corrected during the routine checks, the farmers should notify the organisation responsible for the overall maintenance.

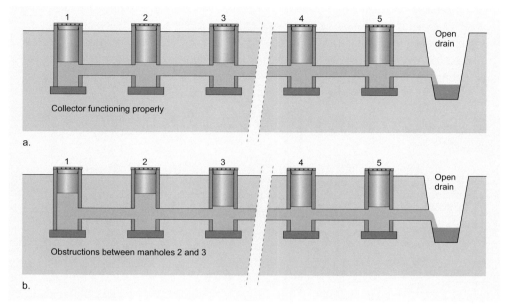

Figure 64   Visual inspection of the water level in the manholes to check the hydraulic performance of a collector line: (a) collector is functioning according to the design (= no overpressure); (b) overpressure in manholes 1 and 2 indicates an obstruction in the collector between manhole 2 and 3

I.8.4.6   Periodic integral check of the functioning of the system

It is advisable to do an integral check of the system periodically, namely, once or twice a year. The faults found during the checks can then be remedied at an early stage. The checking method is described in Part II-E. There will of course be some staff costs involved because time has to be spent on it (man-hours).

I.8.4.7   Periodic cleaning of the system

Since there will always be some sedimentation in the pipes it is advisable to remove this sediment periodically to prevent any excessive build-up. Sediment can be removed from a pipe drainage system by flushing (Figure 65). Theoretically, the sediment ought to be removed when it covers more than 25% of the cross section of the pipes (Figure 66). For practical reasons, especially in areas where the drain flow is seasonal, it may be better to remove the sediment earlier. Note, flushing can damage the envelope so less frequent flushing is better. Exactly how long it will take for this build-up to occur is not known and will have to be determined by monitoring sediment built up in the pipes. The cleaning of a subsurface drainage system by flushing is a specialised job that requires trained personnel and special equipment, and is normally done by a contractor or a specialised unit. The job is even more complex for composite drainage systems than for singular systems. Details of the flushing operation are described in Part II-E. Flushing by gravity with irrigation water from the upstream or top end of the system is practiced in some countries. This method is not recommended because it is likely to carry sediments further into the system accumulating in the downstream part where it can cause obstructions.

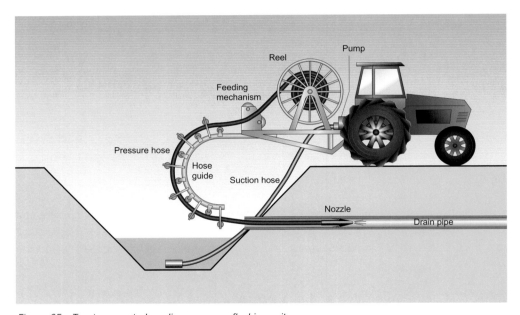

Figure 65   Tractor-mounted medium-pressure flushing unit

Figure 66
Plastic corrugated collector pipe half full with sediment
(example from Pakistan)

The costs of flushing are machinery and staff costs. As a rule of thumb a fully equipped flushing unit can flush some 3 - 4 km of pipes per day. Calculation of the costs should take into account that flushing can only be carried out when there is a drainage flow. In the case of composite systems, crop growth may limit the period when flushing can be carried out.

I.8.4.8   Carrying out repairs on the different parts of the system if and when needed

The need for repairs is indicated by the farmers or during the yearly or half-yearly inspections of the maintenance entity. Repairs may consist of:
- Repair of manholes (breakage, leakage, covers etc.);
- Flushing one or more pipe lines that are obstructed;
- Repairing one or more drain pipes at place of obstruction, breakage etc.;
- Repair of pumps (if relevant);
- Repair of outlets (in case of composite systems);
- Repair of end pipes (in case of a singular system).

The costs are difficult to estimate, nevertheless, if no wilful damage is done to the system, the regular checking and arranging minor problems is well done and the system is properly installed, the costs will be minimal.

I.8.4.9   Preventive maintenance and repair of pumps

The manufacturers of the pumps prescribe regular maintenance. These instructions have to be followed and should be given adequate attention the maintenance planning. In areas with a serious frost hazard, it may be necessary to carry out frost protection of the pumps.

I.8.5   Cost of operation and maintenance

As can be concluded from the paragraphs above, the actual cost of operation and maintenance of subsurface drainage systems are site-specific and influenced by a number of unforeseeable parameters. If no operation and maintenance experience is available, the best is in the planning phase to obtain a pessimistic estimate of the cost so that budgets can be made available. If the activities and cost of operation and maintenance are carefully recorded in the course of the first years, a more realistic estimate can be made for subsequent years on the basis of these records. The costs can be calculated making use of the cost calculation methods as indicated in Chapter I.9.

I.9   Cost of Subsurface Drainage Systems

I.9.1   General

The construction costs of subsurface drainage systems are substantial (Box 9.1), therefore, it is of utmost importance that accurate cost estimates are made. The costs to be considered include:
- Preparation costs, including the cost of feasibility studies, field investigations and design, tender preparation and tendering (investment costs);
- Construction costs (investment costs);
- Operation and maintenance costs (recurrent costs);
- Cost of accompanying measures, both investment cost and recurrent costs;
- Financing costs.

And where no drainage tradition or industry exists in the country:
- Training costs of staff;
- Investment costs to set up a drainage industry and/or equip the various government units.

Costs, of course, result in benefits. Estimating the direct and indirect benefits of drainage systems requires special studies that are not the subject of this handbook, but a few general observations are presented in Section 9.1.2.

Box 9.1   Construction costs of subsurface drainage systems

Construction costs of subsurface drainage vary from country to country and from situation to situation. Costs also depend on whether or not an open main drainage system, complicated outlets or pumping stations are required. A cost survey done in several countries with large-scale installation infrastructures and a more or less mature drainage industry resulted in a cost price that varied between € 750 and € 1500 per hectare (prices in 2002) for the construction of subsurface drainage systems, excluding the open main drainage systems.

These cost estimates play a role in each step of the implementation process, namely, (Figure 67):
- During decision-making by national or regional government;
- During the detailed planning process;
- As part of the design process (Engineers estimate);
- For budget planning;
- For cost control during construction.

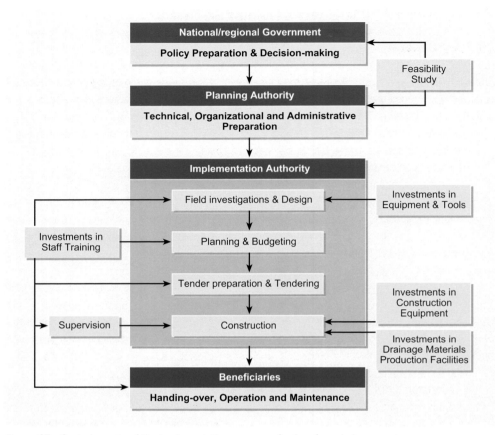

Figure 67   Cost elements of the implementation process of subsurface drainage systems

In the following paragraphs the outlines of cost calculations are presented. In Part II-B detailed instructions for cost calculations are worked out.

I.9.2   Considerations for determining cost, benefits and financing of drainage projects

I.9.2.1   Cost estimates during the implementation process

Cost estimates during decision-making by national or regional government
During the decision-making process at government level, the following questions concerning costs have to be answered:
- Is the implementation of drainage systems financially and economically feasible? (Determining the cost benefit relationship is the main objective of a feasibility study).
- What are the benefits of the systems to be installed compared with other possible investments of (scarce) government resources?

- Can the required one-time investment costs such as preparation and construction costs be made available from government sources, international financers or private sources?
- Can budgets be made available for the recurrent costs and from what source?

If a drainage industry needs to be set up in the country in question, answers to the following questions will also have to be obtained:
- Can the required investment cost of setting up a drainage industry be made available and, if so, from which sources and in which form?
- Is there enough scope for future use of the plant and equipment to justify the investments therein?

Financing from private sources is a (theoretical) possibility, but in most cases the government or a government agency will in someway be involved in the financing and thus the decision-making. The involvement can be as a direct financer, regulator, subsidiser, organisation responsible for accompanying measures, or the entity responsible for the future management and maintenance. All these (partial) involvements have consequences for the government budget.

The accuracy of the cost estimates at this stage of the implementation process is the so-called "feasibility" level precision, which can vary by 10% either way. The cost estimates in a feasibility study include the estimated costs, overhead costs and if applicable general costs, risks and profits and contingencies (often around 10%). The information about the costs can be obtained from the following sources:
- Previous projects in countries with experience with drainage;
- Feasibility studies, because cost estimates are a vital part of feasibility studies, certainly if international financing is involved, in countries or regions with little or no experience with large-scale drainage implementation;
- International prices as a first estimate, if there is no local experience and no market prices are available.

Cost estimates during the detailed planning process
The planning authority has to prepare a detailed cost calculation, preferably divided into:
- Preparation costs;
- Construction costs;
- Possible investment costs in setting up a drainage industry;
- Cost of accompanying measures (if any) and operation and maintenance costs.

If a feasibility study has been done during the decision-making phase, then most of the cost calculations required for this phase will already have been made. In this phase, the cost calculations are also used to compare alternative technical solutions and to select the least costly ones. The investment costs for setting up a drainage industry are long-term investments that have to be written off over many years thus over many drainage systems. Although it is seldom done, during this phase an estimate should also be made of the financing cost of each cost element. The financing costs refer to the unavoidable banking costs and interest payments if capital has to be made available from commercial sources or development banks. If part or all of the implementation activities are carried out by private entities the costs that these entities incur and/or will invoice covering risks, overheads and profits must be included.

Cost estimates as part of the design process
Detailed cost calculations are made during the design process when all details are known. These estimates, based on well-established unit prices, are reported on in a *Bill of Quantities* (Chapter I.9.4.9). This total cost or "*Engineers Estimate*" is input for the detailed budget preparation and tender procedures. When design engineers are asked to prepare adequate designs that are cost effective, they are often also asked to determine the most cost effective and technically acceptable alternatives.

Budget planning
Budget planning is done to determine which payments have to be made during the construction process and when. Budget planning can only be made at the end of the design process after a detailed construction schedule has been prepared. In the case of tendering, the resulting payment schedule will be included in the conditions of payment of the contract and has consequences for the possible financing costs. Contractors interested in the tender will also prepare their own detailed cost estimates for their tender price, including coverage for risks, overheads and profits. These costs should be part of the engineer's estimate, albeit possibly at another rate.

Cost control during construction
Supervisors and contractors will both carry out their own individual cost control during construction to suit their own purposes.

I.9.2.2   Benefits of drainage systems

Quantification of the benefits is a complicated thing to do because it is difficult to separate the diverse direct and indirect effects of drainage from other variables that can also influence the yields, production costs and so forth. Data on the actual effects and benefits of drainage systems based on field verification are scarce, and a so-called post-construction verification and quantification study is complicated because the implementation period of drainage systems stretches over a number of years. Moreover, the full effects may only emerge several years after the implementation has been completed. During this period many parameters influencing the benefits will have altered and the process of identifying the direct benefits from the drainage from other factors will be a complicated business. This type of study is not a component of the implementation process and should preferably be carried out by specialised research organisations. Estimating the benefits of drainage systems along the lines as described below is one of the major components of a feasibility study.

Benefits of agricultural drainage can be divided into direct, associated and secondary benefits, i.e. one or more of the following:

Direct benefits:
- Increase in yield due to absence of water logging;
- Increase in yield due to reduced soil salinity.

Associated benefits:
- Better access to fields for mechanised operations resulting in lower production costs and reduced risk that activities cannot be carried out on time;
- Opportunity to grow other, higher value, crops;
- Opportunity to grow an extra crop each year.

Secondary benefits:
- Controlling a salinisation process will also stop environmental deterioration;
- Deeper groundwater levels will facilitate sanitation in an area and thus improve public health;
- Removal of standing water will reduce or eliminate water-borne diseases and thus improve public health.

These secondary benefits are particularly difficult to quantify.

The "without drainage" case
Drainage is primarily a measure to reduce water logging and to control salinity. Salinisation is a dynamic process that causes a slow but sure decline in the productivity of the land. Thus, an important invisible "benefit" that is considered in most feasibility studies is stopping the progressive reduction of the productivity that would just simply continue if the drainage systems were not implemented. This can be quantified by comparing the expected development of the pro-

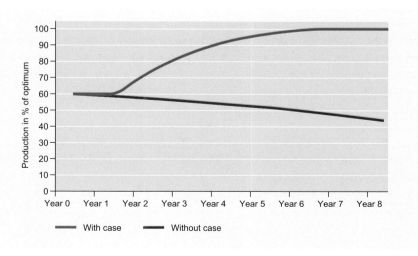

Figure 68   Expected development of the productivity of the area after the implementation of the drainage system ("with drainage" case) compared to the expected decline of the productivity of the area if no drainage systems were implemented ("without drainage" case)

ductivity of the area after the implementation of the drainage system in the "*with drainage*" case, with the expected decline of the productivity of the area if no drainage systems were implemented, the "*without drainage*" case (Figure 68). The production decline in the "*without drainage*" case can be estimated by extrapolating the production decline of the last years (decades). As can be seen in the figure the production in the "*with drainage*" case rises from 60% to 100% of the potential in 5 years. The first year is the construction year during which a decline in yield may occur. The direct benefit of the drainage system for each year is the difference of the value of the production between the "with" and the "without" project situation. The benefit of the project as a whole is the integration of the discounted annual benefits.

I.9.2.3   Influence of the existence of a national drainage industry on budgetary requirements

The budgetary requirements for implementing drainage systems depend very much on the existence of a drainage industry in the country. In general, subsurface drainage is only economically/financially justified if it is carried out on large scale. To make economical sense, the investments required for setting up a drainage industry including pipe and envelope production facilities, installation machines and equipment, and training of staff (Box 9.2) all of which easily amounting to several millions of euros, has to be written off over long periods and covers large areas. Apart from the cost of the preparation and construction, a budget has to be made available for the creation of such an industry. If the industry is going to be privatised, the private sector has to provide either all the investments or part of it with government support. The private sector will only be ready to do this if there are guarantees that there will be adequate work during the lifetime of the investments so that the investments can be written off over a reasonable period. If there is a drainage industry in existence then there will be no need for the additional investment. The proportional depreciation of the investment costs already incurred are partly reflected in the unit costs for drainage materials, drain installation and overheads. A similar situation can be created if the construction of the drainage system is tendered internationally. As international contractors will include a fee for risks and will try to write off as much machinery and plant costs as possible for their "one time" project, the costs will tend to be higher than if a national drainage industry exists.

Box 9.2   Investment costs needed for the implementation of subsurface drainage systems

A drainage machine costing between € 200,000 and € 250,000 (Table 9.2) can easily install 2000-3000 km of drains over its economic lifetime of 10,000 hours (or 10 years). Assuming an average drain spacing is 50 m, this will cover 10,000-15,000 ha.

A pipe production line for three diameters of pipes costs between € 1.2 and € 1.5 million and can produce 2500 km of Ø 100 mm pipe (550 tons) per year in 1 shift. Assuming again a drain spacing of 50 m, this covers 12,500 ha per year or 125,000 ha over a 10-year period (its life time).

I.9.2.4   Financing of drainage projects

As stated earlier, drainage projects can either be partly or wholly financed by a government from public funds as part of a public task to improve the production potential and/or to arrest further deterioration of the production potential and environment. The national benefits are expected to be an increase in local and, hence, national income. This can be translated into an improved tax base, better living conditions and perhaps reduced health costs. If the government does not have the budget to finance the drainage systems, it can try to obtain loans from the capital market or from development banks. Private initiatives for construction and financing of large-scale drainages systems are rare. In western countries, however, the construction or improvement of field drainage systems by owners of privately owned areas is quite common.

Organising the financing and recovery of the cost is largely dependent on the national customs and policies. It can range from being completely financed by government funds with the expectation that costs will be recovered through taxes, to being completely financed by the direct beneficiaries, either directly or through loans. All intermediate solutions are also possible. An approach often used is as follows:
- The main infrastructure, i.e., the main drainage system including the outlets and/or pumping stations, is considered a public good and is entirely financed by the government with public funds either directly or though loans. Repayment is eventually expected to come from an increased tax base;
- The on-farm works, i.e., the field drainage systems, are considered to be the direct benefit of the land owner/user. Therefore, the landowners have to finance these works, either fully or partly. Partly, because in some cases governments subsidise these works. Again the government expects repayment of their subsidies through additional tax revenues in the future;
- Landowners finance their part with a loan with a commercial loan or a subsidised loan. The repayment conditions of the loans (grace period, repayment period etc.) can be made on the basis of projected yield improvements.

I.9.3   Estimating the cost of drainage projects

I.9.3.1   Principles of estimating costs

A total cost estimate can be made by breaking down the implementation process into its components and subsequently breaking down these components into the constituent elements (Figure 67). The total implementation cost is the sum of the costs of all the components. The constituent elements are some or all of the following:
- *(Base) material costs* including transport and insurance to site and the normal breakage and or other losses;
- *Staff costs* including direct salaries, social charges, cost of schooling, cost of downtime, general overheads, specific overheads like tools, instruments and consumables;

- *Equipment costs* including running cost (consumables), repairs, spare parts, depreciation, storage costs, insurance, financing costs and cost of downtime;
- *Management costs* including time of managers, administration costs and contracting costs;
- *Financing costs,* namely, cost of bank credits or loss of interest;
- *Overhead costs.* The term "overhead cost" is a "catch all" phrase for all costs that are not accounted for elsewhere. They are often the costs that can be called "general running costs" of an entity or establishment and can include the cost of renting offices, secretarial assistance, professional insurance and services to personnel. Most of these costs cannot be attributed to only one project and are therefore accounted proportionally to the turnover of a project or contract;
- *Taxes and duties;*
- *Insurance, risks and profits.*

If some or all activities are contracted out to private entities the provision for risks and profits should be estimated for the contracted parts. In the case of an entirely government designed and implemented drainage system, the overhead costs are often part of the government's general budget and the state takes all the risks of cost or time overruns. These costs are then still real but less visible.

I.9.3.2   Methodologies for estimating costs

The easiest and most realistic way of calculating the cost of the components of a drainage system is to base the unit costs on market prices, if available. For instance, if there is a regular production of drainage pipes in the country with listed market prices, these prices can be included in the cost estimate. As a precaution, because some prices could fluctuate with world market prices, it may be wise to make appropriate allowances in the budget for them. If there are no market prices available in the country costs will have to be estimated. The methodology for calculating the "cost types" is given in Part II-B and includes: cost of staff, cost of machinery and equipment, cost of transport and cost of base material.

I.9.3.3   Cost estimates in this handbook

The discussion of cost estimates for subsurface drainage systems in this handbook will be confined to the costs related to the implementation of subsurface drainage systems, excluding the open drainage systems, associated works and associated measures. The cost of open drainage system is basically the cost of soil movement and civil engineering works (bridges, culverts, bypasses etc,) that are generally well known. The associated works are specific for every area thus no general suggestions can be made. The cost of operation and maintenance will be discussed in a non-quantitative way for the sake of completeness.

In the following sections some guidelines will be given for calculating the investments costs in case there is no drainage industry in the country and for construction costs.

I.9.4 Investments for the creation of a drainage industry

I.9.4.1 General

If no drainage industry exists and it is decided that such a drainage industry is to be established, long-term investments have to be made in staff training, machinery and the plants specific to subsurface drainage. The investments cost of machinery and plants must include all costs, including taxes and duties, transport, erection and test runs. The investments should be depreciated (amortised) over their lifetime, which can be calculated as an economic lifetime and/or as technical lifetime. Even if equipment has been received as a gift it is advisable to depreciate it, in this way a capital can be built up for replacements once the equipment has exceeded its lifetime. The investment costs are proportionally written off and are accounted for in the cost of drainage materials and the costs for drainage construction.

I.9.4.2 Investments in staff training

Specialised knowledge is required for the design and implementation of subsurface drainage systems (Table 9.1). Depending on the national customs and systems this can apply to the government or private staff. Since training needs vary with the basic education of the selected staff, the organisational set-up and local customs, no basis for cost calculation can be suggested. The possible training required for producing drainage materials and maintaining equipment is not included. The intensity and level of training that will be required has to be determined on a case-by-case basis. In most countries the basic knowledge will be available. For the calculation of training costs the following items can be taken into account:
- Training fees;
- Travelling and boarding costs of trainees;
- Training materials;
- Salaries and other cost of trainees.

Table 9.1   Training subjects

Preparation & tendering	Installation	Management & supervision
• Collection of field data	• Operation trenchers	• Contracting
• Topographic surveys	• Managing laser	• Progress control
• Soil surveys	• Operation tractors	• Quality Control
• Soil chemical and physical testing	• Operation excavators	• Budget control
• Defining drainage criteria	• Operation loaders	• Handing over procedures
• Defining design criteria	• Application of gravel envelopes	• National regulations
• Design of subsurface drainage systems	• Topographic survey	• Relations with stakeholders
• Calculation of unit prices	• Mechanical servicing and repair of equipment	
• Preparing Bills of quantities	• Setting out of field	
• Least cost analyses	• Quality control of installation	
• Preparing installation instructions	• Quality control drainage materials	
• Contracting	• Economic installation	
• Preparing tender documents	• Managing installation process	
• Tender procedures		

I.9.4.3   Investment in drainage equipment

The equipment used for drain installation consists of (Chapter I.5):
- *Specific drainage machinery* that can only be used for subsurface drainage installation including: trenchers or trenchless machines equipped with lasers, and if necessary gravel trailers as support equipment;
- *General construction equipment,* meaning equipment required for drainage though commonly also used for other purposes, which includes: excavators, bulldozers, tractors, trailers, front loaders and topographic equipment.

The equipment that will be required and how much of each item is very dependent on the system to be installed and the methods used. For the installation of subsurface drainage systems in large areas, working in units of 2-3 trenchers has proven to be economical for organisational purposes and for effective use of the support equipment and support staff.

The economic life of mechanical equipment in western countries is considered to be 10,000 hours or some 10 years. Under normal conditions drains of up to 2500 km can be installed with a drainage machine over this lifetime (Box 9.2). Beyond a period of 10 years, the cost of maintenance and repairs together with the time losses due to mechanical failures are thought to be greater than the costs of new equipment. In some countries, especially where import duties are high and/or exchange control problems exists, it may be logical to keep the equipment functional for a longer period.

The cost estimate of equipment for subsurface drainage installation depends on what equipment is required for the implementation of a specific design. It also depends on what is available in the country and what has to be purchased at the international market. Transport cost, import duties, insurance cost and exchange rates also play an important role in the final price. A general estimate for two basic units for drainage installation, namely, one with granular envelopes and one without granular envelopes is given in Table 9.2. Both units consist of one drainage machine for the field drain installation and one for the collector installation. The collector machine can also install field drains. The minor support machines like agricultural tractors, trailers etc. are not valued, since these are normally available in a country and prices can differ very much from world market prices.

Table 9.2   Cost estimate of drainage installation unit (both field and collector drains) with granular and pre-wrapped envelopes around the field drains (costs based on international market F.O.B. prices of tenders in year 2002)

Item	Unit	Quantity	Unit price (€)	Total price (€)
Drainage system with granular envelope				
Field drain installation machine equipped with laser	unit	1	200,000	200,000
Gravel trailer	unit	6	20,000	120,000
Collector installation machine with laser	unit	1	250,000	250,000
Excavator	unit	2		
Tractors for gravel trailers >75 HP	unit	3		Local market price
Bulldozer	unit	1		Local market price
Front loader (gravel)	unit	1		Local market price
Agric. tractor + trailer	unit	2		Local market price
Servicing/maintenance truck	unit	1		
Topographic equipment	set	2		Local market price
Quality control	set	1		Local market price
Spare parts imported equipment 20%				134,000
Total Drainage system with granular envelope				
Drainage system with pre-wrapped envelope				
Field drain installation machine equipped with laser	unit	1	200,000	200,000
Collector installation machine with laser	unit	1	250,000	250,000
Excavator	unit	2		
Bulldozer	unit	1		
Agric. tractor + trailer	unit	2		Local market price
Servicing/maintenance truck	unit	1		
Topographic equipment	set	2		Local market price
Quality control	set	1		Local market price
Spare parts imported equipment 20%				90,000
Total Drainage system with pre-wrapped envelope				

I.9.4.4   Investment in a plastic drain pipe production plant

The following considerations play a role if investment is required in drain pipe manufacturing plants (Chapter I.4.2.3):

- A pipe manufacturing plant consists of the following components: extruders, corrugators, perforators and coilers. The most expensive parts are the corrugators and perforators;
- A drain pipe production line can manufacture a range of diameters roughly measuring Ø 60-125 mm and Ø 100-200 m. The extruder requires a specific die head for each diameter and the corrugators and perforators require specialised components. Thus the investment increases considerably for each additional diameter needing to be produced. Limiting the number of diameters of drain pipes during the design can be economical;
- A pipe manufacturing line requires a constant supply of electricity and cooling water. Depending on the conditions in de area this supply may require additional investments;
- A pipe manufacturing line requires a production hall with adequate storage room (plastic drain pipes have to be stored outside the direct sunlight);
- The cost of a corrugated drain pipe is directly related to its weight per m'. The weight per m' is a function of the diameter and the pipe thickness;
- The form of the corrugations is related to the required pipe thickness to obtain the norm strength of the pipe. The most optimal form of the corrugation is thus the form that gives the pipe its required strength with the minimum pipe thickness and thus the lowest weight per m. An indicator of quality of the production line is the required weight per m' pipe to obtain the norm strength. Although production lines that produce the same pipe strength with less weight per m' tend to be more expensive, the saving on base material normally offsets the extra cost of the line within a short period of time;
- Transport of pipes is costly since the pipes are voluminous. Thus, the location of the factory in regard to the installation site can have an important influence on the cost price of pipes "delivered onsite";
- If transport distances are excessive relocation of the production line to a location closer to the site may be considered. Mobile pipe production lines were manufactured in de 1970s and 1980s, however, the cost and limitations of mobile production lines proved to be higher than moving the components of a fixed production line to other premises;
- Importing pipes is normally not a feasible option. The cost of transport very quickly exceeds the value of the pipes;
- Importing base material for the production of pipes can be a reasonable solution;
- PE production lines tend to be somewhat cheaper than PVC production lines. However, PE requires about 20% extra base material and on the world market PE tends to be more expensive per kg than PVC;
- The capacity of production lines tends to be very high compared to the installation capacity of trenchers, namely, a production line can produce in 24 hours a quantity of pipes that 8 -10 trenchers can install per day. Buying a line with a reduced capacity, however, will hardly save any costs since the extruder determines the capacity and is only a minor part of the total cost.

The production capacity of a production line is usually expressed in kg base material per hour. Outputs per line vary from 500-800 kg/hour. For Ø 100 mm pipes this can be translated into 1150-1800 m/hour. If required the drain pipe production line can work 20-24 hours per day all year round. The technical lifetime of a production line is approximately 80 000 hours (10 years of 8000 hours per year), the tooling has to be replaced after approximately 25 000 hours.

Conclusions
The investment costs of a pipe manufacturing line is dependent on: (i) the diameters and the number of diameters that are to be produced; (ii) whether PVC or PE pipes need to be made; (iii) the available facilities in the country (electricity and cooling water); and (iv) the cost of the civil works, and the like. The following are the indications of the investment costs: a good quality production line itself without generators including extra cooling facilities etc., costs vary between € 1.2 and 1.8 million for a line with three diameters. For each additional diameter an investment of approximately € 150 000 is needed.

I.9.4.5   Investments in drain envelope production

Drain envelopes can be either made of granular or a pre-wrapped synthetic material (Chapter I.4.4).

Granular envelopes
Granular envelope production is a question of transport and sieving with or without the crushing of natural gravel. If a gravel production is to be set up the investment will consist of sieves, possibly crushing plants and transport equipment. These costs are largely locally dependent and mostly well known.

Synthetic envelope
The production of most synthetic envelopes requires complicated industrial processes, which have no economic justification if they are only used to produce drain envelopes. If the appropriate envelope material cannot be made locally, it has to be imported. The volumes and the weight are relatively limited so transport costs are not excessive. Wrapping the envelope around the pipes is most logical done at or close to the place where the pipes are produced. The equipment required therefore depends very much on the enveloping material and the preparations that have to be made before it can be wrapped around the pipes. Cost can vary from € 5000 - € 250 000 in prices of the year 2002.

I.9.5   Cost calculation of the pre-construction activities

I.9.5.1   Preparation of a feasibility study

Feasibility studies can be useful for the decision-making process at government level, especially when foreign financing is required and in countries with no drainage tradition and thus no experience of costs and benefits. The costs of preparing a feasibility study with the precision and contents acceptable to international development banks can be important. No general estimates can be given since it very much depends on the extent of the study, the readily available basic information, the possible complications of lowering groundwatertables for surrounding areas, the drain water disposal, the possible environmental impact and problems in estimating the benefits. Preparation costs of a multidisciplinary feasibility study is mainly based on an estimate of the time and unit costs of the required specialists.

I.9.5.2   Field investigations

Field investigations consist mainly of (Chapter I.1.4.2):
- Topographic surveys;
- Pre-drainage soil surveys.

If there is little or no information of the geo-hydrology and geology of an area, surveys such as these may also be required although their outcome will have a much wider application than purely for drainage. The cost of these additional surveys should also be taken into account.

Topographic surveys
Detailed topographic information is required for the design of a drainage system that can seldom be extracted with enough precision from existing topographic maps, and consequently, additional surveys are needed. Calculation of the costs of these topographic surveys is mostly done per hectare, and only if long alignments need to be levelled outside the direct area to be drained, the alignments may be calculated per km.

Pre-drainage soil surveys
The requisite soil information for determining drainage requirements is seldom found in existing soil maps. For drainage purposes hydraulic conductivity has to be determined, and information about soil salinity and groundwater levels and salinity is required as well as soil texture and the occurrence of impermeable layers. Since the required information is quite well defined (see ILRI publication 16) as well as the density, a costing on a per hectare basis can be estimated (Box 9.3).

Box 9.3   Cost estimate pre-drainage soil survey

If the required survey density is about one observation point per 5 - 10 ha a survey team can survey at least 4 locations per day depending on local conditions such as transport. Thus pre-drainage soil survey can have a daily output of some 20 to 40 ha (excluding laboratory work).

I.9.5.3   Design

A detailed design of drainage systems is based on reliable field information and a set of clear design criteria (Chapter I.1.4.3). The latter are prescribed by the implementation authority (Chapter I.1) and specify the groundwater levels that have to be maintained and the capacity required of the system, including practical information on available materials, installation equipment, desired layouts and so forth (Chapter I.3). The design process itself can quickly become a routine in which computers play an important role. The cost of the design of the subsurface system itself is mainly a question of the cost of the designer's time and can be accounted for on a per hectare basis. Special features like road crossings, pumping stations or complicated outlet structures are normally less routine-like in nature and should be considered separately.

I.9.5.4   Tender preparation and tendering

The tender preparation, the tendering, the supervision of the construction and the design are often combined in the one contract. It is quite common for the cost of these services are expressed as a percentage of the contracting construction costs. The amount of work depends on the existence of tender routines in the country with standard procedures, standard contract forms and specifications etc. If all of these have to be developed the work and the costs can be considerable. But, if properly drawn up in line with the national policies they can serve as a model for a following contract and thus have an application beyond the drainage system(s) for which they have been prepared (Chapter I.2). The cost can be calculated as: (i) a lump sum; (ii) a percentage of the contract sum; or (iii) on the basis of estimated expert time required.

I.9.5.5   Summary pre-construction costs

Table 9.3 presents the cost calculation of the preparation of the construction of a drainage system. In this table the cost of the governmental interventions are not taken into account.

Table 9.3   Sample of bill of quantities for budgeting of preparation costs

Item	Unit	Unit cost	Quantity	Total cost	Sub total
Feasibility study:					
• Time input	Person days				
• Associated cost	Lump sum				
Subtotal Feasibility study					
Field investigations:					
Topographic survey:					
• Area topography	ha				
• Alignments	km				
Pre-drainage soil survey:					
• Area soil survey	ha				
• Laboratory analysis	No. samples				
Subtotal Surveys					
Design:					
• Design of subsurface network	ha				
• Design of associated work	unit				
Subtotal Design					
Tender preparation and tendering:					
• On percentage basis	% of constr.				
• On time basis	days				
• Lump sum					
Subtotal Tendering					
Total Pre-construction Costs					

I.9.6   Construction costs

Methodologies for cost calculation of the major activities required for the construction of subsurface drainage networks are discussed in the following sections. The basic cost elements of the construction process are: staff costs, equipment cost, transport cost and material costs.

I.9.6.1   Field preparation

Field preparation consists of a number of activities (Chapter I.6.6) that have to be priced separately:
- Setting out alignments and levels: this includes staking out of the locations where the drains and manholes have to be installed with indications of levels. The cost can be calculated in staff time, some materials (stakes, bench marks, etc.) and equipment time;
- Accessibility of fields for drainage equipment: This includes the making of temporary passes of canals or drains and removing obstructions. It can be estimated in machine hours and staff time. Sometimes temporary bridges or culverts have to be installed

requiring the necessary materials for the purpose. The costing should include the removal after the construction is completed;

- Levelling alignment of drains: this involves the preparation of an alignment so that the drain machine can drive unobstructed. Normally, it is a matter of levelling a path with a bulldozer or grader. In case gravel is used with gravel trailers the path must be wide enough to accommodate the gravel trailers. The cost is calculated on the basis of machine (bull-dozer, grader) hours;
- Preparation of a gravel storage place (if required): this involves the smoothing of a stra-tegic location with good accessibility for both delivery trucks and gravel trailers with tractors. The cost can be calculated on the basis of machine hours;
- Preparing field storage place for drain pipes, manholes and the like: in the case of plastic drain pipes this often involves a shaded place. The cost is calculated in machine hours, staff time and materials;
- Camp preparation: for large projects sometimes contractor camps are made for lodging of the personnel, equipment maintenance facilities, etc. Costs depend very much on local conditions;
- The equipment has to be transported to the site, the cost depending on where the equipment comes from and on local transport costs and available transport equipment.

I.9.6.2   Drainage materials

The type and quantity of drainage materials to be used is determined according to the selected construction method (Chapter I.6). Cost estimates can be obtained as indicated below.

Plastic drain pipes
The price of plastic pipes varies considerably worldwide, partly caused by supply and demand, and partly by the volume that is produced. A factory that has a full workload can produce more cheaply than a factory that only works occasionally. The cost of plastic drain pipes can be calculated from the following:

- Commercial market prices plus transport costs, if there is an industry in the country;
- Base material costs (world market prices fluctuate!), production equipment costs plus transport costs, if there is no industry in the country and the industry is going to be set up;
- World market prices plus import duties plus transport costs, if imported pipes are going to be used.

Tips:
- Include in the cost 5-10% extra pipes for losses, damage and waste;
- A first approach for a price can be: 2 x the cost of base (raw) materials + transport cost.

Accessories for plastic drain pipes
The cost of accessories like connectors, reducers, end stops and pipe ends should be based on market prices or production costs similar to the plastic pipes above.

Rigid plastic pipes
Rigid plastic pipes are often required as end pipes, outlets, drain bridges and the like. The prices can mostly be derived from local manufacturers.

Concrete drain pipes
The cost of concrete drain pipes can best be based on the local cost of such pipes that are used for other purposes. If these costs are not available an estimate can be based on the national cost of m^3 of high quality concrete. Transport to the site must be added.

Granular envelopes
The cost of granular envelopes is a sum of the costs of all or some of the following items:
- Quarry rights (locally variable mostly a cost per m^3);
- Crushing (labour costs, cost of crusher equipment) if required;
- Sieving (labour costs plus minor costs of sieves and internal transport);
- Loading (labour + conveyor belts);
- Transport.

Synthetic envelopes
If there are no commercial listed prices for synthetic pre-wrapped envelopes, the price can be estimated from the cost of:
- The base material including transport costs to the factory;
- Thread to tie the material around the pipe;
- Wrapping machinery including, if necessary, the preparation of envelope material;
- Transporting the pipes from pipe factory to wrapping plant.

Note: if pipes with a pre-wrapped envelope are used, the price is based on the pipe with envelope.

Structures
Structures, in particular manholes, sumps, drain bridges, end structures and outlets, are mostly made of concrete the cost of which can be based on the volume of (different classes of) concrete in accordance with the design and unit cost of concrete per m^3.

I.9.6.3   Drain installation

Depending on the design, drain installation consists of some or all the following activities (Chapter I.6.6):
- Installation of field drains;
- Installation of end pipes;
- Installation of joints with collectors;
- Installation of manholes;
- Installation of crossings (drain bridges);

- Closing of field drain trenches;
- Installation of collector drain;
- Installation of joints field drains/collector drains;
- Installation of manholes and sumps;
- Installation of outlets;
- Closing of trenches of collectors.

The cost of installation is a total of the machine costs and labour costs. Since both costs are daily or hourly based, it is crucial to know the productivity per day or the length of drains that can routinely be installed per day. The required machinery, equipment and personnel for installation is dependent on the local situation, the design and the used materials, such as singular or composite system, concrete or plastic pipes and granular or pre-wrapped envelopes, for instance.

To calculate the cost of the installation, the composition of an efficient working installation unit in terms of machinery, equipment and personnel needs to be determined first. Costs per day of such a unit can then be calculated from the unit cost of each component. The cost of the drain installation can then be calculated by dividing the daily cost by the expected daily productivity of the installation unit.

Table 9.4 and 9.5 presents examples of installation cost calculations for field drains and collector drains, respectively. These are fictitious examples both as far as the unit cost is concerned and the equipment and personnel required. These two tables together provide the model for the cost calculation of composite systems with granular envelope. The installation units for the installation of singular systems or systems with pre-wrapped envelopes will be smaller than the units given in the example. In Part II-B details of cost calculations are further elaborated.

Comments
The cost of the installation very much depends on how the installation is organised. Often the cost of the installation machines is the single most expensive item. Consequently, the use of these machines should be optimised, meaning that everything must be done to keep them working continuously. Because the quantity of collectors is generally less than 20% of the quantity of field drains, the collector installation machines are idle for part of the time if they work in tandem with the field drain machines. This can be prevented by either having a number of field drain installation machines working together with one collector machine or by using the collector drain installation machine also for the installation of field drains by attaching another trench box.

Table 9.4   Example (fictitious) of the methodology for cost calculation for field drain installation. It is assumed that the collector installation machine can install both collectors and field drains. The cost per m' installed is the cost of an average m' of field and collector drains

Item	Quantity	Unit cost per day (€)	Total Cost per day (€)
Machinery and equipment:			
Field drain installation machine + laser	1	570	570
Gravel trailer	3	25	75
Tractors for gravel trailers	3	50	150
Excavator	1	450	450
Bulldozer	1	250	250
Front loader (gravel)	1	50	50
Agric. tractor + trailer	2	25	50
Servicing/maintenance truck	1	75	75
Topographic equipment	2	10	20
Car for field manager	0.5	40	20
Field transport for topographic and control personnel	1	30	30
Subtotal machinery and equipment			**1740**
Staff:			
Field manager	1		
Gravel manager	1		
Mechanics	1		
Topographers group	1		
Laser management	1		
Labourers	5		
Quality control	2		
Subtotal personnel			
Total daily cost Field Drain Installation			
Length of drain installed per day in m' drain [a]			
Cost per m' drain			

[a] The number of m' of field drains installed by a field drain installation machine depends on logistics, management, local conditions, capacity of the machine etc. For plastic flied drains, installation rates between 1500 m and 2500 m per day can easily be reached.

Table 9.5 Example of the methodology for cost calculation for collector drain installation (In this fictitious example, the cost of a composite system with granular envelope is taken into account, the assumption being that the collector installation does not require an envelope)

Item	Quantity	Unit cost per day (€)	Total Cost per day (€)
Machinery and equipment:			
• Collector/field drain installation machine + laser	1	650	650
• Excavator [a]	1	450	450
• Bulldozer [a]	1	250	250
• Agric. tractor + trailer [a]	1	25	25
• Servicing/maintenance truck [a]	0.33	75	25
• Topographic equipment [a]	2	10	20
• Car for field manager [a]	0.25	40	10
• Field transport for topographic and control personnel [a]	0.33	30	10
Subtotal machinery and equipment			**1440**
Staff [a]:			
• Field manager	1		
• Gravel manager	1		
• Mechanics	1		
• Topographers group	1		
• Laser management	1		
• Labourers	5		
• Quality control	2		
Subtotal personnel			
Total daily cost Collector Drain Installation			
Length of collector installed per day; in m' drain [b]			
Cost per m' drain			

[a] The quantities of these machines are to be taken up in proportion of the time spend for field and collector drain installation and can thus be a fraction. So if one collector machine works with two field drain installation machines 1/3 of the cost must be attributed to the collector installation.

[b] The number of m' installed per day by a collector machine depends on logistics, management, local conditions, capacity of the machine etc. For plastic collector pipes a installation rate of 1000 - 1500 m per day can easily be reached. The installation rate for concrete collector pipes is considerably lower (700 m/day).

I.9.6.4 Installation of manholes, sumps and joints

The cost of the installation of manholes/sumps, crossings, joints, outlet pipes and the like is an integral part of the drain installation. The cost also represents a combination of the cost of the staff and machinery. Most practical would be to foresee in the composition of the installation unit adequate staff and machinery for this installation and calculate the cost as an integral part of the drain installation. The cost of the supply of pipes if contracted out is sometimes separated from the cost of the pipe installation as such. If this is the case the costs are based on the machine hours and staff costs.

I.9.6.5   Backfilling of trenches

When drain pipes are installed using trenchers, the trenches have to be filled back, preferably with some overfill to compensate for subsidence. This can be done manually or mechanically (bulldozer, grader tractor with grader or bulldozer blade). The cost thereof is thus the cost of the machinery and/or the staff.

I.9.6.6   Construction and Installation of pumps/pumping stations

Construction of pumping stations is a civil engineering task the details of which are outside the scope of this book. Installation of pumps includes the supply of pumps and the connection to electric lines. The cost of the pumps can be obtained from manufacturers or suppliers based on the specifications. The cost of electric lines, transformers and so forth can be obtained from local electricity companies.

I.9.6.7   Cost of quality control and supervision

The cost of quality control and supervision can be divided into the cost of:
- Quality control of the materials: this is a cost that is part of the production cost of these materials, with a final check on the site, which is part of the "regular" supervision task. No extra costs have to be included;
- Quality control of the installation during the installation process: this is basically checking of the vertical and horizontal alignment of the drain pipes and levels of the manholes, sumps and outlets.

I.9.6.8   General Costs

Besides the direct construction costs, there are the so-called general costs such as:
- *Clearing of the site:* After the construction has been completed the site must be cleared of all leftover materials, refused materials and temporary constructions. The costs amount to mainly machinery and staff costs;
- *Quality control:* A final quality check has to be one to determine whether the system is functional as part of the handing over procedure of the site to the future users. This is mainly a staff cost;
- *As-built drawings:* Precise maps need to be made of where the drainage systems are located at the end of the installation, so that they can be traced for maintenance purposes. In most cases the exact location of the drains does not always coincide with the designed location;
- *Organisation overheads:* These costs include the time of the general management, accounting and administration, which is often carried out in parallel with similar tasks for

other projects. These costs are normally taken as a percentage of the construction costs. The overhead cost of the individual staff members is included in their unit cost;

- *Profit and risk:* If the installation is carried out by a private entity they have to make allowance for profits and for risks. After all they may be held responsible if something goes wrong, for any miscalculations or for human error. If government entities carry out the work they also run risks, but usually the government will pay for the extra cost. The amounts charged for overheads, profits and risks might vary considerably. They depend on the experience in the country, the trust in supervisors, the quality of the design, the general business risks in the country, and so forth. Figures varying between 20 and 50% have been known to occur;
- *Contingencies:* Most cost calculations reserve an amount for contingencies, namely, 10 - 20%. This is a reservation for extra work, unforeseen problems, price rises and such like. The conditions of contract determine how and when contingencies payments are to be made.

I.9.6.9   Total cost of construction

The total cost of construction is often summarised as a bill of quantities. Here the aggregated unit prices are given for the main items (Table 9.6).

Table 9.6   *Bill of Quantities for the construction of a composite drainage system (items marked* are not relevant for all projects)*

No.	Item	Units	Unit cost	Quantity	Total Cost
1	**Field Preparation:**				
1.1	Setting out of field	ha			
1.2	Accessibility of field	unit			
1.3	Levelling drain alignments	m'			
1.4	Preparing gravel storage*)	unit			
1.5	Preparing pipe storage	unit			
1.6	Preparing camp*)	unit			
1.7	Transport equipment to site	unit			
	Subtotal Field Preparation				
2.	**Field drain Installation:**				
2.1	(Pre-wrapped) drain pipes on site Ø 80 mm	m'			
2.2	(Pre-wrapped) drain pipes on site Ø 100 mm	m'			
2.3	Connections*)				
2.4	End-caps and couplers on site	no			
2.5	Rigid end pipes/bridges	m'			
2.6	Granular envelope (if relevant)	m³			
2.7	Installation drain pipes plus envelope	m'			

Table 9.6   Continued

No.	Item	Units	Unit cost	Quantity	Total Cost
2.8	Installing joints to collectors*)	no.			
2.9	Installing manholes*)	no.			
2.10	Installing end pipes*)	no.			
2.11	Installing crossings*)	no.			
2.12	Trench backfilling	m'			
2.13	Quality control	m'			
	Subtotal Field Drain Installation				
3	**Collector Drain Installation:**				
3.1	Collector pipes on site Ø .... mm	m'			
3.2	Collector pipes on site Ø .... mm	m'			
3.3	End-caps and couplers on site	no.			
3.4	Rigid end pipes/bridges	m'			
3.5	Installation collectors	m'			
3.6	Installing manholes*)	no.			
3.7	Installing sumps*)	no.			
3.8	Installing outlets*)	no.			
3.9	Installing crossings*)	no.			
3.10	Trench backfilling	m'			
3.11	Quality control	m'			
	Subtotal Collector Drain Installation				
4	**Additional works:**				
4.1	Construction pumping stations	no.			
4.2	Supply of pumps	no.			
4.3	Installation of pumps	no.			
4.4	Electrical connections	no.			
4.5	Transformers type ...	no.			
4.5	Electricity supply lines	km.			
	Subtotal Additional Works				
5	**General Cost:**				
5.1	Clearing of site	unit			
5.2	Final Quality Control	unit			
5.3	Management and accounting	unit			
5.4	As-built drawings	unit			
	Subtotal General Costs				
	Total Net Cost				
	Overhead profit and risk	% of total net cost			
	Contingencies	% of total net cost			
	Total Cost of Construction				

I.9.7   Cost of operation and maintenance of subsurface systems

The cost of operation and maintenance depends on many factors and can very considerably, namely:

- *Operation cost* (Chapter I. 8.3): The operation is generally confined to the pumping cost (if there is pumping). This involves energy costs (diesel or electricity) and some times staff costs. Operation costs can also be mentioned in the regular inspections, the staff cost for supervision and complaints management;
- *Maintenance* (Chapter I.8.4): Maintenance is mainly the cleaning and repairing of the subsurface drains (field drains and collector drains) and the associated structures (outlets, manholes, crossings, pumping stations etc.). Some maintenance work can be carried out by the landowners as part of their general field maintenance, and will thus have no direct cost consequence. This for instance applies to the checking of the drains, cleaning of the manholes, the checking and clearing of the outlets. The flushing of the drain pipes with flushers is a professional job. The cost is mainly determined by the required frequency of flushing, so no general rules can be applied. The required frequency depends on the soil types, envelopes, quality of installation, intensity of use and climate, among other things. For budgetary purposes a frequency of flushing one every 3-5 years is a good estimate. The length of drain that can be flushed per day depends very much on local situations and equipment. Until experience is available one can consider a potential production of 2 km per day for budgetary purposes. The cost of flushing is the cost of staff and equipment. Other maintenance costs pertain to the maintenance of the pumps and repairs of drains (mainly outlets and manholes). These costs are mainly staff costs, some equipment and spare parts.

Part II

Detailed Instructions for the Implementation of Subsurface Drainage Systems

General introduction to Part II

Contents
In Part I the planning of the implementation process and the organisational aspects of operation and maintenance of subsurface drainage systems were discussed. In Part II, the detailed methodologies and techniques of the implementation and operation and maintenance are dealt with. Part II is confined to the essential aspects of implementation that cannot easily be found in other literature, with the emphasis on construction, operation and maintenance of subsurface drainage systems.

Organisation
Implementation and maintenance of subsurface drainage systems is a complex process demanding the cooperation of many parties, of which the success depends entirely on the quality of the individual components. Since the responsibility is with different people and organisations, the contents of part II are presented in the form of '*instruction sheets*', organised in subject chapters. In this way instruction sheets dealing with only one activity or sub-activity can be copied and used by the staff responsible for that particular activity. Consequently at times there are repetitions, this is done to assure that each of the instruction sheets can be used independently.

Instruction sheets
Part II contains instructions sheets for:
A Planning and monitoring of the construction of subsurface drainage systems. Although the planning methodologies described are not unique to drainage implementation and hardly useful for smaller projects, international banks sometimes insist on the preparation of such planning.
B Instructions and models for cost calculations.
C Construction of subsurface pipe drainage systems. These instruction sheets focus on the construction of pipe drainage systems with plastic drain pipes with drainage trenchers. For the sake of completeness instructions are attached for installation by hand and installation of pipes in trenches dug by excavators. Instructions for trenchless drain installation are also included.
   Part C is subdivided in three sub-parts:
   • Organisation of the implementation;
   • Machinery and equipment;
   • Installation of drain pipes.
D Quality control of pipe drainage systems and monitoring of the performance of pipe drainage Systems.
E Operation and maintenance of pipe drainage systems.

Contents

Instruction sheet number	Subject and title	Target groups	Page
A	**Planning and Supporting Research**		
A.1	Network planning for the construction of subsurface drainage systems	Planners, supervisor, field manager	189
A.2	Operational monitoring for machine performance	Researchers, planners, monitoring staff	197
A.3	Time and motion studies	Researchers, monitoring staff	201
B	**Cost Calculations**		
B.1	Methodology for the calculation of staff cost	Planners, contracting department, contractors	207
B.2	Methodology for the calculation of the cost of equipment and machinery	Planners, contracting department, contractors	209
B.3	Methodology for the calculation of the cost of transport	Planners, contracting department, contractors	213
B.4	Methodology for the calculation of the cost of raw material	Planners, contracting department, contractors	215
C	**Installation of Subsurface Drainage Systems** **Organisation of the Implementation of Subsurface Drainage Systems**		
C.1	Requirements for the implementation of singular drainage systems	Planners, field manager, supervisor	227
C.2	Requirements for the implementation of composite drainage systems	Planners, field manager, supervisor	229
C.3	Task descriptions for key installation staff	Planners, field manager, supervisor	231
	Machinery and Equipment *Trenchers*		
C.4	Description of trenchers	Planners, operators, mechanics, field manager, supervisor	239
C.5	Maintenance of trenchers	Planners, operators, mechanics, Field manager, supervisor	245
C.6	Adjustment of trench box and digging chain	Planners, operators, mechanics, field manager, supervisor	253
C.7	Minimising the operation costs of trenchers	Operators, mechanics, field manager, supervisor	259

Instruction sheet number	Subject and title	Target groups	page
C.8	Operation of trenchers for corrugated plastic drain pipe installation	Planners, operators, mechanics, field manager, supervisor	263
C.9	Working with a liftable trench box	Operators, mechanics, field manager, supervisor	267
	Trenchless drainage machines		
C.10	Description of trenchless drainage machines	Planners, operators, mechanics, field manager, supervisor	271
C.11	Maintenance of trenchless drainage machines	Planners, operators, mechanics, field manager, supervisor	275
C.12	Operation of trenchless drainage machines	Planners, operators, mechanics, field manager, supervisor	283
	Laser equipment for grade control		
C.13	Description of laser equipment	Operator, surveyor, field manager, supervisor	287
C.14	Management of laser equipment for grade control	Operator, surveyor, field manager, supervisor	291
C.15	Determining the extension of laser mast on trencher	Operator, surveyor, field manager, supervisor	295
C.16	Verification of correctness of laser transmitter in the field	Operator, surveyor, field manager, supervisor	297
C.17	Manual grade control in absence of laser equipment	Operator, surveyor, field manager, supervisor	299
	Gravel trailers		
C.18	Description and maintenance of gravel trailers	Operator, mechanic, field manager, supervisor	303
	Installation of Drain Pipes		
	General activities		
C.19	Preparatory activities	Field manager, supervisor	307
C.20	Sequence of drain installation	Field manager, supervisor, field staff [1]	311
C.21	Setting out of field	Surveyors	317
C.22	Site preparation	Field manager, supervisor, field staff [1]	321
	Installation		
C.23	Installation of drains in a straight line and with correct grade	Operators, surveyors, field manager, supervisor	325
C.24	Installation of drains in saturated and/or unstable subsoils	Field staff [1], operators, field manager, supervisor	331

Instruction sheet number	Subject and title	Target groups	page
C.25	Installation in fields with standing surface water	Field staff[1], field manager, supervisor	333
	Installation of singular systems		
C.26	Installation of field drains starting from an open ditch	Operators, surveyors, field manager, supervisor	335
C.27	Installation of outlets of field drains into an open ditch	Field staff[1], field manager, supervisor	339
	Installation of composite systems		
C.28	Installation of sumps at the start of collector drains	Operators, surveyors, field staff[1], field manager, supervisor	341
C.29	Levels of manholes and starting levels for field drain installation	Surveyors, field manager, supervisor	343
C.30	Installation of manholes and preparation of start holes for field drains	Operators, surveyors, field manager, supervisor	349
C.31	Installation of pipe connections and joints	Field staff[1], field manager, supervisor	353
C.32	Completion of manhole/sump installation	Field staff[1], field manager, supervisor	355
	Singular and composite systems		
C.33	Backfilling of trenches	Field staff[1], field manager, supervisor	359
C.34	Cleaning up of site after installation	Field staff[1], field manager, Supervisor	363
C.35	Application of gravel	Gravel manager, field manager, supervisor	365
	Manual installation of drains and envelope materials		
C.36	Manual installation of drains	Field staff[1], field manager, supervisor	373
C.37	Manual installation in trenches dug by excavators	Field staff[1], field manager, supervisor	379
C.38	Wrapping a synthetic sheet envelope around the pipes in the field	Field staff[1], field manager, supervisor	385
D	**Quality Control**		
D.1	Quality control of drainage materials	Field manager, supervisor	391
D.2	Quality control of installation of pipe drainage systems	Field manager, supervisor, surveyors	397

Instruction sheet number	Subject and title	Target groups	page
D.3	Checking the functionality of composite drainage systems	Field manager, supervisor, surveyors	403
D.4	Methodology for checking the grade of installed drain and collector pipes during installation	Field manager, supervisor, surveyors	407
D.5	Post construction verification of drain pipes	Field manager, supervisor	413
E	**Operation and Maintenance**		
E.1	Checking the functionality of a subsurface drainage system	Maintenance staff, farmers	421
E.2	Principles of flushing subsurface systems	Maintenance staff, farmers	427
E.3	Management, maintenance and repair of high pressure flushers	Operators, field staff[1]	433
E.4	Flushing of collector drains	Operators, field staff[1]	435
E.5	Flushing of field drains from a ditch	Operators, field staff[1]	439
E.6	Flushing of field drains from a manhole	Operators, field staff[1]	443

[1] Field staff comprises all people involved including bulldozer operators, excavator operators and labourers.

II-A

Planning and Supporting Research

Planning and supporting research	Instruction sheet A.1
Subject: **Network planning for the construction of subsurface drainage systems**	
Target group: Planners, supervisor, field manager	

A.1 Network planning for the construction of subsurface drainage systems

A.1.1 Introduction

To set up a network planning of the construction of subsurface drainage systems the work necessitates detail inventory of the processes and working methods. In Part I Chapter 1.4.4 a number of planning methods have been discussed. As indicated therein the preparation of the network planning, as sometimes required by international financers, is a specialised job needing special software. In this instruction sheet we discuss the information that needs to be collected so that the professional can carry out the planning tasks. For the details of the network planning process see the relevant literature.

A.1.2 Information required at the start of the planning

Detailed planning of the construction can only start once the full design has been completed and technical specifications and the Bill of Quantity are available. In case of tendering the tender documents must also be available.

The information required for planning of the construction of the subsurface drainage system can be summarised as follows:
- The complete design, including:
  - Drawings of the layout of the subsurface drainage system;
  - Construction drawings of specific structures;
  - Technical specifications of all the works;
  - Technical specifications of the drainage materials;
  - The volume or quantity of work (Bill of Quantities). Table A.1-1 presents an example of the Bill of Quantities.
- The working methods and installation equipment to be used:
  - Installation methods of the pipe drains be (trenchers, trenchless, manually);
  - Installation equipment and capacity.
- The conditions under which the construction (installation) has to be carried out insofar as they influence the installation capacity and time requirements, such as:
  - Dimensions of the field;
  - Type of drains: open, subsurface, irrigation canals;

- Type of vegetation (crops, grass);
- Condition of the soil surface (trafficability, subsoil conditions);
- Water levels in open watercourse.
- The required start and end date of the construction as well as the factors affecting the time during which the fieldwork can be carried out, such as:
  - Number of working hours per day/number of working days per week;
  - Official holidays;
  - Periods during which the construction can take place (dry seasons, no crops in the fields etc.);
  - Effects of the climate on the work progress during specific periods.
- Manpower requirement and availability of manpower for each activity;
- Machinery and equipment requirement and availability for each activity;
- Responsibilities for transport of drainage materials to the site (if transport is to be included in the planning, then:
  - Availability of transport equipment;
  - Accessibility of the project area, infrastructure, roads and their quality (all-weather roads);
  - Distance of the factories to regional distribution centres and from there to the site;
  - Availability of support services;
- Time requirement for communication with the farmers and agreement with them about the schedule of construction in compliance with cropping calendars.

Now, an operational schedule for the construction of the drainage work can be prepared based on the above information.

Table A.1-1   Bill of Quantities for the construction of a composite drainage system

No.	Item	Units	Unit cost	Quantity	Total cost
1	**Field preparation**				
1.1	Setting out of field	Ha			
1.2	Accessibility of field	Unit	LS		
1.3	Levelling drain alignments	m'			
1.4	Preparing gravel storage*)	Unit	LS		
1.5	Preparing pipe storage	Unit	LS		
1.6	Preparing camp*)	Unit	LS		
1.7	Transport equipment to site	Unit	LS		
	Subtotal				
2	**Field drains**				
2.1	(Pre-enveloped) drain pipes on site Ø (80) mm	m'			
2.2	(Pre-enveloped) drain pipes on site Ø (100) mm	m'			
2.3	Connections*)				
2.4	End-caps and couplers on site	No.			
2.5	Rigid end pipes/bridges	m'			

No.	Item	Units	Unit cost	Quantity	Total cost
2.6	Gravel envelope (if relevant)	m³			
2.7	Installation drain pipes plus envelope	m'			
2.8	Installing joints to collectors*)	No.			
2.9	Installing manholes*)	No.			
2.10	Installing end pipes*)	No.			
2.11	Installing crossings*)	No.			
2.12	Trench backfilling	m'			
2.13	Quality control	m'			
	Subtotal				
3	**Collector drains**				
3.1	Collector pipes on site Ø .... mm	m'			
3.2	Collector pipes on site Ø .... mm	m'			
3.3	End-caps and couplers on site	No.			
3.4	Rigid end pipes/bridges	m'			
3.5	Installation collectors	m'			
3.6	Installing manholes*)	No.			
3.7	Installing sumps*)	No.			
3.8	Installing outlets*)	No.			
3.9	Installing crossings*)	No.			
3.10	Trench backfilling	m'			
3.11	Quality control	m'			
	Subtotal				
4	**Additional works*)**				
4.1	Construction pumping stations	No.			
4.2	Supply of pumps	No.			
4.3	Installation of pumps	No.			
4.4	Electrical connections	No.			
4.5	Transformers type ...	No.			
4.5	Electricity supply lines	Km			
	Subtotal				
5	**General cost**				
5.1	Clearing of site	Unit	LS		
5.2	Final Quality Control	Unit	LS		
5.3	Management and accounting	Unit	LS		
5.4	As-built drawings	Unit	LS		
	Subtotal				
	Total net cost				
	Overhead profit and risk	% of total net cost			
	Contingencies	% of total net cost			
	Total				

*The items marked *) are not relevant to all projects.*

A.1.3   Detailed information about the activities to be carried out

For each activity an estimate needs to be made of:
- The required time to carry out the activity with the available manpower and equipment;
- The activity that must be completed before the next one can start;
- Activities that can take place at the same time;
- Which activity can succeed another upon its completion;
- The periods during which the activity can be carried out (rainfall, crops in the field etc.).

A.1.4   Activities required for the construction of subsurface systems

The activities required for the construction of subsurface drainage system are listed below. Note that not all of the listed activities are relevant to all systems to be installed:
1. Ordering/tendering machinery and equipment (if required)
   - Drainage machines;
   - Excavators;
   - Tractors;
   - Trailers;
   - Gravel trailers;
   - Low-bed trailers;
   - Trucks;
   - Mobile workshops.
2. Ordering drainage materials
   - Drain pipes;
   - Envelope materials;
   - Ordering Gravel (if required).
3. Tender and contract preparation
4. Tendering
5. Awarding of contract
6. Establishment of camp/workshops/depots
7. Transport of materials to the field
8. Field preparation and setting out
9. Installation of subsurface drainage system
   - Construction of sump (if relevant);
   - Installation of outlet structure (if relevant);
   - Construction of power lines/transformers (if relevant);
   - Construction of dewatering drain (if relevant);
   - Dewatering (if relevant);
   - Installation of collector drain (composite systems only);
   - Installation of manholes (composite systems only);
   - Installation of field drain-collector connection and flushing entrance (composite systems only);
   - Installation of field drains, if relevant with gravel envelope;

- Quality control;
- Backfill of trenches;
- Checking functionality of the drainage system;
- Cleaning the site.

10. Reception of the subsurface drainage systems

A.1.5   Network diagram

A specialist subsequently processes the activities and all the relevant information about each activity into a planning network diagram. The network diagram indicates the sequence in which the activities will be implemented and the interdependency of the activities.

In Figure A1.1 the network diagram for the construction of a subsurface drainage project with sump construction and horizontal dewatering of the collector drains is presented as an example.

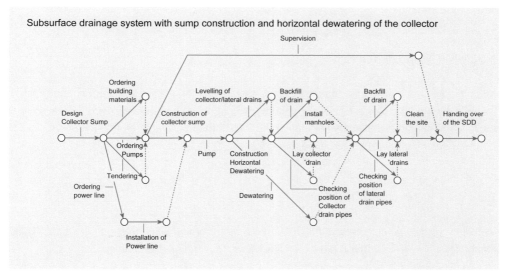

Figure A1.1   Network diagram for construction of a subsurface drainage system with sumps and horizontal dewatering of collector drains

A.1.6   Results and use of network planning

A.1.6.1   Fitting the planning into the allotted times

Whether or not the construction can be completed within the allotted time period with the available means and equipment can be determined from the first result of the planning procedure. If this is not the case either the means will have to be increased or the time period will need to be extended.

Once the decision has been made about increasing the time or getting more equipment and manpower a new run of the planning process is made. The planning will need regular revision while the project is running in keeping with the actual process made.

A.1.6.2   Completion of the network

The actual time calculations can be made once agreement has been reached about the total time allotted and all the necessary means have been made available for each activity. The result is that for each activity the following will be known:
- Earliest start date;
- Latest finish date;
- The float.

The float is the difference between the period available for implementing the activity and the time required for doing it. The integration of all the activities results in the start date and earliest finish date of the project.

A.1.6.3   Determine the critical path

When the earliest start dates and latest finish dates of all the activities have been determined, the critical path - the longest path of the network in terms of time requirements where no float is available - can be identified by calculating the *total float* of each activity. The method for calculating the total float is presented in Table A.1-2.

Table A.1-2 Calculation of Total Float

Activity (node no.)	Description	Latest finish time	(-)	Earliest Start time	(-)	Time estimate for Completing activity	=	Total float

The primary benefits to be derived from the critical path timing calculations are:
1. Establishment of the project duration for the plan;
2. Identification of the longest path through the project;
3. Identification of jobs for which there is scheduling flexibility without lengthening the project duration;
4. Identification of the activities on the critical path that do not allow any 'float' and therefore need to be carefully watched by the management.

The critical path activities can very well change in the course of the project when regular revisions of the planning are made based on the actual progress of each activity.

A.1.6.4   Periodic analysis of the results

Periodic analyses of the results of the regularly updated network diagram will allow the management to determine whether or not the actualised total project duration is in keeping with the allotted time for the project implementation.
- If not, the activities should be rescheduled and additional time or means will have to be made available;
- If the timing is within the allotted time the implementation can proceed without changes.

A.1.7   Simplified planning tools

A bar chart schedule can be prepared on the basis of the same information as given above. It is a simple planning tool that does not require highly specialised staff. It can be done either manually, in case of a small project, or using computer software programs, like the bar chart function of *MS-project*, for large-scale projects (Figure A1.2)

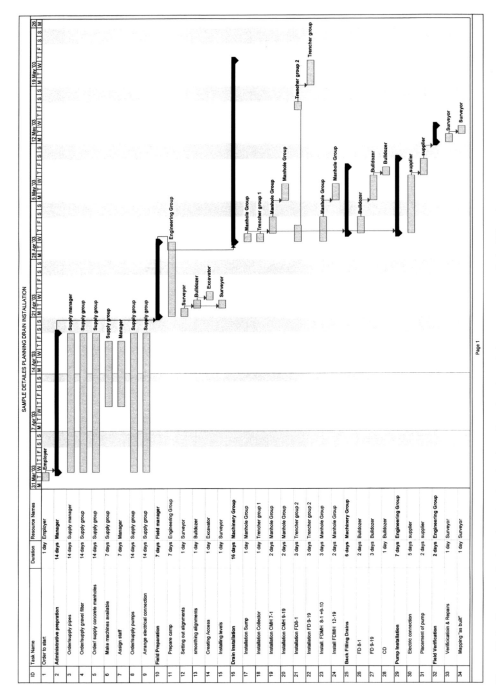

Figure A1.2   Example of a bar chart for the planning of a subsurface drainage system made by MS-project

Planning and supporting research	Instruction sheet A.2
Subject: **Operational monitoring for machine performance**	
Target group: Researchers, planners, monitoring staff	

A.2 Operational monitoring for machine performance

A.2.1 Introduction

Operational monitoring is a tool to determine the realistic standard time requirements for performing installation activities. These time requirements are basic inputs for the planning process. The monitoring of the performance of drainage machines during the installation process can, over time, result in realistic information about the installation capacity of these machines. This is valuable information for planning, cost estimates and the estimates of the quantity of machines required to install drainage systems per defined time limits.

A.2.2 Terminology

The common terms used in operational monitoring are:
- *Element:* A clearly defined part of an activity;
- *Build-up Time:* The time of an element in which Time and Work Standards are built up;
- *Time Standard:* Time unit (hour, minute) per production unit (ha, km, ton, etc.);
- *Work Standard:* Production unit per time unit;
- *Capacity:* Output in production units per time unit;
- *Efficiency:* Ratio of the useful output to the total input of a system.

Time is the most decisive factor, which to be measured accurately should be divided into small time units (Figure A2.1):
- *Total Machine Time.* The number of days in a year that the machine can be made available for the work, namely, 365 (or 366) calendar days minus all weekends and public holidays in that year, and minus seasonal days during which the machine will not be operating because of harvesting or planting activities. For drainage machines the Total Time varies between 190 and 200 days, depending on local conditions;
- *Non-Available Time.* The time that the machine is unable to operate, because of bad field conditions (weather, irrigated fields or major technical breakdowns, which require extensive repairs in the workshop);
- *Available Time.* The time that the machine is actually operational. It can be really available for the actual work: Total Time minus Non-Available Time. It can be divided into Non-Effective Time and Effective Time;

- *Non-Effective Time.* The time that the machine is available but unable to operate due to daily maintenance, organisational losses (for example non-availability of pipes) and daily rests or breaks of drivers and workers. Effective Time is obtained by subtracting the Non-Effective Time from the Available Time;
- *Effective Time.* The time that the machine is actually operational, namely, Available time minus Non-Effective Time. It can be divided into Direct Effective Time and Indirect Effective Time:
  - *Effective Time.* The time spent on the Main Elements of the work process, e.g. pipe laying, or removing weeds and/or silt;
  - *Indirect Effective Time.* The time spent on Support and Additional Elements of the work process. Support Elements are elements that are part of the work cycle but not the main element. They are necessary to implement the work such as lifting and lowering of the trench box of a drainage machine, and turning and driving back of the drainage machine. Additional Elements include short breakdowns of the machine, transport of the machine to the parking place and daily maintenance shop.

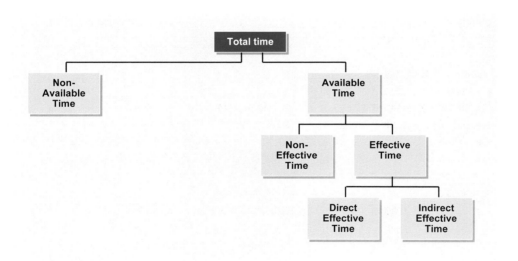

Figure A2.1   Total machine time can be divided in smaller time units

There are two methods to measure these various time units: 1) time (or efficiency) studies and 2) time and motion (or capacity) studies. These two methods will be discussed in the following sections.

Important elements of the installation of drains by drainage machines are:
Direct Effective Time
- Laying pipe
Indirect Effective Time
- Support elements

- Driving back
- Lifting trench box
- Lowering trench box
- Digging connections
- Connecting outlet
- Filling water tank, if applicable

Indirect Effective Time
- Additional Elements
  - Short technical breakdown
  - Short organisational delays:
    * Laser
    * Pipes
    * Fuel
    * Field obstruction
    * Gravel
  - Field transportation

A.2.3 Time Studies

Time or efficiency studies are used to determine the total time that a machine is working such as time lost by repairs, non-working days (e.g., holidays) and lunchtime. The Total Time is divided into Non-Available Time and Available Time. The Available Time is divided into Non-Effective Time and Effective Time (Figure A2.1). To note down the time used for the various activities it is advisable to use a standard time registration form (Figure A2.2). The following data should be collected for a time study to assess the performance of drainage machines:

- General information such as the date, project, name of observer, machine and field conditions;
- Information on the working condition of the machine: time the machine was working and the time the machine was not working, including the reasons why the machine was not working.

The form should be filled in preferably by an observer or the field engineer and not by the driver. To adequately assess the performance of the machine (and its driver) the time study must cover an entire working day or a series of days. The data is used to calculate the Effective and Non-Effective Time, including the reasons for the Non-Effective Time. By making observations throughout the year, the actual available working days can also be determined. It is important to record why a machine is not working, whether this is due to holidays or stoppage due to crops, irrigation activities, breakdowns, labour disputes, and so forth. Only then can the Available Time be determined, including the length of an average working day. This type of information can be used for planning. Note, time studies do not tell us anything about the output (kilometres of drain lines installed etc.). To get to know this time & motion studies will have to be done.

Efficiency Study on Drainage Machines
Time Registration Sheet

General information:	Date:　　　　　Name of observer:													
Project information:	Directorate:													
	Project name:													
	Collector number:													
	Contractor:													
Machine information:	Kind of machine:　　　Lateral / Collector													
	Manufacturer and type:													
	Year of manufacturing:　　Chassis number:													
Conditions:	Crop:　　　　　Use of gravel:　No / Yes													
	Soil type and condition:　　　Dry / Wet													
Description	Daily hours													
	7	8	9	10	11	12	13	14	15	16	17	18	19	20
A Working														
B Not working														
* Maintenance														
* Technical problems														
- Engine														
- Digging mechanism														
- Hydraulic system														
- Frame														
* Organisational problems														
- No driver														
- No labourers														
- No pipes														
- No gravel														
- No preparations														
- No fuel														
* Field conditions														
- High water level														
- Crop damage														
- Other problems														
* Personal care														
Lunch break														
Rest														
Production of the machine:	.... m^1 / day　　　EFFSTUDY.SHT													

Figure A2.2　Time Registration Sheet for drainage machines

Planning and supporting research	Instruction sheet A.3
Subject: **Time and motion studies**	
Target group: Researchers, monitoring staff	

A.3   Time and motion studies

Time and motion studies are used to determine the capacity of drainage machines. The Effective Time (outcome of the time study) is divided in Indirect and Direct Effective Time. The time for each element of the work process is measured using a stopwatch in, for example, centi-minutes (0.01 part of a minute). The elements must be clearly defined, with a proper indication of the beginning and end of the elements. Again it is recommended to use standard data sheets, for time and motion studies. Two sheets are used:
• Survey Sheet Time and Motion Study to record general data: date, name of observer, project information, machine information, general working conditions, data on the drainage system and general remarks (Figure A3.1);

Survey Sheet Time and Motion Studies Drainage Machines		
Observation date: **Observation number:**	**Name observer:**	
Project:	Directorate:	
	Project name:	
	Collector number:	
	Contractor:	
Machine information:	Kind of machine:	Lateral / Collector
	Manufacturer:	
	Type specification:	
	Year of manufacturing:	
	Chassis number:	
	General Condition:	Good / Moderate / Bad
General conditions:	Weather condition:	Good / Moderate / Bad
	Soil type:	Heavy clay / Clay / Silty clay / Sandy
	Soil condition:	Dry / Wet / Very wet
	Crop:	Non / Berseem / Wheat / Cotton / Rice / Potato / Barley / ....
	Crop height:	Low / Medium / High
Drainage system:	Distance between drains:	(metres)
	Length of drains:	(metres)
	Depth of drains:	(metres)
	Pipe material:	Cement / PVC - PE
	Pipe diameter:	(mm)
	Envelope used:	Non / Gravel /Synthetic
General remarks:		
T&MGEN.SHT		

Figure A3.1   Survey Sheet for drainage machines

- Time and Motion Study Sheet to record time and motion, when the time (in centi-minutes) for each successive element of the machine's working cycle is measured. The best way is to keep the stopwatch running continuously because the end-time of one element is the begin-time of the next element. Apart from general data, the following data is also recorded: the real starting time of the main elements; the name of the element or activity; length and depth of the drain trench; unusual events or incidents and changing conditions (Figure A3.2).

Time and Motion Study Sheet

Drainage machine:			Project name	Collector number		Date		Sheet number
Manufacturer	Year of manufacturing	Chassis number						
(7)	Measurement [cmin]	Activity		Lateral		Soil type	Remarks	
				Depth	Length			
↓	↓	↓		↓	↓	↓	↓	

Figure A3.2   Study Sheet for drainage machines

The data collected with the survey and study sheets is used to calculate work and time standards. This can be done by hand (Figure A3.3) or by computerised calculation programmes. The output is the average time for each element of the work process. The output can be related to different types of machines, areas, soils, working conditions and any other variable that is important for managing the construction process. Examples are presented in Part III.

Work Standard Calculation Form

Method:

Laying plastic pipes of 80 mm diameter from both sides of the collector drain.
Average length of the drain is 200 m. Depth of trench 1.20 m. to 1.50 m.

Machine: All lateral-laying drainage machines

Envelope: None

Work Standard per km lateral drain

Elements of work process	Min./ element	Total minutes
1 Laying pipes		*112.0*
2 Turning and driving back	24.7	
Lifting shoe	1.8	
Lowering shoe	1.8	
Digging connection	8.7	
Inlet outlet connection	6.4	
Filling water tank	0.9	
Subtotal		44.3
3 Short technical breakdowns	1.6	
Subtotal		1.6
4 Short organisational breakdowns		
- Stop for pipes	18.0	
- Stop for fuel	3.7	
- Adjustment laser	1.8	
- Field obstructions	1.9	
Subtotal		25.4
- Stop for gravel		
5 Transportation in the field	0.7	
Subtotal		0.7
Total minutes per km of lateral drain		*184.00*
Work norm: Metres / Hour {[1000: total minutes] * 60}		*326.09*
Time norm: Hours / Kilometre {Total minutes: 60}		*3.07*

Figure A3.3   Work Standard Calculation Form

II-B

Cost Calculations

Cost Calculations	Instruction sheet B.1
Subject: **Methodology for the calculation of staff cost**	
Target group: Planners, contracting department, contractors	

B.1   Methodology for the calculation of staff cost

The staff costs are calculated on a monthly or daily basis. Staff costs are generally considerably more than salary costs. It is composed of all or some of the items as given in Table B.1-1. All costs, also for tools etc., have to be calculated on a time basis (for instance, per day or per month).

Table B.1-1   Staff cost components

Cost items	Explanation	Unit
Salary	Paid out salary plus possible withholdings for taxes and social charges	Amount/month
Bonuses	Extra payments for special work or gratifications	Amount/month
Overtime payment	Average overtime payments for same category staff	Amount/month
Taxes paid by employer	Depending on national tax law	Amount/month
Social charges paid by employer	Depending on national laws and regulations, either fixed sum or percentage of salary	Amount/month
Insurance paid by employer	Health insurance, accident insurance, unemployment insurance, third party insurance etc., depending on national legislation and customs	Amount/month
Additional allowances	Depending on labour contract	Amount/month
Transport cost	Cost of transport to office or site; car allowances	Amount/month
Field allowances	Allowance paid for work out of office, depending on national legislation and customs	Amount/month
Clothing allowances	Depending on local customs.	Amount/month
Tools and instruments	Essential tools that employer provides to staff for carrying out their tasks such as measuring instruments, shovels and computers	Monthly charge
Consumables	Provisions that employer provides such as paper, writing materials and lubricants for instruments	
Overhead	See below	Amount/month
Total Cost		

If costs are calculated per month, as proposed in Table B.1-1, the daily cost can be obtained as follows:

Total monthly salary costs x 12 divided by the number of working days per year.

Overhead costs

The term 'overhead cost' is a 'catch all' phrase for all costs that are not accounted for elsewhere. It often has to do with the cost that can be called 'general running cost' of an entity or establishment and can include the cost of renting offices, secretarial assistance, professional insurance, services to personnel and so forth. Most of these items provide services to or are used for a number of projects simultaneously. They can thus not be attributed to one project or contract only. A common practice is to attribute these costs to all projects or contracts served in proportion to the turnover of each. (see also Part I.7.1.5).

Cost Calculations	Instruction sheet B.2

Subject:	**Methodology for the calculation of the cost of equipment and machinery**
Target group:	Planners, contracting department, contractors

B.2 Methodology for the calculation of the cost of equipment and machinery

Calculation of equipment and machinery costs is complicated by the fact that these are so-called capital goods. The cost of the use of capital equipment is divided into two components:
- Fixed costs or owing costs: costs that are incurred even if the machine is not working;
- Operation costs or variable costs: costs that are incurred only if the machine is working.

A complication may occur when not all costs are incurred in the same currency. For example, if most of the fixed costs are incurred in an international currency to finance the purchase and most of the variable costs are incurred in the national currency. If this is the case, then the realistic exchange rate is to be used and the costs have to be converted into one currency.

The lifetime of capital goods, like drainage machines, is in most cases considerably longer than the time necessary to complete the installation of a drainage project. Thus:
- The cost of each activity carried out by the machinery includes part of the write-off of the investment made for the machinery. If the money destined to compensate the write-off is systematically put into a savings account, a capital will have been built up at the end of the lifetime of the machine to purchase a new one;
- The money spent for the purchase of the machine is taken out of circulation and does not accrue interest. If the machine would not have been purchased the owner could have put the money in the bank and this sum would have generated interest. Thus the purchase of the machine results in a loss of interest. This loss has to be compensated in the cost of the machine which includes an item "loss of interest". If the equipment is bought on credit (with a loan) then interest will have to be paid to the credit provider (bank). In that case the interest payments are a cost element of the machinery.

The cost calculation of machinery or equipment can be made on the basis of Table B.2-1 given below, which has been derived from the cost calculation methods of Caterpillar handbook and is one that is internationally accepted. As the table only allows for one currency, we have selected the Euro for our example.

Table B.2-1   Sample calculation method of cost of equipment

No	Item	Unit/formula	Quantity	No	Item	Unit/formula	Quantity
Basic information							
A.	Purchase price	Euro	250,000	H.	Insurance	% of A/year	1
B.	Depreciation period	Hour	10,000	I.	Shelter	Euro/year	0
C.	Annual use	Hour/year	1,200	J.	Lubricants/year	15% of F x G	1152
D.	Life time	Years (B/C)	8	K.	Personnel cost	Euro/hour	2.5
E.	Interest rate	%	9	L.	Spare parts	% of A/life time	65
F.	Fuel price	Euro/litres	0.50	M.	Repair	% of A/life time	10
G.	Fuel consumption	litres/year	15,360	N.	Residual value	% of A	10

	Owing Costs	Formula	Euro/year	Formula	Euro/hour	Formula	Euro/day
O.	Depreciation	(A-N)/D	27,000	O/C	22.50	O/C*8	180
P.	Loss of interest	A/2*E	11,250	P/C	9.38	P/C*8	75
Q.	Insurance	H*A	2,500	Q/C	2.08	Q/C*8	17
R.	Shelter	I	0	R/C	0	R/C*8	0
S.	**Total**		**40,750**	**S/C**	**33.96**	**S/C*8**	**272**

	Operation Cost	Formula	Euro/year	Formula	Euro/hour	Formula	Euro/day
T.	Fuel	F*G	7,680	T/C	6.40	T/C*5	32
U.	Lubricants	J	1,152	U/C	0.96	U/C*5	5
V.	Spare/wear parts	A*L/D	19,500	V/C	16.25	V/C*5	81
W.	Repairs	A*M/D	3,000	W/C	2.50	W/C*5	13
X.	Personnel	K*C	3,000	X/C	2.50	X/C*5	13
Y.	**Total**		**34,332**		**28.61**		**143**

	Total Cost		Euro/year	Formula	Euro/hour	Formula	Euro/day
S.	Owing		40,750	S/C	34	S/C*8	272
Y.	Operation		34,332	Y/C	29	Y/C*8	143
Z.	Contingencies	(S+Y)*0.05	3,754	Z/C	3	Z/C*8	21
	Total		**78,836**		**66**		**435**

Explanation of the table: (for the sake of simplicity only the term equipment has been used).

Part 1   Basic information
A. Purchase price: is the price of the equipment including all costs such as transport insurance, taxes, assembling and test runs;
B. Depreciation period (working hours): the period over which the equipment has depreciated or the technical lifetime of the equipment. The end of the technical lifetime is the moment that repair/revision of the equipment is economically more costly than purchasing a new one. The lifetime of modern machinery in the western world is estimated at 10 000 hours. In reality the lifetime may be considerably longer depending on the local cost of mechanics, spare parts and the like;
C. Annual use (working hours per year): refers to the number of hours the equipment is used annually;
D. Lifetime (years): is the lifetime of the equipment in years, which can be obtained by dividing the depreciation period by the annual use;

E. Interest rates in %: the current interest rate in the country or the expected average annual interest rate over the lifetime of the equipment;

F. Fuel price in Euro per litre;

G. Fuel consumption in litres/year. This can be obtained from the number of working hours per year (C) and the hourly consumption (The hourly consumption can be estimated from the manufacturer's information, which if difficult to obtain can be estimated as follows: hourly consumption at full power is 200 gr./fuel per horsepower, or 0.16 litres/HP/hour. Since most of the equipment is not continuously working at full power the actual consumption is 50%-70% of 0.16 litres/HP/hour). If electrically or gas driven equipment is used, then obviously fuel will be replaced by electricity or gas;

H. Insurance (Euro per year): insurance of the equipment is often arranged to cover accidents so that the investment is not lost. The insurance rate varies per company and per country. The rates can be obtained from insurance companies and often amounts to a percentage of the insured value;

I. Shelter (Euro per year): the equipment requires storage and shelter (garage). The cost thereof depends on the local conditions and prices;

J. Lubricants (Euro per year): Lubricants are needed for most equipment. If actual costs are not known they can be estimated for diesel powered equipment as being 15% of the fuel costs. For electrically powered equipment the information can be obtained from the manufacturer;

K. Personnel costs: (Euro/hour); The costs of the personnel required to operate and do the regular maintenance of the equipment (see B.1) depends on the local cost levels, salary levels and so forth;

L. Spare parts (Euro over life time): the cost of spare parts including wear parts[1] over the lifetime of equipment can be expressed as a percentage of the purchase price. The use of wear parts is especially high for drainage machines so this can be an important cost item (75-100%);

M. Repairs (Euro over lifetime). This concern the cost of mechanics and small items required for repairs, it is a local cost based on the hourly cost of mechanics. It is generally expressed as a percentage of the purchase price;

N. Residual value (in Euro): at the end of the life of the equipment it may still be of value be it second hand value, spare parts that can be cannibalised, or as scrap. The value will vary from country to country and from situation to situation and is often estimated at between 0% and 10% of the new value;

Part 2   Owing costs (in Euro per year)

O. Depreciation (Euro/year): this is calculated as the purchase price minus the residual value divided over the lifetime. (A-N)/D;

P. Loss of interest (Euro/year): is the amount of money that would be lost had the equipment been purchased as opposed to it gaining interest in the bank. Since the value of the

---

[1] Wear parts are parts that regularly wear out because of the activity of the equipment. With a trencher, for instance, these are the digging chains and sprocket wheels, with cars: tires and oil filters, with drain pipe production lines: needles or knives for punching the holes.

equipment depreciates every year the amount of money that could have gained interest in the bank also depreciates year by year. Thus, the loss of interest also becomes less and less. To make it simple, the average amount that could have been deposited in the bank would be 50% of the purchase price. Thus, the annual loss of interest is calculated as being 50% of the purchase price in Euro times the interest rate in percentage;

Q. Insurance cost (Euro/year): calculated as insurance rate in % multiplied by the new value in Euro;

R. Shelter (Euro/year): the annual cost of shelter in Euro;

S. The total owing costs (Euro/year): addition of O, P, Q and R. The total owing costs can be calculated per hour by dividing all the costs by the number of hours the equipment is used (C). The daily price for drainage - a convenient basis for cost calculation - is the hourly cost multiplied by the daily working hours;

Part 3   Operation costs (in Euro per year)

T. Fuel (or energy (Euro/year): calculated as the annual fuel or electricity use multiplied by the unit cost;

U. Lubricants (Euro/year): cost of lubricants per year;

V. Spare/wear parts (Euro/year): Total value of spare/wear parts over the lifetime divided by the number of years;

W. Repairs (Euro/year): Total value of repairs over the lifetime divided by the number of years;

X. Personnel costs (Euro/year): Cost of personnel per hour multiplied by the number of hours per year;

Y. Total operation costs (Euro per Year): addition of T, U, V, W and X. The total operation costs can be calculated per hour by dividing all the costs by the number of hours the equipment is used (C). The daily price, that for drainage a convenient basis for cost calculation, is the hourly cost multiplied by the daily working hours.

Part 4   Total costs

The total costs are the sum of the owning costs (S) and the operation costs (Y). For eventualities that may occur, price rises, exchange rates changes, 5 or 10 per cent is normally added for contingencies (Z).

In Table B.2-1 a cost price has been calculated based on fictitious data for a drainage trencher, that cost 250,000 Euro, and works 1200 hours per year for 8 hours working days.

Cost Calculations	Instruction sheet B.3

Subject: **Methodology for the calculation of the cost of transport**

Target group: Planners, contracting department, contractors

B.3 Methodology for the calculation of the cost of transport

The transport requirements for the construction of drainage systems can be international and national or local transport.

B.3.1 International transport

International transport (sea freight or air freight) has its own particularities, which vary considerably. Since it is a question of a world market price there is no direct relationship between distance, volume and costs. Moreover charges for ports, port storage handling, insurance and paper work can be significant and out of all proportions to the actual cost of transport.

The calculation of international transport costs is specialist work that can be circumvented by requesting an international supplier to do the job and quote a CIF price (Cost Insurance Freight is then included in the price). Initial quotations are often FOB (Free On Board) prices, meaning the cost of the equipment includes the transport to the harbour and the loading onto the ship.

B.3.2 Local transport costs

Local transport costs can be calculated in the following ways:

Contracted transport

If there are reliable transport companies to whom one can contract out the transport, these companies often have km/ton charges, meaning the cost of transport of one ton over one km distance. They may also have various prices for different road conditions. If light materials need to be transported (drain pipes) they may quote a price according to m^3/km. Insurance for the transport is extra.

Transport by own organisation

If transport is going to be taken care of by the entity responsible for the drainage construction, the cost of transport has to be calculated in detail as follows:
- Cost of loading: is the cost of labour and possible tools, instrument lifting devices;
- Cost of transport: can be calculated in the same way as the cost of equipment presented in instruction B.2;
- Cost of discharge: is the cost of labour and possible tools, instrument lifting devices;
- Cost of Insurance: if required, to be obtained from local insurance companies;

213

Cost of losses and damages: losses or damages depend on what precisely is transported. Gravel will only have losses, culverts may be damaged as can happen to drain pipes. Initially an estimate can be made of the losses and damages, but as experience is gained regular corrections may be made.

B.3.3   Suppliers transport

Suppliers can be requested to take care of the transport and deliver on site. This will circumvent some of the difficulties as long as the contracts are properly drawn up. They will then be accountable for all losses and damages. The consequence is that they will include the risk of the transport in their cost.

Cost Calculations	Instruction sheet B.4
Subject: **Methodology for the calculation of the cost of raw material**	
Target group: Planners, contracting department, contractors	

B.4 Methodology for the calculation of the cost of raw material

Under raw material for the construction of drainage systems is understood to be materials like PVC powder, PE powder, cement and to a lesser extent fuel and electricity. The basic material for synthetic envelopes such as polypropylene, nylon thread for the windings may also be included. The cost calculation of base materials can be based on national (sometimes controlled) prices or world market prices.

B.4.1 PVC and PE powder

These materials are international commodities that are governed by world market prices. If there is a national industry that produces either one of these powders, the price is possibly a set national price. Therefore, the national price is required for the cost calculation. For the feasibility study, however, the world market (economic) price may be required. The prices of PVC and PE powder fluctuate continuously on the world market as a reaction to supply and demand. International prices can be obtained from international publications on commodity prices and national prices from the national industry. If the powder is purchased internationally the cost of transport may have to be added as well as the cost of import duties.

B.4.2 Cement

Cement prices are in most cases nationally set or have a national market price. Other raw materials have to be obtained from the national or international suppliers.

II-C

Installation of subsurface drainage systems

Preamble

The installation process starts as soon as the design has been completed and approved, the installation mode has been decided and all the relevant contracts have been signed.

A prerequisite for the start of the installation in countries without an existing drainage industry is the availability of the equipment and production facilities for drainage materials in country in question or, in special cases, arrangements for the import of drainage materials. Obviously, when the installation process commences the equipment and drainage materials that will be used will already be known.

The minimum information that the organisation in charge of construction should be provided with is as follows:
- Map with the layout and levels of the drainage system relative to a benchmark and base-line;
- List of the field drains and collectors to be installed indicating: the locations, levels, lengths and diameters of the drains;
- Bill of Quantity in which the required quantities of drainage materials are listed.

Drainage materials

The procurement of drainage materials can, depending on local customs, be done directly by the implementing organisation or is included in the construction contract. Whatever method is used, the instructions sheets are based on the assumptions that:
- Drainage materials of acceptable quality has been transported to the site;
- Plastic (PVC or PE) corrugated field drain and collector pipes will be used;
- Either gravel or pre-wrapped envelope material will be used.

Installation equipment

The instruction sheets for installation are written for using trenchers with laser guided depth and grade control. Instructions for the use of trenchers can vary depending on the make of the trenchers. These are general instructions that need to be completed or modified according to the instructions provided by the manufacturers of the equipment. Instructions for manual grade control can be found in instruction sheet C.17 for the rare instances when no laser is available. For the sake of completeness a guideline is given in instruction sheet C.36 for the installation of drain pipes by hand (see also Chapter 6, Part I). In instruction sheet C.37 guidelines are given for the installation of drain pipes by hand in trenches dug by excavators (see also Chapter 6 of Part I).

Layouts

As far as the layouts are concerned the instructions are written for:
- Singular systems, which are systems in which field drains discharge into an open drain (Figure C0.1);
- Composite or collector systems where the field drains discharge into a subsurface collector drain that in turn discharges into an open ditch or a sump from where the water is pumped into an open ditch (Figure C0.2).

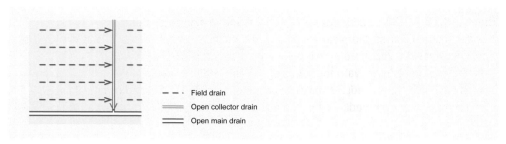

Figure C0.1   Layout of singular drainage system discharging into an open drain

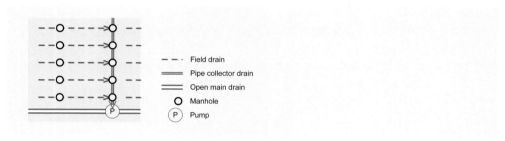

Figure C0.2   Layout of composite drainage system discharging into a sump

Organisation of the instruction sheets

The instructions only contain a limited amount of background information, they are purely and simply a practical guide to the process of drainage installation and the technical aspects of the maintenance of drainage systems. For other aspects of the implementation process reference is made to the specific Chapters in Part I.

The following groups of instruction sheets are provided:

Sheet II.C.1 - C.3   Organisation of the implementation of subsurface drainage systems

Provides information about the organisation required and how the organisation can be staffed and the special skills required.

Sheet II.C.3 - C.18   Machinery and equipment

Provides information about the machinery and equipment required, the maintenance and management thereof and, in particular, the adjustment of the trencher.

Sheet II.C.18 - C-38   Installation of subsurface drainage systems

Provides instructions on the main aspects of the implementation of subsurface drainage systems. These instructions sheets have been organised per subject as follows:

- General procedures, valid for both singular and composite layouts;
- Implementation procedures for singular systems, with pre-wrapped or gravel envelope;
- Implementation procedures for composite drainage system with pre-wrapped or gravel envelope;
- Management of gravel as an envelope;
- Installation of drain pipes by hand;
- Installation of drain pipes by hand in trenches dug by excavators;
- Trenchless installation of drain pipes.

II-C/1

Organisation of the implementation of subsurface drainage systems

General

Implementation of subsurface drainage systems requires a systematic organisation. The precise form of this organisation will depend on the local customs and conditions as well on the institutional set up of the local drainage industry (see also Part I, Chapter 6). The following sections contain the requirements in terms of machinery, equipment, tools and staff for the implementation of both singular and composite drainage systems.

Installation of Subsurface Drainage Systems	Organisation of the Implementation of Subsurface Drainage Systems	Instruction sheet C.1
	Subject: **Requirements for the implementation of singular drainage systems**	
	Target group: Planners, field manager, supervisor	

C.1 Requirements for the implementation of singular drainage systems

C.1.1 Required machinery equipment and tools

The following equipment and tools are required for the installation of singular drainage systems:
- Trencher(s) for installing field drains (including tools, fuel, etc.);
- At least 5 boning rods (delivered with the trenchers);
- Laser equipment;
- Levelling instrument including the measuring staff;
- Measuring tape of 2 metres;
- Measuring tape of 50 metres;
- Bulldozer;
- In some cases a hydraulic excavator.

Support equipment:
- Transport equipment material for infield transport of drainage materials (agricultural tractor with trailer);
- Fuel tanker;
- Servicing/maintenance truck (pick-up);
- Transport equipment for staff (motorcycles, cars, busses);
- Communication equipment (walky-talkies, cell phones, or other).

Additionally if gravel envelope is used:
- Three tractors and gravel trailers for each trencher, for infield transport of gravel envelope;
- Front loader for loading of gravel into gravel trailers.

C.1.2 Required staff

The following staff is required for the installation of singular drainage systems:
- Field manager for the overall organisation;
- Trencher operator (one for each trencher);
- Assistant trencher operator (one for each trencher);
- Technical assistant to assist the field manager and as deputy field manager when the field manager is absent;

- Two surveyors per trencher for setting out the field and quality control;
- Three labourers per trencher for unrolling the drain pipe (if pipes are not delivered on rolls and/or the trenchers are not equipped for handling rolls);
- Ore person for guiding the drain pipe on the machine (operators assistant);
- Ore person for installing the outlet, checking the pipe position and initial backfilling of trench;
- Tractor driver for driving the transportation material for supply of drainage material.

Support personnel:

- Mechanic for infield maintenance (depending on customs, conditions and proximity of mechanical services);
- Fuel tanker tractor driver (perhaps not full-time);
- Car driver(s) for driving transporting field staff.

In case of gravel envelope application:

- Three tractor drivers;
- Front loader driver;
- Gravel manager.

Installation of Subsurface Drainage Systems	Organisation of the Implementation of Subsurface Drainage Systems	Instruction sheet C.2
	Subject: **Requirements for the implementation of composite drainage systems** Target group: Planners, field manager, supervisor	

C.2 Requirements for the implementation of composite drainage systems

C.2.1 Required machinery equipment and tools

The following equipment and tools are required for the installation of composite drainage systems. The equipment is based on the use of one trencher for field drain installation and one trencher for collector installation:

- Excavator(s) for digging the starting hole of the collector trencher and for installation of collector outlet, manhole and starting holes of field drain trencher;
- Trencher for installing collector drains;
- Trencher for installing field drains;
- At least 2 x 5 boning rods (delivered with the trenchers);
- Laser transmitter (preferably 2);
- Battery charger for laser transmitter (if required);
- Levelling instrument including the measuring staff (preferably 2 sets);
- Measuring tape of 2 metres;
- Measuring tape of 50 metres;
- Mud pump.

Support equipment:

- Transport equipment material for infield transport of drainage material (agricultural tractor with trailer);
- Fuel tanker;
- Servicing/maintenance truck (pick-up);
- Transport equipment for staff (motorcycles, cars, busses);
- Communication equipment (walky-talkies, cell phones, or other).

Additionally if gravel envelope is used:

- Three tractors and gravel trailers for infield transport of gravel envelope;
- Front loader for loading of gravel into the gravel trailers;
- Transportation material for supply of drainage material;
- Transportation equipment for staff (motorcycles, cars, busses).

C.2.2   Required staff

Requirements for the staff for the installation of composite drainage systems are as follows:
- Field manager for the overall organisation;
- Trencher operator (2-4 depending on workload and customs);
- Technical assistant to assist the field manager and to be deputy field manager when the field manager is absent (depending on the size of operation);
- Two surveyors for setting out the field and quality control;
- Three labourers per trencher for unrolling the drain pipe (if pipes are not delivered on rolls);
- One person per trencher for guiding the drain pipe on the machine (operators assistant);
- One or more assistants per trencher for installing outlets making connections, checking pipe position and initial backfilling of trench;
- Tractor driver for driving the transportation material for supply of drainage material.

Support personnel:
- Mechanic for infield maintenance (depending on customs, conditions and proximity of mechanical services);
- Fuel tanker tractor driver (perhaps not full-time);
- Car driver(s) for transporting field staff.

In case of gravel envelope application:
- Three tractor drivers;
- Front loader driver;
- Gravel manager.

Installation of Subsurface Drainage Systems	Organisation of the Implementation of Subsurface Drainage Systems	Instruction sheet C.3
	Subject: **Tasks descriptions for key installation staff**	
	Target group: Planners, field manager, supervisor	

C.3   Tasks descriptions for key installation staff

C.3.1   Field manager[1]

Profile

The expertise of the field manager must cover drainage in general and the practical implementation of pipe drainage systems in particular. He needs to be conversant with the operation and maintenance of trenchers, surveying techniques and will have a clear understanding of the design principles of drainage systems. The field manager, if appointed by a contractor, represents the contractor in the field and is directly responsible to the supervising authority.

Responsibilities

The field manager will be responsible for the following:

General responsibilities

- Supervision and guidance of the implementation process and staff including the operator(s) of the trencher(s);
- Assuring that the system is implemented according to the design. If local conditions require adjustment of the design, he needs to act as coordinator with the designers. If he is appointed by a contractor he will have to obtain permission from the supervisor representing the implementation authority;
- Continuously carrying out infield quality control;
- The total organisation of the installation process especially focused on;
  - Assuring availability of staff, pipes, fuel, trenchers + laser, excavators, transport equipment;
  - Assuring supply of materials and the availability of equipment in sufficient quality and quantities;
  - The preparation of as-built drawings.

---

[1] For large projects with more than one installation unit a field manager will have a more general managerial task. Unit managers will then have the specific task of managing the unit in the field. If the installation is done by only one installation unit, the field manager will be responsible for all the tasks described.

Specific responsibilities:
- Familiarisation with the design. (Designs data, maps and sheets are to be available in the field);
- Guiding and checking the staking out in the field of the design before installation starts;
- Guiding and checking that the field is prepared for the installation (obstructions removed etc.);
- Guiding and checking that proper levels are available according to the design (benchmarks);
- Guiding and checking that the individual drain lines are properly set out;
- Guiding and checking the levels and the installation of outlets, sumps and manholes;
- Organising and checking that the drainage materials are available and properly prepared (pipes rolled out and joints correctly made);
- Guiding and checking the provision of start levels of the drains, collectors and manholes as well as the placement of the laser and settings thereof;
- Organising and checking the total installation sequence (outlets, collector, field drain);
- Assuring that the drain pipe is installed in the proper alignment and grade and that the pipe is properly entered into the trench box (limited tension);
- Checking the correct position of the drain pipe in the trench;
- Checking the preliminary backfilling of the trench (covering the drain pipe with a first layer of soil to prevent the pipe of moving and floating in the trench);
- Overall guidance and supervision the field staff, activities of the labourers;

C.3.2   Supervisor

Profile
The supervisor represents the "client" in the field. In FIDIC contracts the supervisor is named: supervising engineer. In the case of important contracts the supervisor is the so-called "engineers representative". The client (or principal) is usually the implementation authority. The main task of the supervisor is to check that the installation of the subsurface drainage system is carried out according to the design, the norms and specifications as described in the technical specifications of the contract. His powers and authority are described in the conditions of contract. The supervisor must have a good knowledge of drainage, be able to read and interpret designs, have a thorough understanding of the designs and a profound knowledge of the specifications and checking methods. For some legal details see Chapter 2 of Part I. The method for checking the quality in the field is given in Section D of Part II.

General responsibilities
This involves checking and approving all activities of the installation according to the design and specifications. If discrepancies arise the supervisor will need to take the necessary actions to assure that a good quality installation will result. The tasks include: disallowing the use of faulty materials and working with faulty machinery and equipment, order corrections for the placement of sumps and manholes, order replacement or correction of drain outlets, rejecting a faulty

aligned drain line and order correction or reinstallation and so forth. His administrative authorities (including his right to stop the work) are described in the conditions of the contract.

Responsibilities for materials and equipment
- Checking and approving the drainage materials when delivered to the site;
- Checking and approving storage of the materials;
- Checking that the machinery and equipment used by the contractor/installation unit is in good condition and can be expected to install the system correctly;
- Checking and approving the certificate of the laser;
- Checking and approving the regular checking of the laser.

Responsibilities for drain installation
- Checking the setting out of the field and (levels and alignment);
- Checking the starting levels of the drainage systems;
- Checking levels, positioning, structural integrity of sumps and manholes as well as backfill;
- Checking levels and grade of installed drain pipes during/directly after installation;
- Checking damages to drain pipes during installation;
- Approving the closure of trenches;
- Checking and approving the backfill of trenches;
- Checking the functionality of the system;
- Checking the cleaning up of the site.

Responsibilities for final approval/reception of the works
This entails approval of the system and its recommendation to the implementation authority. If active supervision is carried out the supervisor must carry out all the checks in person or through a representative. If passive supervision is carried out the supervisor must verify the work carried out by the contractor/installation unit as well as carry out double checks on-the-spot.

C.3.3 Trencher operator

Profile
The trencher operator is fully trained in the operation of the trenchers and laser equipment. He is capable of carrying out or guiding the daily and regular maintenance of the trenchers. Background knowledge of drainage in general is preferred.

Responsibilities
- Daily and regular maintenance of the trencher;
- Operating of the trencher;
- Adjusting the trencher;
- Carrying out small repairs;
- Assisting with big repairs of the trencher;
- Handling of the laser equipment on the trencher;

- Reporting maintenance, and repairs and problems with the trencher;
- Filling in daily and weekly maintenance sheets (see C.5).

Observation
It is preferable to have one assistant trencher operator per trencher. In this way while one operator operates the trencher and the other one assists the operator with alignment activities such
as placing the boning or ranging rods and removing them.

C.3.4   Assistant trencher operator

Profile
The assistant trencher operator will have a basic knowledge of operating hydraulic equipment
and will be trained in the operation of the trencher and the laser equipment, and the maintenance
of the trenchers.

Responsibilities
Same as the trencher operator, but working under his guidance:
- Daily and regular maintenance of the trencher;
- Operating of the trencher;
- Adjusting the trencher;
- Carrying out small repairs;
- Assisting with big repairs of the trencher;
- Informing trencher operators of problems with the trencher during operation;
- Placing boning rods in the alignment and the timely removal of them;
- Supervising the supply of drain pipes and guiding them into the trench box.

C.3.5   Excavator operator

Profile
The excavator driver is fully trained in operating and handling of a hydraulic excavator. He is capable of carrying out or guiding the daily and regular maintenance of the excavator.

Responsibilities
The excavator operator is responsible for:
- Daily and regular maintenance of the excavator;
- Operating the excavator to:
    - Remove obstructions in the field;
    - Dig starting holes up to the instructed level;
    - Place sumps and manholes.

Observation
Background knowledge of field drainage in general is preferred.

C.3.6   Surveyor

Profile
The surveyor is familiar with the setting out of lines, levels, handling of levelling instruments, laser equipment, and processing of field date in map and graphical form.

Responsibilities
- Setting out of the field with levels;
- Setting up and checking the laser transmitter;
- Providing the trencher operator with start levels;
- Providing and checking levels of manholes and sumps;
- Checking laser and level instruments;
- Assisting with staking out drain lines;
- Quality control of installed drain (checking levels of the drains directly after installation);
- Assisting with preparing as-built drawings;
- Processing field information.

Observation
Background knowledge of field drainage in general is preferred.

C.3.7   Labourers/Operators assistants

Profile
No special skills are required. However experience with soil movement is recommended.

Responsibilities
- Laying out of pipes in the field and preparing connections;
- Installing outlet;
- Connecting pipes to manholes/outlet/connector drains;
- Initial backfilling trenches, if required;
- Assisting surveyors (setting out of field and drain lines, measuring drain levels);
- Guiding the drain pipe in the trench box and checking pipe and joint quality;
- Installing the outlet, checking pipe position and preliminary backfilling of trenches;
- Clearing of field from obstacles;
- Guiding the gravel trailers/opening and closing of valves of gravel trailers (if applicable);
- Other fieldwork when circumstances demand.

C.3.8   Tractor driver/Front loader driver

Profile
The tractor driver is fully trained in driving and handling of tractors/front loaders. He is capable of carrying out or guiding the daily and regular maintenance of the tractor/front loader.

Responsibilities
The tractor driver is responsible for:
- Daily and regular maintenance of the tractor/front loader;
- Driving and operating the tractor/ front loader;
- Managing/loading and unloading the gravel trailers (if applicable).

C.3.9   Gravel manager

Profile
The gravel manager is trained in handling and managing tractors and gravel trailers and further-more is capable of judging the quality of gravel and managing relative complex situations.

Responsibilities
The gravel manager is responsible for:
- Regular, uninterrupted supply of gravel to the trenchers;
- Ordering new gravel (if circumstances demand);
- Selecting the best location of field depots of gravel;
- Controlling/correcting proper supply of gravel to and placement of gravel around the drain pipes;
- Managing the loading and unloading the gravel trailers (if applicable).

II-C/2

Machinery and Equipment

Installation of Subsurface Drainage Systems	Machinery and Equipment *Trenchers*	Instruction sheet C.4
Subject: **Description of trenchers**		
Target group: Planners, operators, mechanics, field manager, supervisor		

C.4 Description of trenchers

C.4.1 General

In the following instructions sheets reference is often made to components of the trencher and commands to be given to the trencher. A schematic drawing of the trencher and its main components is presented (Figure C4.1). The figures presented in this section are based on a commonly used trencher. The different makes of trenchers differ in detail. The manuals and technical information provided by the manufacturers with the drainage trenchers will give the exact information about the particular trencher used.

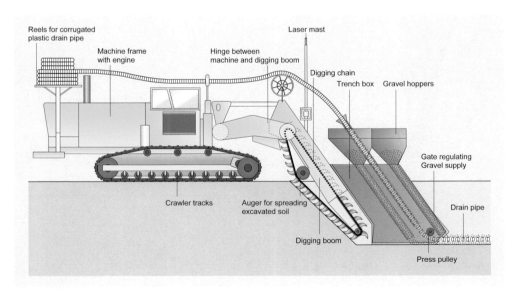

Figure C4.1 Schematic drawing of a trencher

C.4.2 Trencher

In Figure C4.1 is a schematic drawing of a drainage trencher. The following components of the trencher require additional comments:

Press pulley

For the installation of corrugated plastic pipes the trench box is equipped with a press pulley above the outlet opening for the drain pipe in the trench box (Figure C4.2). The press pulley pushes the drain pipe towards the bottom of the trench, which is the designed level for the pipe. Because the drain pipe is relatively light, installing it without this press pulley can cause the soil to slip underneath the pipe. This might result in differences in level.

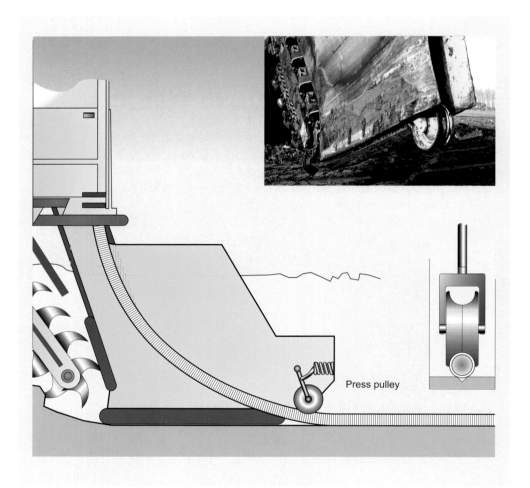

Figure C4.2   Press pulley in the trench box

The press pulley should not be used when a gravel envelope is applied, because a space for the gravel is required between the bottom of the trench and the bottom of the drain pipe. The pulley can be either removed or fixed in an upward position.

The auger

Most of the lateral drainage machines are equipped with an auger, which is meant to move the excavated soil sideways. If an auger is not used there will be a larger friction area (Figure C4.3).

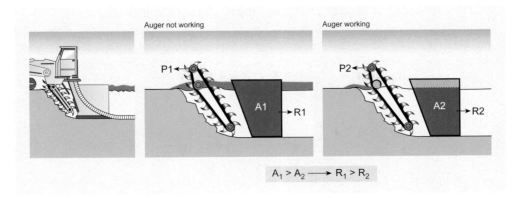

Figure C4.3   Use of auger reduces friction

Water tanks

If installation takes place in sticky clay the friction between the sides of the trenches and the trench box can be significant, slowing down the speed of the trencher. This requires extra power. The friction can be significantly reduced by spraying water along the sides of the trench box and on the digging chain. Therefore, trenchers for use in clay soils can be equipped with a water tank (Figure C4.4). The need of such a tank should be stipulated in the purchasing contract or in the contract with drainage contractors.

Figure C4.4   Trencher with water tank

C.4.3   A model of a operators command panel of a trencher

Below, in Figure C4.5, is a schematic layout of the driver's console from which the operator gives the required commands. The various command buttons/handles are referred to in the instruction sheets that follow:

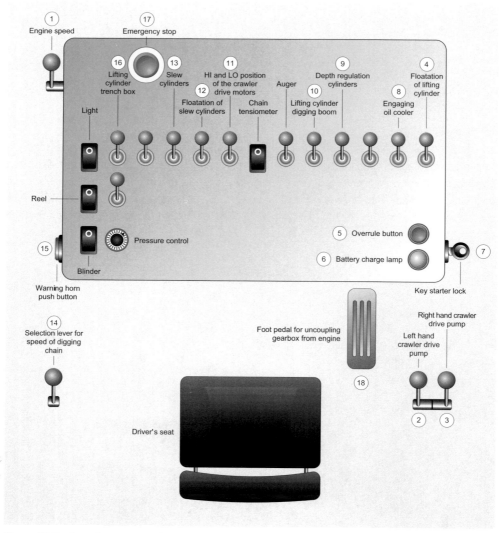

Figure C4.5   Operators command panel of a trencher

No.	Function of command	No.	Function of command button/handle
1.	Engine speed	11.	HI and LO position of the crawler drive motors
2.	Left-hand crawler drive pump	12.	Floatation of slew cylinders
3.	Right-hand crawler drive pump	13.	Slew cylinders
4.	Floatation of lifting cylinder	14.	Selection lever for speed of digging chain
5.	Overrule button	15.	Warning horn push button
6.	Battery charge lamp	16.	Lifting cylinder trench box
7.	Key starter lock	17.	Emergency stop
8.	Engaging oil cooler	18.	Foot pedal for uncoupling gearbox from engine
9.	Depth regulation cylinders		
10.	Lifting cylinder digging boom		

Installation of Subsurface Drainage Systems	Machinery and Equipment *Trenchers*	Instruction sheet C.5

Subject: **Maintenance of trenchers**

Target group: Operators, mechanics, field manager, supervisor

C.5 Maintenance of trenchers[1]

C.5.1 General

Maintenance of a trencher consists of:
- Daily maintenance, including the starting up procedures;
- Weekly maintenance;
- Regular maintenance: maintenance needing to be done after every 100 hours of operation;
- Yearly maintenance and storage.

In the following sections simplified checklists and action lists are given. However, it is of great importance that the people in charge of the machines have knowledge of and access to the manuals. Sample forms that need to be filled in by the persons responsible for the daily maintenance and for the weekly maintenance are provided at the end of this instruction sheet. These forms can serve as maintenance records or logs.

C.5.2 Daily checks and maintenance

Daily checks and maintenance includes the starting up procedures.

C.5.2.1 Before starting engine

Engine
Check:
- Water level (if too low: add water);
- Oil level (if too low: add oil);
- Hydraulic oil (if too low: add hydraulic oil).

---

[1] Instructions are based on a trencher of a specific manufacturer, which generally applies to trenchers of other manufacturers as well. However, for other trenchers the manufacturers instructions in the manuals must be checked and adjustments made (if required).

Cleaning and draining:
- Drain the water separator so that the water is removed;
- Clean pre-air filter (by hand).

Other parts of the trencher
Greasing:
- All cardan shafts;
- Final drive digging chain;
- The nipples of the auger should be greased after every 500 m of drain installation.

Check and repair:
- Broken or loose bolts (tighten or replace);
- Oil leaks (tighten couplers if necessary);
- Fuel leaks;
- Digging chain (Figure C5.1):
  - Tightness of bolts and broken knives (tighten bolts and replace knives if necessary);
  - Digging chain tension;
  - Difference between scraper blades and trench box;
  - Lubricate rotating points every 1 or 2 hours.

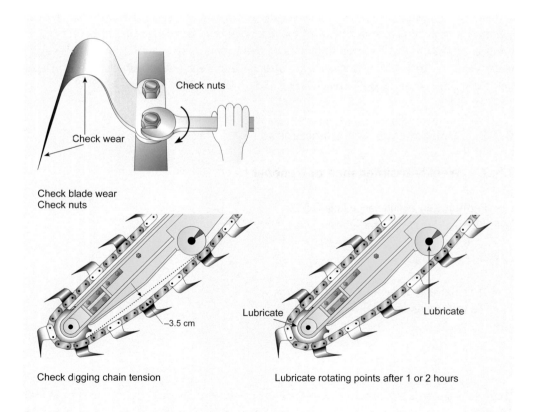

Figure C5.1   Check blade wear, nuts, digging chain tension and lubrication

C.5.2.2   After starting the engine

Wait five to ten (5-10) minutes until engine is warmed up (length of time depends on the outside temperature).

After that check on dashboard:
- Oil pressure engine indicator (if too low, call mechanic!);
- Fuel level indicator (if too low: add fuel);
- Air filter indicator (if flashing: clean filter);
- Hydraulic filter indicator (if flashing: check vacuum gauges on machine);
- Hydraulic oil tank.

Check on the machine: Vacuum gauges of the hydraulic drive.

C.5.2.3   Re-fuelling

Re-fuelling the trencher should preferably be done after work, not in the morning (to prevent condensation forming in the tank).

C.5.2.4   General

- During the checking and starting up procedures a general cleaning of the machine is recommended;
- The daily maintenance should not take more than 30 minutes.

C.5.3   Weekly maintenance of trencher

- Perform daily maintenance (see C.5.2);
- Check acid levels in the batteries (if too low: add distilled water);
- Check oil levels of all the gearboxes in the machine (if too low: add oil);
- Grease all grease nipples on machine;
- Check tightness of duplex or triplex chain in chain case[1] (tighten if necessary, see manual);
- Change the fuel filters if the engine power had been noticeably less;
- Clean machine and make intensive checks for:
  - Fuel leaks;
  - Oil leaks;
  - Water leaks.
- Carry out repairs, if necessary.

---

[1] Only in case of mechanical driven digging chain.

C.5.4   Regular maintenance of trencher

Carry out the following activities after every 200-300 running hours of the engine:
- Change engine oil and oil filter;
- Clean bleeder of crankshaft;
- Check tension of V belts and tension if necessary.

Other parts of the trencher:
- Adjust digging chain (Figure C5.2)

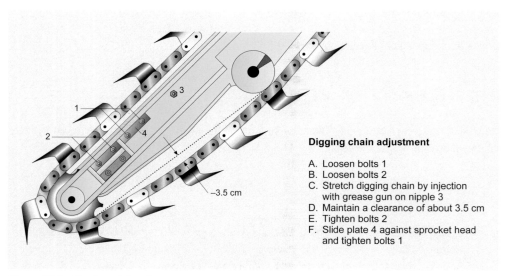

Digging chain adjustment

A. Loosen bolts 1
B. Loosen bolts 2
C. Stretch digging chain by injection with grease gun on nipple 3
D. Maintain a clearance of about 3.5 cm
E. Tighten bolts 2
F. Slide plate 4 against sprocket head and tighten bolts 1

Figure C5.2   Digging chain adjustment

C.5.5   Annual maintenance and winter storage

- Check and if necessary adjust valves (see manufacturers manual);
- Clean and grease whole machine, and check for leaks;
- Repair leaks before the winter storage of the trencher;
- Drain cooling water from engine;
- Put tracks of machine on wooden beams;
- Change engine oil and oil filter;
- Change oil in gear boxes (every 1000 hours or once a year; check the manufacturers manual);
- Change filters of hydraulic system; (every 500 hours or once a year; check the manufacturers manual);
- Cover machine against dust.

C.5.6   Replacement of digging chain, digging knives, sprockets and auger blades

The digging assembly of a trencher is subject to wear and tear, requiring regular checks and replacement of digging knives, auger blades, sprocket wheels and the chain itself. The digging chain and sprocket wheels are the parts that suffer the most wear and tear (see also C.7). Figure C5.3 shows the digging boom with the digging chains, knives, auger and the position of the sprockets.

Digging chain
Digging chains and the two sets of digging knives have to be replaced when they are worn out. The replacement depends on the soil texture. On average the replacement takes place after 60 km of drain pipe installation. But situations are known where this has to be done after 40 km (sandy soils) or 80 km (clay soils).

Digging knives
The wear of the digging knives depends on the soil conditions, for instance, in sandy soil the wear is much faster than in clay soil. On average, the knives need to be welded after some 10-15 km of drain installation, depending on the soil texture and the installation speed. The welding of the knives can be done twice. For the welding of each knife one electrode is used to create a 1.5 cm wear strip.

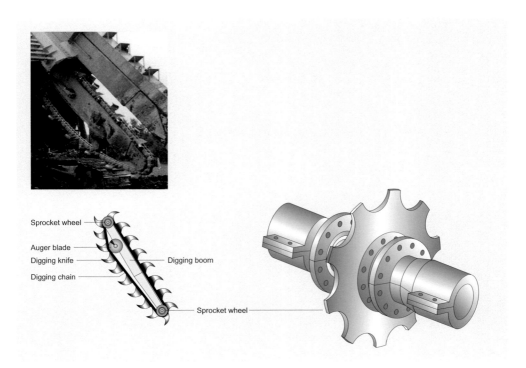

Figure C5.3   Details of digging assembly

Sprockets
The drive sprocket at the top of the digging boom needs to be replaced after approximately 60 km, so at the same time the digging chain and digging knives are also renewed. The bottom sprocket and the auger sprocket should be replaced after approximately 120 km.

Auger blades
The wear of the auger blades also depends on the type of soil in which the trencher is operating. On average the auger blades have to be welded at the same time as the digging knives. After 10 -15 km of drain pipe installation, wear strips are welded on the auger blades.

C.5.7   General warning for trencher

- If welding is done on the machine disconnect three (3) cables from control box and disconnect the battery;
- Do not drive the machine at high speed over long distances!!

C.5.8   Model maintenance record

On the following pages examples of daily and weekly maintenance records for drainage trenchers are given.

DAILY MAINTENANCE OF TRENCHER: (type en number)

DAILY MAINTENANCE OF TRENCHER: (type en number)						
Report no:						
Daily Record	Date:					
Working area						
Drains installed (no)			**Work hours**	**Time**		**hours counter of the machine**
Metres installed			Start:		Hour	hours
Fuel use (litre).			End:		Hour	hours
			Total		hours	hours
DAILY MAINTENANCE CARRIED OUT						
Before starting engine						
Engine						
Water level:	Checked	Yes/no	Water added:		Litre	
Oil level:	Checked	Yes/no	Oil added:		Litre	
Water drained in fuel:	Checked	Yes/no			cm	
Air filter:	Cleaned	Yes/no	Water drained:			
Greasing						
Cardan shaft 1, .. nipples	Greased	Yes/no				
Cardan shaft 2, .. nipples	Greased	Yes/no				
Final drive digging chain	Greased	Yes/no				
Auger	Greased	Yes/no	How many times:			
Checking/ repairing			Result OK	Activity		Number
Bolts	Checked	Yes/no	Yes/no	Repaired:		
Oil leaks	Checked	Yes/no	Yes/no	Couplers tightened:		
Fuel leaks	Checked	Yes/no	Yes/no	Leaks repaired:		
Digging chain						
Bolts	Tightened	Yes/no				
Knives replacement	Checked	Yes/no		Knives replaced:		
After starting engine 5-10 minutes			Result OK	Activity		
Oil pressure	Checked	Yes/no	Yes/no	Corrected	Yes/no	
Fuel level	Checked	Yes/no	Yes/no	Fuel added		Litre
Air filter indicator	Checked	Yes/no	Yes/no	Cleaned	Yes/no	
Hydraulic filter indicator	Checked	Yes/no	Yes/no	Oil added		Litre
Hydraulic oil indicator	Checked	Yes/no	Yes/no	Oil added		Litre

Observations

Operator: Supervisor:

WEEKLY MAINTENANCE OF TRENCHER: (type en number)

WEEKLY MAINTENANCE OF TRENCHER: (type and number)					
Report no:					
Weekly Record	Week	Start:		End:	
Working area: Drains installed: (no) Metres installed: Fuel use (litres)		**Work hours during past week** Start: End: Total			
Maintenance record		Date:	At.............................hours (reading on the hours counter of the machine)		
Previous weekly maintenance:				hours	
100 hours maintenance carried out:				hours	

WEEKLY MAINTENANCE	Carried out at .... Hours (Reading on the hours counter of the machine)				
Batteries	Checked	Yes/no	Water added:	Yes/no	
Oil in gearboxes of:	Checked	Oil added	Quantity	Unit	
Pump case	Yes/no	Yes/no		Litre	
Main gearbox	Yes/no	Yes/no		Litre	
Angle gearbox	Yes/no	Yes/no		Litre	
Chain drive gearbox	Yes/no	Yes/no		Litre	
Final drive track L	Yes/no	Yes/no		Litre	
Final Drive Track R	Yes/no	Yes/no		Litre	
Grease nipples greased	Yes/no	Number:			
Fuel Filter changed	Yes/no				
Duplex chain checked	Yes/no	Tightened: Yes/no			
V belts tension checked	Yes/no	Tightened: Yes/no			
Wear plates checked	Yes/no	Replaced: Yes/no			
Trencher cleaned	Yes/no				
Oil leakage checked	Yes/no	Leakage found: Yes/no			

Oil and filters		Last time		This week		
	Interval	Date	Hours	Yes/no	Quantity	Unit
Engine oil changed every 250 hours				Yes/no		Litres
Hydraulic oil changed every 1000 hours				Yes/no		Litres
Engine oil filter changed every 250 hours				Yes/no		Litres
Hydraulic oil filters changed every 500 hours				Yes/no		No.

Other repairs carried out:

Observations:

Installation of Subsurface Drainage Systems	Machinery and Equipment *Trenchers*	Instruction sheet C.6

Subject: **Adjustment of the trench box and digging chain**

Target group: Operators, mechanics, field manager, supervisor

C.6 Adjustment of the trench box and digging chain

C.6.1 General

The trench is dug to the required depth by the digging chain and the trench box mounted immediately behind the digging chain (see schematic layout of trencher in Figure C4.1). The function of the trench box is to:

- Keep the trench walls apart and prevent collapse during the process of positioning the drain pipe in the trench. This also facilitates the checking of the installation depth of the pipe;
- Guide the drain pipe from the top of the trencher towards the bottom of the trench;
- Make a V-profile in the bottom of the trench in order to position the drain pipe in a straight line;
- Act as float for the whole rear end of the trencher.

The depth of the trench box can only be adjusted when the machine is moving and digging. When the trench box is pointed upwards, it will result in a lifting of the trench box and a shallower trench. When the trench box is pointed downwards, it will result in a lowering of the trench box and a deeper trench. This adjustment is done by retracting or expanding the depth regulation cylinder B using the command button no.9. The lifting cylinder A (with command button no.4) should be in the floating position, so that the trench box rests on the trench bottom (Figure C6.1). If the lifting cylinder is not in the floating position, the trench box will not rest on the trench bottom and the drain pipe alignment will be incorrect (Figure C6.2). An exception is the installation in unstable soil (see C.24).

C.6.2 Adjustment of the trench box in relation to the digging chain

The bottom of the trench box must be in a horizontal line with the lowest point of the digging chain if the soil is soft and stable but not very hard or stony. When the trench box is lower than the chain, the machine will require much power and the trench box might get damaged. When the trench box is higher than the bottom end of the digging chain, the V-profile in the bottom of the trench is not created. The result is that the drain pipe cannot be installed in an absolute straight line. In the case of a hard and stony soil the digging chain has to be adjusted in such a way that it is 5-10 mm under the trench box. The adjustment of the digging chain relative to the trench box, for different soil conditions, is given in Figure C6.3.

C.6.3   Adjustment of the knives on the digging chain

The knives on the digging chain vary in size. The number of different sized knives to be used on the digging chain depends on the width of the trench to be dug. The trench width, in turn, is dependent on the width of the trench box. The diameter of the drain pipe to be installed, and, if required, provisions for the application of gravel around the drain pipe determine the width of the trench box.
Sizes of the knives to be used also depend on the soil conditions.
Generally, the following sizes are used:
  • Sand: 16 cm, 24 cm, 30 cm, 38 cm, 46 cm, 50 cm, and 60 cm
  • Clay: 16 cm. 24 cm, 30 cm, 40 cm, 50 cm, and 60 cm

The sizes and intervals can be adjusted, if required.

In sandy soils the interval will be smaller than in clay soil. In clay soil the larger intervals of diameter facilitates the loosening of the clay from the knives. In sandy soils the smaller intervals prevent the soil from falling back into the trench. The knives are fixed to the digging chain in a V-shaped pattern, as presented in Figure C6.4 on the outer links of the chain on the left and right side, starting with the smallest size (forerunner). The digging width of the forerunner is 16 cm, then comes the next size and so on until the width of the trench is reached. The forerunner digs a V-shaped groove in the bottom of the trench.

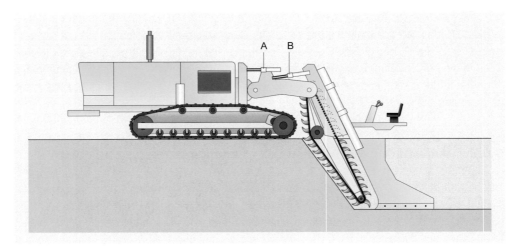

Figure C6.1   Lifting cylinder (A) and depth regulation cylinder (B) on the intermediate frame of a trencher

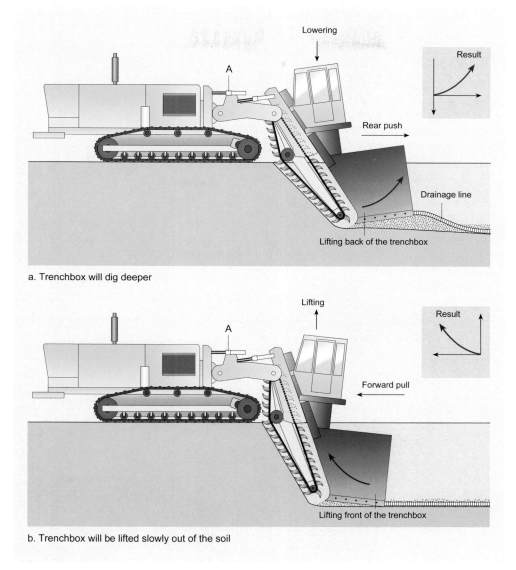

a. Trenchbox will dig deeper

b. Trenchbox will be lifted slowly out of the soil

Figure C6.2   If the lifting cylinder is not in the floating position, the trench box will not rest on the trench bottom and the drain pipe alignment will be either too deep (a) or too shallow (b)

Figure C6.4a shows the digging chain and the positions of the different sized knives of a trencher digging a trench of 24 cm width, for field drain pipe installation. Figure C6.4b shows the digging chain and knives of a trencher digging a trench of 50 cm width for collector drain pipe installation.

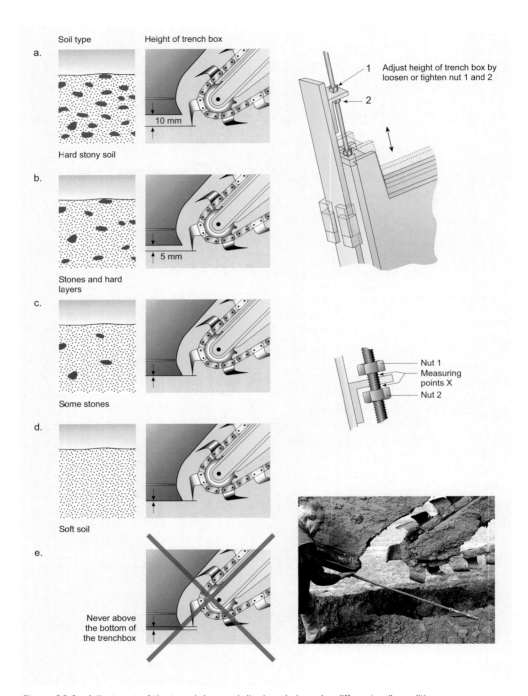

Figure C6.3   Adjustment of the trench box and digging chain under different soil conditions

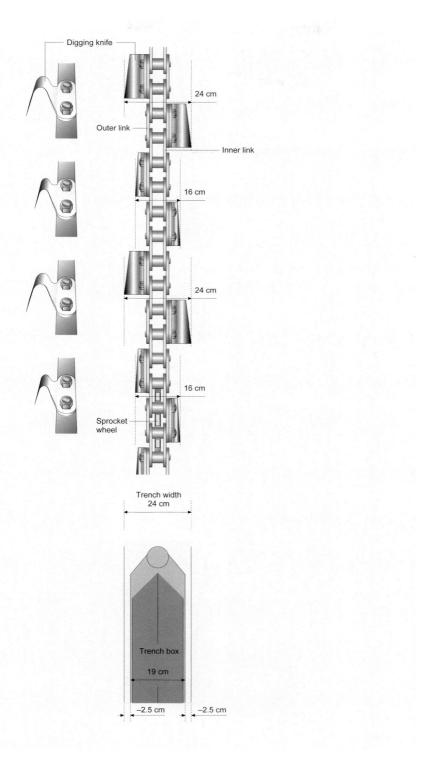

Figure C6.4a   Digging chain with positions of the knives for a trench width of 24 cm

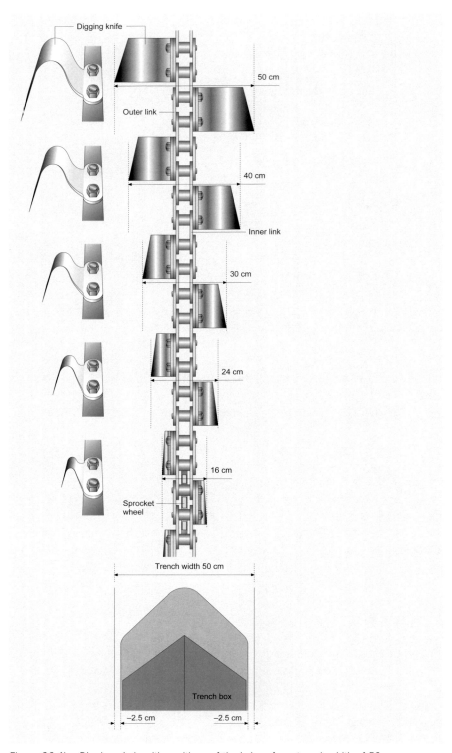

Figure C6.4b   Digging chain with positions of the knives for a trench width of 50 cm

Installation of Subsurface Drainage Systems	Machinery and Equipment *Trenchers*	Instruction sheet C.7
	Subject: **Minimising the operation costs of trenchers**	
	Target group: Operators, mechanics, field manager, supervisor	

C.7 Minimising the operation costs of trenchers

C.7.1 General

Trenchers are expensive items of equipment with many so called "wear parts"(parts which will wear out with use). The main wear parts are the digging chain and sprocket wheel. The quantity of wear parts used per km of drain installed is an important cost factor in the total cost of the installation. Increasing the lifetime of wear parts results in minimising the cost of installation. Taking special care when operating the trencher can extend the life of the wear parts. In the following sections the methods to reduce wear and tare and thus costs, are discussed.

C.7.2 Reduction of wear on the digging chain and sprocket wheel

C.7.2.1   If the machine is digging: reduction of wear of the digging chain

The digging chain of the trenchers wears out regularly because of the abrasive working of the soil on the digging knives. The wear can be reduced, thus extending the lifetime, by installing the drains more quickly. The reasons are as follows:
- If the chain is digging (in the ground) it wears out with the same velocity, no matter how fast the chain is digging;
- The faster the machine is driven, the quicker a drain is installed and the less the wear per km of installed drain. The wear of the chain is a function of the hours of working and thus digging by the chain. The wear can be calculated as follows:
    Examples of how much a chain can dig in a certain soil for a period of 100 hours before being worn out:
    - If the installation speed is 600 m/h a drain of 1200 m can be installed in 2 hours. A chain can then install a total of 60 km drain;
    - If the installation speed is only 400 m/h a drain of 1200 m will be installed in 3 hours and the chain can then only install 40 km of drain. Thus, the cost per metre of drain installed in this case is higher.
The conclusion is that fast work when digging reduces the cost of drain installation!
Fast digging is also recommended for the cleaning of the knives, because if too slow the mud will stick to the knives and digging will be less efficient.

C.7.2.2   If the machine is not digging: reduction of wear on the sprocket wheel

- The sprocket wheels that drive the chain are expensive spare parts;
- The sprocket wheels wear out quickly when the chain turns around without digging;
Thus:
- To prevent wear and tear do not run the chain at fast speed when not digging.

C.7.3   Reduction of wear on the engine

- The engines of most trenchers have been designed and built to perform under maximum power;
- The engine has the longest lifetime if it is run at around 2150 RPM (on most engines);
Thus:
- Try to keep the engine speed always between RPM 2000 and 2150;
- Drive, during installation, as fast as possible for reduced chain cost and wearing of the engine.

C.7.4   Reduction of wear during transport of the trencher

C.7.4.1   In field transport

1. Drive from one drain to the next preferably in reverse because turning around costs time and wears the tracks (this only for short drains);
2. Drive to the following drain in second gear;
3. During transport to new fields, drive in second gear.

C.7.4.2   Transport to other areas

The trenchers are not built and equipped for driving fast over long distances (distances of more than 1 km). Therefore, always use a low loader to travel to other areas or other parts of a drainage area!
If low loaders are not available, drive and transport the trencher at "low speed" (low gearing) with a speed of not more than 1.5 km/hour. After every 30 minutes stop for a while (5-10 minutes).

If the trenchers are driven at too high a speed for too long a time the under-rollers in the tracks become too hot and the seals will be damaged so that it loses oil. Then, the only repair possible is replacement of the under-rollers, which is very expensive!

C.7.5 Concluding recommendations to reduce cost of trenchers

- Dig as fast as possible;
- Do not run chain at high speed when not digging;
- Do not transport trencher over long distances under its own power, use a low loader (Figure C7.1);
- If it is necessary to drive over longer distances then drive slowly and stop for cooling every half hour.

Figure C7.1   Trencher on low loader

Installation of Subsurface Drainage Systems	Machinery and Equipment *Trenchers*	Instruction sheet C.8

Subject: **Operation of trenchers for corrugated plastic drain pipe installation**

Target group: Operators, mechanics, field manager, supervisor

C.8 Operation of trenchers for corrugated plastic drain pipe installation

C.8.1 General

The procedures for operating the trencher for the installation of drain pipes are given below as a sequence of events for installing a field drain, starting with a trencher at an open drain. The principles apply also when starting at either a manhole or a piped collector drain, in a starting hole previously dug. The procedure needs to be adjusted if the drain trencher, equipped with a liftable trench box, digs its own starting hole (see C.9)

C.8.2 Procedures

1. Reverse the trencher until the trench box and digging chain are above the open drain. When doing so, the operator must take care that the vertical direction rod is exactly in line with the boning or ranging rods that mark the drain line;
2. Lower the trench box and digging chain with the lifting cylinder (see C.4, command button 16) until the top of the trench box is horizontal, and the bottom of the trench box is at the starting level of the pipe drain;
3. Adjust laser mast so that the top orange light is flashing (see C.15);
4. Insert the drainage pipe into the trench box, extend it so far that the rigid pipe can be connected to it (see also C.27);
5. Shift the digging chain into gear and drive forward slowly, while manually adjusting the depth to keep the top orange coloured light flashing. Stop the trencher at the moment that all of the trench box is inside the side slope of the drain;
6. Switch on slew (see C.4, command button 12) and lift "float" (see C.4, command button 4) and set laser to "automatic";
7. When digging starts, the trench box and digging chain will automatically rise a bit until the green light flashes;
8. As the machine starts moving forwards the pipe should be kept in place by hand, so that the end that has been fitted with the rigid pipe is pulled to its final position. Release the pipe when the rigid pipe is in the correct position and immediately fix it in this position by backfilling and carefully compacting the soil over the rigid pipe;

9. To prevent the drain pipe from being displaced, preliminary backfilling could be done by throwing some soil on the pipe at regular intervals;

C.8.3   Accidental stopping of engine

Sometimes (if hard objects or clay layers are encountered), the engine may stop running when laying pipes and the gearbox is still in gear. At the moment it stops, considerable friction will occur on the gear sprockets as the trencher will have been working under full load conditions, making it very difficult to shift the gear into neutral. It requires strength and parts may break or be damaged. So, two persons will be required to solve the problems. The operator should start the engine while at the same time the assistant operator pulls the gear stick into neutral.

C.8.4   Changing the trench box

Some trenchers are equipped with the facility to remove with a quick release system the trench box from the intermediate frame so that another trench box can be attached to the trencher. This quick release system may be necessary if:
- Trench boxes of different width have to be used;
- The trencher operates in stony soil.

If a different sized trench box has to be mounted the following actions are to be taken:
1. Lift the trench box so that a transport trailer can be moved under the trench box;
2. Lower the trench box so that it rests on the transport trailer;
3. Remove the safety pin and unlock the upper trench box clamp;
4. Lift the digging mechanism and remove the transport trailer with trench box from the trencher;
5. Drive the transport trailer with the other trench box to be used near the trencher;
6. Lower the digging mechanism so that it slides into the bushing of the trench box;
7. Remount the upper bushing and safety pin;
8. Lift the trench box and remove the transport trailer.

C.8.5   Operating in stony soil

If a digging mechanism is blocked by an obstruction, for example stone or stump (Figure C8.1a), then the operator has to act as follows:
1. String out or cut off the flexible drain tube (Figure C8.1b);
2. Remove the safety pin and unlock the upper trench box clamp (Figure C8.1c);
3. Lift the digging mechanism and drive forward until the obstruction can be removed (Figure C8.2d);

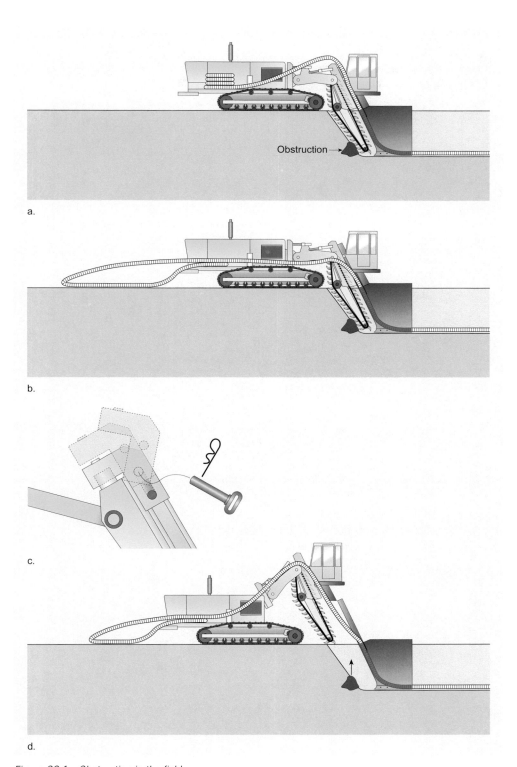

a.

b.

c.

d.

Figure C8.1   Obstruction in the field

4. Drive the trencher backwards again and lower the digging mechanism so that it slides into the bushing of the trench box;
5. Remount the upper bushing and safety pin;
6. Roll up the flexible tube again or reconnect the tube.

Installation of Subsurface Drainage Systems	Machinery and Equipment *Trenchers*	Instruction sheet C.9

Subject: **Working with a liftable trench box**

Target group: Operators, mechanics, field manager, supervisor

C.9 Working with a liftable trench box

C.9.1 General

Some trenchers are equipped with a liftable trench box. The trench box can then slide upwards along the digging boom. With this attribute of the trencher it is possible to start installing field drains and connect them to manholes without a starting hole. The maximum depth to which a machine with liftable trench box can dig without a starting hole is approximately 1.25 m in stable soils. If a deeper start is needed and/or the installation has to be done in unstable soils, it is better and faster to dig a starting hole using an excavator.

Reference is made to C.4 for the commands on the drivers command panel.

C.9.2 Operation of the liftable trench box

1. Switch the float of the lifting cylinders to "off" (button 4, C.4);
2. Lift the trench box completely (Figure C9.1a);
3. Extend the trench box cylinder completely (if this is not done there is a risk that the trench box starts bouncing on the soil surface);
4. Start digging the starting hole (Figure C9.1b):
   - Start the digging chain, let the engine run at approx. 1500 rpm;
   - Lower the digging boom with the lift cylinder until the trench box (or cabin platform if the cabin platform is attached to the digging boom) is completely horizontal;
   - Start digging slowly;
   - Advance slowly with the machine approx. 3 m, so that a trench is dug that is long enough to accommodate the full length of the trench box;
   - After the 3 m are dug, lift the digging boom out of the trench and drive 3 m backwards;
   - Lower the digging boom with the depth regulation cylinder some 50 cm and start digging;
   - Lower the digging boom every run (3 m) 50 cm deeper until the desired depth is reached (Figure C9.1c)
5. After the start hole has been dug return the trench box to its original position (in lock position) in the following way:
   - Keep the digging chain running (to prevent soil from falling in between digging boom and trench box);

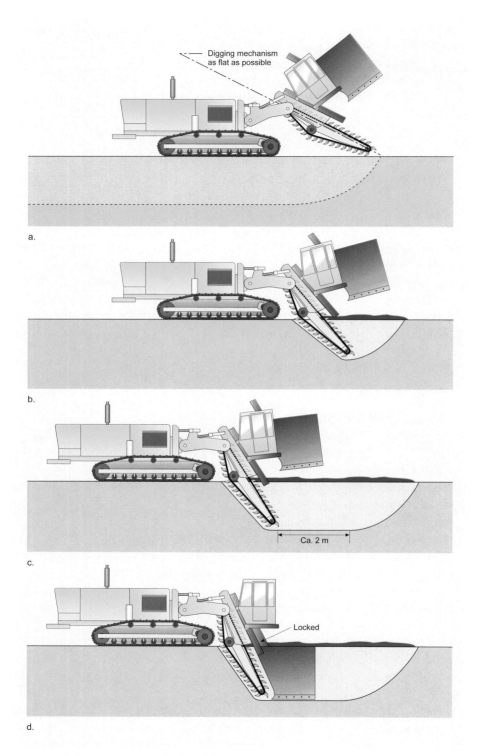

Figure C9.1   Operation of a liftable trench box

- Lower the trench box with trench box cylinder. Be sure that the trench box hook is secured;
- If trench box hook is not automatically secured:
  - Lift digging boom with lift cylinder;
  - Lift trench box with trench box cylinder again and lower it completely so that trench box hook is secured. Repeat this until there is certainty that trench box hook is in place.
6. Lower the digging boom with trench box in the trench (Figure C9.1d);
7. Connect the drain pipe;
8. Switch the float lifting cylinders switch to "on" and start installing.

a.

b.

c.

d.

Installation of Subsurface Drainage Systems	Machinery and Equipment *Trenchless drainage machines*	Instruction sheet C.10

Subject: **Description of trenchless drainage machines**

Target group: Planners, operators, mechanics, field manager, supervisor

C.10 Description of trenchless drainage machines

C.10.1 General

Two types of drainage machine machines have been developed for trenchless drain installation:
- Vertical plough;
- V-plough.

The main components of the vertical plough and the V-plough are presented in Figure C10.1 and C10.2. The major difference compared to a trencher is that the digging mechanism and the trench box are replaced by a plough-type assembly with a guidance tube/box for the drain pipe. No engine power has to be transferred to moving parts at the rear end. So, the operating panel for the operator (Figure C4.5) does not have the functions no. 10 (lifting cylinder digging boom), no.14 (selection lever for speed of digging chain) and no.16 (lifting cylinder trench box). This is replaced by one new function for lifting of the plough assembly.

The drain pipe is guided through a pipe box behind the plough (vertical plough-type) or through a tube in one of the legs of the plough (V-plough).

An iron flap with knives at both sides is attached to the rear-end of the V-plough (Figure C10.3), near the outlet of the drain pipe. This has the same function as the press pulley in a trench box. It cuts soil on both sides of the drain pipe to keep the drain pipe in the correct position.

In principle, the installation of drains by a trenchless drainage machine is not very different from installation by trenchers. The major differences are:
- Only field drains can be installed (the size of the drain pipes should not exceed 125 mm (V-plough) and 200 mm (vertical plough);
- A gravel envelope cannot be used, only pre-wrapped drain pipes;
- In stony soil the vertical plough should be used;
- Laser has to be used for grade control. The laser set-up is the same as for a trencher (C.11);
- Installation speed is much higher speed. Logistics (supply of drainage materials in the field) have to be very well organised;
- In the case of installation of composite systems, starting holes have to be pre-excavated. An excavator should be available.

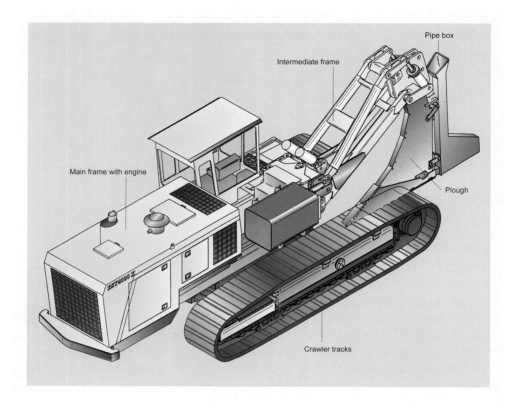

Figure C10.1   Schematic drawing of a vertical plough

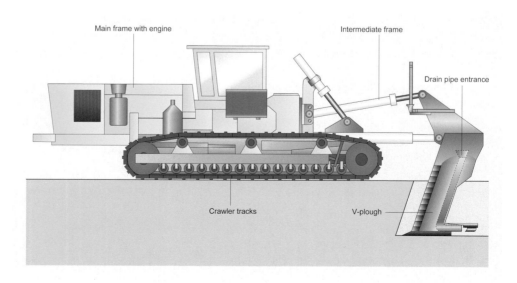

Figure C10.2   Schematic drawing of a V-plough

Figure C10.3   Iron flap with knives at the rear end of the V-plough

Installation of Subsurface Drainage Systems	Machinery and Equipment *Trenchless drainage machines*	Instruction sheet C.11

> Subject: **Maintenance of trenchless drainage machines**
>
> Target group: Planners, operators, mechanics, field manager, supervisor

C.11 Maintenance of trenchless drainage machines

C.11.1 General

Maintenance of a trenchless drainage machine consists of:
Daily maintenance, including the starting up procedures;
- Weekly maintenance;
- Regular maintenance: maintenance needed to be done after every 100 hours of operation;
- Yearly maintenance and storage.

In the following sections simplified check and action lists are given. It is however of great importance that the people in charge of the machines have knowledge of and access to the manuals. For the daily maintenance and for the weekly maintenance sample forms to be filled in by the responsible persons are provided at the end of this instruction sheet. These forms can serve as maintenance records or logs.

C.11.2 Daily checks and maintenance

Daily checks and maintenance includes the starting up procedures.

C.11.2.1 Before starting the engine

Engine
Check:
- Water level (if too low: add water);
- Oil level (if too low: add oil);
- Hydraulic oil (if too low: add hydraulic oil).
Cleaning and draining:
- Drain the water separator so that the water is removed;
- Clean pre-air filter (by hand).

Other parts of the trenchless drainage machine
Greasing:
- All cardan shafts;

Check and repair:
- Broken or loose bolts (tighten or replace);
- Oil leaks (tighten couplers if necessary);
- Fuel leaks;

C.11.2.2 After starting the engine

Wait five to ten (5- 10) minutes till engine is warmed up (length of time depends on the outside temperature).

After that check on dashboard:
- Oil pressure engine indicator (if too low, call mechanic!);
- Fuel level indicator (if too low: add fuel);
- Air filter indicator (if flashing: clean filter);
- Hydraulic filter indicator (if flashing: check vacuum gauges on machine);
- Hydraulic oil tank.

Check on the machine: vacuum gauges of the hydraulic drive.

C.11.2.3 Refuelling

Refuelling the trenchless drainage machine should preferably be done after work, not in the morning (to prevent condensation forming in the tank).

C.11.2.4 General

- During the checking and starting up procedures a general cleaning of the machine is recommended;
- The daily maintenance should take not more than 30 minutes.

C.11.3   Weekly maintenance

- Perform daily maintenance (see C.11.2);
- Check acid levels in the batteries (if too low: add distilled water);
- Check oil levels of all the gearboxes in the machine (if too low: add oil);
- Grease all grease nipples on machine;
- Change the fuel filters, if it was noted that engine power is less;

- Clean machine and make intensive checks for:
  - Fuel leaks;
  - Oil leaks;
  - Water leaks.
- Carry out, if necessary, repairs.

C.11.4   Regular maintenance

Carry out the following activities after every 200-300 running hours of the engine:
- Change engine oil and oil filter;
- Clean bleeder of crankshaft;
- Check V belts and tension if necessary.

C.11.5   Annual maintenance and winter storage

- Check and if necessary adjust valves (see manufacturers manual);
- Clean and grease entire machine, and check for leaks;
- Repair leaks before the winter storage of the trenchless drainage machine;
- Drain cooling water from engine;
- Put tracks of machine on wooden beams;
- Change engine oil and oil filter;
- Change oil in gear boxes every 1000 hours or once a year (check manufacturers manual);
- Change filters of hydraulic system every 500 hours or once a year (check manufacturers manual);
- Cover machine to protect against dust.

C.11.6   General warning for trenchless drainage machines

- If welding is done on machine disconnect three (3) cables from control box and disconnect the battery;
- Do not drive the machine at high speed over long distances!!.

C.11.7   Replacement and welding of plough parts

The wear and tear of the plough parts is much less than that of the digging assembly of a trencher.

C.11.7.1 V-plough

The wear parts on the trenchless drainage machines that have to be replaced are: the knives at the front, the inner plates of the plough and the tip (Figure C11.1). The time after which these have to be replaced depends on the soil characteristics. The average length of drain pipes installed after which replacement is required, is:

- The knives at the front (both sides) that are fixed with bolts: 150 km or earlier if the knives are damaged by stones;
- The inner plates of the plough: 250 km;
- The tip:150 km. The lifetime of the plough tip can be extended by welding;
- The V-shaped bottom profile: 250 km. The underside of the plough has a V-shaped metal reinforcement that generally needs to be changed together with the plough plates. This V-shaped metal part has to be attached in such a way that the bottom front of the plough is 2 cm higher than the bottom end (i.e., the plough has to be tilted upwards slightly).

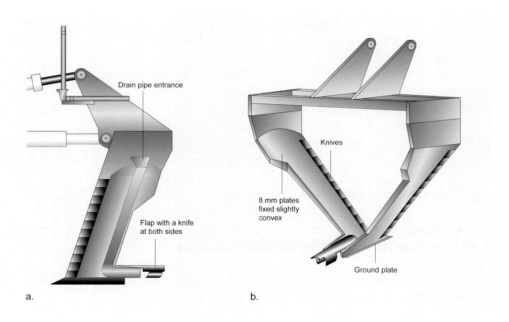

a.   b.

Figure C11.1   Parts of a V-plough that are subject to wear and tear

C.11.7.2 Vertical plough

After installing 150-250 km (depending on the soil characteristics) of drain pipes the following parts have to be replaced or re-welded (Figure C11.2):

- Leading edges;
- Nose;

- Bottom profile part;
- Pipe box: the lifetime can be extended by re-welding the lower part of the pipe box.

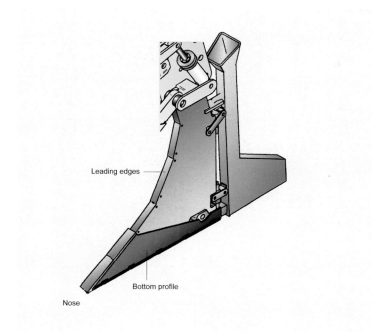

Leading edges

Bottom profile

Nose

Figure C11.2   Parts of a vertical plough that are subject to wear and tear

C.11.8   Model maintenance record

On the following pages examples of daily and weekly maintenance records for trenchless drainage machines are presented in Table C.11-1 and C.11-2.

DAILY MAINTENANCE OF TRENCHLESS DRAINAGE MACHINE: (type en number)

DAILY MAINTENANCE OF TRENCHLESS DRAINAGE MACHINE: (type en number)					
Report no:					
Daily record	Date:				
Working Area					
Drains installed (no)		**Work hours**	**Time**		**hours counter on the machine**
Metres installed		Start:		Hour	_____ hours
Fuel use (Litres).		End:		Hour	_____ hours
		Total	_____	hours	hours
DAILY MAINTENANCE CARRIED OUT					
Before starting engine					
Engine					
Water level:	Checked	Yes/no	Water added		Litres
Oil level:	Checked	Yes/no	Oil added		Litres
Water drained in fuel:	Checked	Yes/no			cm
Air filter:	Cleaned	Yes/no	Water drained		
Greasirg					
Cardan shaft 1, .. nipples	Greased	Yes/no			
Cardan shaft 2, .. nipples	Greased	Yes/no			
Checking/ repairing			Result OK	Activity	Number
Bolts	Checked	Yes/no	Yes/no	Repaired	
Oil leaks	Checked	Yes/no	Yes/no	Couplers tghtened	
Fuel leaks	Checked	Yes/no	Yes/no	Leaks repaired	
Plough parts					
Bolts	Tightened	Yes/no			
Knives replacement	Checked	Yes/no		Knives replaced	
Inner plates	Checked	Yes/no		Inner plates replaced	
Tip	Checked	Yes/no		Tip replaced	
V-shaped bottom plate	Checked	Yes/no		V-shaped bottom plate replaced	
After starting engine 5-10 minutes			Result OK	Activity	
Oil pressure	Checked	Yes/no	Yes/no	Corrected	Yes/no
Fuel level	Checked	Yes/no	Yes/no	Fuel added	Litres
Air filter indicator	Checked	Yes/no	Yes/no	Cleaned	Yes/no
Hydraulic filter indicator	Checked	Yes/no	Yes/no	Oil added	Litres
Hydraulic oil indicator	Checked	Yes/no	Yes/no	Oil added	Litres
Observations					
Operator:		Supervisor			

WEEKLY MAINTENANCE OF TRENCHLESS DRAINAGE MACHINE: (type en number)

WEEKLY MAINTENANCE OF TRENCHLESS DRAINAGE MACHINE: (type and number)					
Report no:					
Weekly record	Week	Start		End	
Working area:		**Work hours during past week**			
Drains installed: (no)		Start:			
Metres installed:		End:		_____	
Fuel use (litres)		Total			
Maintenance record		Date	At...........................hours (reading on the hours counter of the machine)		
Previous weekly maintenance:			hours		
100 hours maintenance carried out:			hours		
WEEKLY MAINTENANCE		Carried out at .... hours (Reading on the hours counter of the machine)			
Batteries	Checked	Yes/no	Water added:		Yes/no
Oil in gearboxes of:	Checked	Oil added	Quantity	Unit	
Pump case	Yes/no	Yes/no	Litres		
Main gearbox	Yes/no	Yes/no	Litres		
Angle gearbox	Yes/no	Yes/no	Litres		
Final drive track L	Yes/no	Yes/no	Litres		
Final drive track R	Yes/no	Yes/no	Litres		
Grease nipples greased	Yes/no	Number:			
Fuel filter changed	Yes/no				
V belts tension checked	Yes/no	Tightened: Yes/no			
Wear plates checked	Yes/no	Replaced: Yes/no			
Trenchless drainage machine cleaned	Yes/no				
Oil leakage checked	Yes/no	Leakage found: Yes/no			
Oil and filters		Last time		This week	
	Interval	Date	Hours	Yes/no Quantity	Unit
Engine oil changed every 250 hours				Yes/no	Litres
Hydraulic oil changed every 1000 hours				Yes/no	Litres
Engine oil filter changed every 250 hours				Yes/no	Litres
Hydraulic oil filters changed every 500 hours				Yes/no	No.
Other repairs carried out:					
Observations:					

281

Installation of Subsurface Drainage Systems	Machinery and Equipment *Trenchless drainage machines*	Instruction sheet C.12

Subject: **Operation of trenchless drainage machines**

Target group: Planners, operators, mechanics, field manager, supervisor

C.12   Operation of trenchless drainage machines

C.12.1   Installation of field drains starting from an open ditch (singular system)

1. Reverse the machine until the V-plough is above the open drain. When doing so the operator must take care that the vertical rod is exactly in line with the ranging rod that marks the drain line (Figure C12.1);
2. Lower the V-plough so that the bottom of the V-plough is at the starting level of the pipe drain;
3. Adjust the laser mast so that the top orange light is flashing (C.15);
4. Insert the drain pipe through the pipe guidance in the leg of the V-plough until it is so far out that the rigid pipe can be connected to it;
5. Drive forwards slowly while manually adjusting the depth to keep the top orange coloured light flashing. Stop the machine at the moment that all of the V-plough is inside the side slope of the drain;
6. Switch on the lift and slewing "float" and set laser to "automatic";
7. Start moving the machine forwards slowly to allow time for the hydraulic system to build up enough pressure;
8. Once the green light on the laser indicator starts flashing the speed can be increased;
9. The drain pipe is placed at the correct level as the machine advances and the green light keeps on flashing;
10. When crossing ditches with high embankments drive extremely slowly and help the plough by making manual adjustments;
11. Lift the plough slowly at the end of the drain line;
12. Once the drain line has been completed the machine is driven backwards with one track over the uplifted soil to press the topsoil down (only in case of the V-plough);
13. If a roller is attached to the front of the machine, the roller is lowered and the machine driven backwards (Figure C12.2);
14. Backfill of the starting hole is best done the same day.

Figure C12.1   V-plough starting installation of a field drain from an open drain

Figure C12.2   Roller in front of trenchless drainage machine

C.12.2 Installation of field drains starting from a collector drain (composite system)

The installation of a field drain starts with digging a starting hole near the manhole or collector using an excavator.

1. Manoeuvre the V-plough into position by driving backwards towards the starting hole until the plough is above the starting hole;
2. Lower the V-plough so far that the bottom of the V-plough is at the starting level of the pipe drain (Figure C12.3);

Figure C12.3 V-plough starting the installation of a field drain at the collector drain (composite drainage system)

3. Adjust the laser mast so that the top orange light is flashing (C.15);
4. Insert the drain pipe through the pipe guidance in the leg of the V-plough until it is far enough for the drain pipe to be connected to the manhole;
5. Drive forwards slowly while manually adjusting the depth to keep the top orange coloured light flashing. Stop the machine at the moment that the V-plough is completely inside the side slope of the starting hole;
6. Switch on the lift and slewing "float" and set laser to "automatic";
7. Start moving the machine forwards slowly to allow time for the hydraulic system to build up enough pressure;
8. Once the green light on the laser indicator starts flashing the speed can be increased;
9. While the machine advances and the green light keeps on flashing, the drain pipe can be placed at the correct level;
10. When crossing ditches with high embankments drive extremely slowly and help the plough by making manual adjustments;
11. At the end of the drain line lift the plough slowly;
12. Once the drain line has been completed the machine is driven backwards with one track over the uplifted soil to press the topsoil down;
13. If a roller is attached to the front of the machine, the roller is lowered and the machine driven backwards;
14. Backfill of the starting hole is best done the same day.

Installation of Subsurface Drainage Systems	Machinery and Equipment *Laser equipment for grade control*	Instruction sheet C.13

Subject: **Description of laser equipment for grade control**

Target group: Operators, surveyor, field manager, supervisor

C.13 Description of laser equipment for grade control

C.13.1 General

Installing a drain or collector pipe at the proper grade (slope) is essential for the functionality of the drain. The laser is the precision tool used for assuring that the pipes are installed at design levels and grades (slopes). There to the laser requires a correct management, handling and control.

The laser equipment consists of:
- Transmitter (modern transmitters are equipped with rechargeable batteries) that is transportable and can be stored in a special case;
- Tripod (transportable);
- Battery (on old models only);
- Receiver (mounted on mast on trencher);
- Expandable/retractable mast for receiver (mounted on trencher);
- A so-called beeper rod, which is a staff gauge with a movable receiver on it. The receiver "beeps" when it is in the plane of the laser beam.

C.13.2 Principles of the laser

The principles of the laser are given in Figure C13.1. Laser equipment for drainage basically consists of two components:
- The *laser transmitter* (Figure C13.2), which is positioned in the field on a stable tripod that is some 2.5 m high, emits through a rotating prism a beam of invisible light that forms a plane. This plane can be a horizontal or at an angle (slope-grade). This plane serves as reference for the level and depth of the trench box of the trencher and consequently for the drain to be installed;
- The *laser receiver* (Figure C13.3) is mounted on the trench box of the trencher and receives the beams of (invisible) light coming from the transmitter. The receiver is fixed on a mast that can be raised and lowered. It contains 3 groups of photocells one above the other: a top group, a middle group and a bottom group.

The receiver is electrically connected to the *hydraulic system* of the lifting cylinders of the trencher and is programmed in such a way that:

- If the bottom cells receive the laser beam light then it means that the trench box is too high and the trench box is automatically lowered until the middle group of cells receive the laser beam;
- If the top cells receive the beam light, then the trench box is too low and the trench box is automatically raised;
- When the middle cells receive the laser beam, the trench box is at the correct height and no change occurs.

There are indictor lights for the photocells on the operator's display (receiver display): when the level is correct the light is green, too high or too low the red or orange indicator lights flash above or below the green indicator.

As is indicated in Figures C13.1 and C13.3, the drain will be installed at the same grade (slope) as the laser beam, as long as the middle cells receive the laser beam.

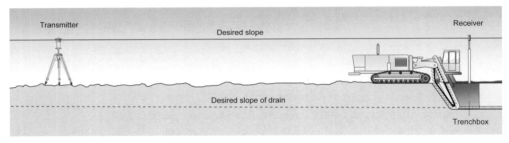

Figure C13.1   Principles of laser

Figure C13.2   Laser Transmitter

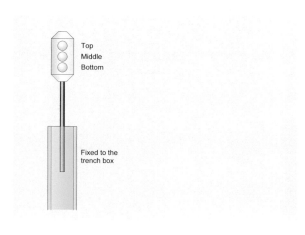

Figure C13.3   Laser Receiver

Installation of Subsurface Drainage Systems	Machinery and Equipment *Laser equipment for grade control*	Instruction sheet C.14

Subject: **Management of laser equipment for grade control**

Target group: Operators, surveyor, field manager, supervisor

C.14 Management of laser equipment for grade control

C.14.1 Tips for operating

Maximum distance during good weather conditions
The *"safe" maximum distance* (in good weather conditions) between the transmitter and the receiver (trencher) is 300 m (thus a drain length of approx. 600 m). For a drain of 400 to 600 m, place the transmitter tripod halfway along the length of the drain.
In the case of a *drain of > 600 m in length:*
- Place the transmitter at a distance of about 250 m from the start of the drain;
- Stop the trencher once the trencher has installed about 500 m of drain;
- Switch the control on the trencher from automatic to manual. (The reason for switching from automatic to manual is to prevent undesired reactions on the receiver when replacing the transmitter);
- Now, replace the transmitter at a distance of about 750 m from the start of the drain (right direction, right slope!);
- Adjust the transmitter to a level to where it can be assumed that the laser beam will be within reach of the receiver;
- Switch the laser to automatic and wait for a green light to appear on the display. During the levelling the mast of the receiver extends or shortens so that the receiver is in the laser beam of the transmitter. The left lamp on the display will flash red during the levelling, which may last for 1 to 2 minutes;
- Continue with drain installation.

Poor weather conditions
During humid weather (hazy, misty, rain) the laser beam will be scattered by the water particles in the air. The safe distance for working with laser will then be reduced, even in extreme cases to < 100 m.

Drain direction - Direction of the slope of the laser beam
The slope or grade of the laser plane has to be in the same direction as the designed slope of the drain to be installed.

C.14.2   Possible problems with the operation of the laser

- *Wind.* The transmitter is mounted on a tripod and is sensitive to wind. If there is a strong wind the transmitter will vibrate, which may result in a flashing indicator light on the receiver display/control box and cause inaccurate levels of the drain. The deviations increase with in-creasing distance from the transmitter. If the wind is strong the following measures can be taken:
  - Erect the tripod as indicated in Figure C14.1;
  - Limit the distance between the transmitter and the receiver (< 300 m);
  - Put weight in the form of sandbags on the legs of the tripod;
  - Decrease the height of the tripod as much as possible;
  - Limit the height of the base of the transmitter in relation to the tripod;
  - Tighten all the bolts of the tripod;
  - Be sure that the legs of the tripod are as far away from each other as possible (chains not fully stretched);
  - Place, if possible, a car in front of the transmitter/tripod as windbreak.

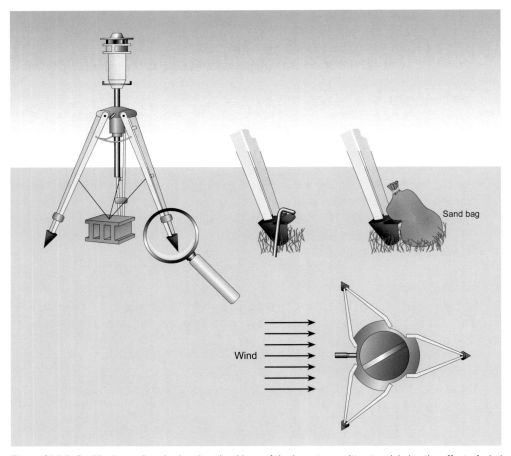

Figure C14.1 Positioning and anchoring the tripod legs of the laser transmitter to minimize the effect of wind

- *Sunlight.* Sunlight and high temperatures may cause inaccurate laser performance;
  Action: shorten distance between transmitter and receiver.
- *Fog/Mist.* Fog can influence laser performance;
  Action: In the case of fog shorten the distance transmitter to receiver.
- *Vibrations of the soil.* Especially when the soil is soft at the place where the transmitter is placed prevent vibrations caused by machines;
  Action: This can be done by making sure that no machines or vehicles are driven close to the transmitter and/or by placing the tripod as far away as possible from the drain line.
- *High-tension lines.* When the laser beam passes a (high-tension) electric line it is possible that the beam is disturbed. If the lights on the machine's display will flash, the depth of the trencher is not correct;
  Action:
  - Do not place the transmitter underneath the electric line and/or;
  - Place the transmitter so that transmitter and trencher are on the same side of the line.
- *Radar.* Nearby radar may disturb the laser beam, which makes its use impossible. Sometimes, in the case of strong radar (e.g., airport), the influence is noticeable over a large distance.

C.14.3 Laser use when two trenchers work side by side in the same field

It is quite possible that two drainage trenchers work in tandem for installing field drains in the same field with the same slope. For the operation of the laser the following aspects have to be taken into account:
- The trenchers operate with *one* transmitter. In this case only one person is to be responsible for the transmitter. Using one laser transmitter prevents interference between two transmitters. If two transmitters are used, one of the trenchers can after some length of installation start to receive the laser beam of the other transmitter, which would make it suddenly alter the depth of the drain;
- Using one transmitter is only possible if:
  - The two drains are designed with *the same slope and run parallel;*
  - The drain lines are not more than 300 m from each other.
- During installation, one trencher should not be between the transmitter and the other trencher. Therefore, it is preferable that the trenchers operate on both sides of the transmitter as indicated in Figure C14.2;
- In practice it means that only one drain on both sides of the transmitter can be installed with the same transmitter position;
- The maximum distance between the transmitter and the receiver(s) should not exceed the safe maximum distance as discussed above;
- In the presence of (high) tension lines, both the trenchers and the transmitter should operate on the same side of the (high) tension line.

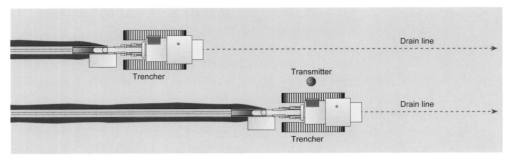

Figure C14.2   Trenchers operating on both sides of the transmitter

C.14.4   Maintenance of the laser equipment

In general the laser can be used without any specific maintenance. Dust and mud spots should however be removed as soon as possible from all parts including the tripod.
Batteries (this only for the older models that have non built-in rechargeable batteries): should be recharged regularly (every two days). It is advisable to keep one extra, charged battery close to the laser for quick replacement.

Winter storage
Store receiver, transmitter, mast, survey rod and control box after cleaning in a heated room;
Every month switch laser on for about 3 hours, recharge the batteries afterwards (this heats the transmitter somewhat and the condense moisture will be expelled).

Installation of Subsurface Drainage Systems	Machinery and Equipment *Laser equipment for grade control*	Instruction sheet C.15

	Subject:	**Determining the extension of laser mast on trencher**
	Target group:	Operators, surveyor, field manager, supervisor

C.15   Determining the extension of laser mast on trencher

C.15.1   General

The laser beam gives a plane with a certain slope (grade) with a level in the middle of the beam at the level of the transmitter. To install the drain at the right level, the receiver of the laser beam on the mast of the trencher should be set so that the trench box bottom is at the design start level for the drain and the middle cell of the receiver is in the middle of the laser beam.

C.15.2   General procedures

Start
1. Read manual, surveyor should be familiar with the contents of the manual;
2. Place tripod at a maximum distance of 300 m from trencher some metres left or right from the drain line;
3. Be sure that tripod is stable (wind direction!);
4. Put transmitter on tripod, adjust to direction of drain;
5. Switch on self level switch;
6. Adjust required slope setting on transmitter (see design and the manual);
7. Open windows of the laser.

Level of laser beam (transmitter)
Determine the level of the laser beam (LBL) relative to the reference level used in the design of the drainage system (this can be the national datum (sea) level or a local reference level) as follows (Figure C15.1):
1. Set beeper rod on peg with known absolute level (peg level = PL);
2. Extend beeper rod until the beep is heard;
3. Measure beeper rod height ("Y");
4. Calculate the absolute level of the laser beam ("LBL") as follows:
   Absolute level of peg (PL) + beeper rod height (Y), or LBL = PL + Y

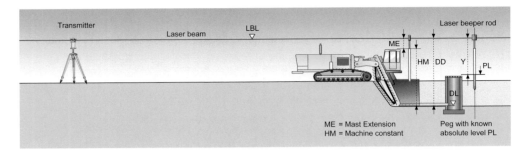

Figure C15.1   Determining the level of the laser beam (LBL) relative to the reference level used in the design of the drainage system

C.15.3   Determine the required mast extension (ME)

1. Determine desired absolute drain pipe bottom level from design, DL;
2. Calculate the depth of drain below laser beam: DD = LBL (-) DL;
3. Calculate the extension of the receiver mast: "ME" = DD - Machine Constant (HM).
   The machine constant is the vertical distance between bottom of trench box and the lowest point of the receiver mast.
   The machine constant for each trencher is different and should be determined separately for each machine (normally between 4 and 5 metres);
4. Give mast extension information to operator who will extend the mast accordingly;
5. Installation can begin.

Installation of Subsurface Drainage Systems	Machinery and Equipment *Laser equipment for grade control*	Instruction sheet C.16

Subject:	**Verification of correctness of laser transmitter in the field**
Target group:	Operators, surveyor, field manager, supervisor

C.16 Verification of correctness of laser transmitter in the field

C.16.1 General

In principle, the laser is a precision tool that is sensitive to rough handling and rough transportation. Its proper functioning should be regularly (monthly) checked, or more often when its proper functioning is doubted.

An easy field test to check the performance of a laser transmitter is described below.

C.16.2 Methodology for testing

There are 2 aspects to test:
- The *horizontal* adjustment of the laser beam or plane;
- The functioning of the *grade control.*

C.16.3 Testing horizontal adjustment of laser beam

1. Erect the tripod and transmitter and adjust the laser plane to horizontal position;
2. Place pegs in a straight line on both sides of the tripod at a distance of 100 and 200 m. Determine the levels of the pegs with a levelling instrument;
3. Though not necessary, for easy comparisons later on it will be useful if the pegs were placed at the same absolute level (Figure C16.1);
4. Set a rod with beeper on pegs 1 and 4, and later on pegs 2 and 3. Calculate for each peg the level difference between the top of the peg and the laser plane. If the level of the 4 pegs is the same (see 3), and the level difference with the laser plane is the same, then the laser plane is horizontal and functions correctly;
5. If the readings between pegs 1 and 2 or between 3 and 4 are different, then there is a deviation in the laser plane related to horizontal adjustment;
6. For adjustment to the correct setting see the instruction book of the laser equipment.

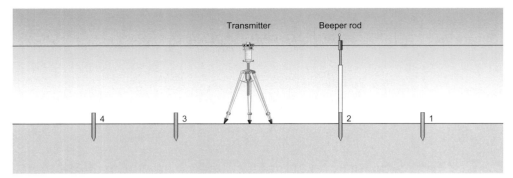

Figure C16.1   Testing the horizontal adjustment of the laser beam

C.16.4   Test for grade control

1. Position the transmitter in the same way as described above. Adjust the grade of the laser plane to $1\,^0/_{00}$ pointing upwards in the direction of pegs 1 and 2;
2. Be sure that the 4 pegs have all the same absolute level. Set the beeper rod on pegs 1 and later on pegs 4 and 3. Calculate for each peg the level difference between the top of the peg and the laser plane. If the transmitter performs correctly then the readings on pegs 1 and 2 should be: 0.001 x 100 m = 10 cm (peg 2) and 0.001 x 200 m = 20 cm (peg 1) more than the reading of the levels measured in C.16.3. The readings for pegs 3 and 4 should read 10 cm and 20 cm lower than the readings of the levels measured in C.16.3;
   If this is not the case then the grade control of the transmitter is not correct: either the angle of the slope is not according to the angle of $1\,^0/_{00}$, or the direction of the slope is not according to the direction of the alignment pegs 1-4.

C.16.5   Observation

If the deviations are considerable and the cause is unclear the transmitter should be sent to the supplier for adjustment. It is advisable to get the laser transmitter regularly checked and certified by the manufacturer or the local representative.

Installation of Subsurface Drainage Systems	Machinery and Equipment *Laser equipment for grade control*	Instruction sheet C.17
	Subject: **Manual grade control in absence of laser equipment**	
	Target group: Operators, surveyor, field manager, supervisor	

C.17   Manual grade control in the absence of laser equipment

C.17.1   General

If no laser equipment is available or if the trencher is not electrically equipped for laser guided grade control, the grade of the drain to be installed has to be checked manually. Manual control can only be practised if[1] the driver cabin is mounted on the trench box and the trencher is equipped[2] with a so-called "sighting bar".

C.17.2   Preparation for manual grade control

Boning rods are used for manual grade control (Figure C17.1). A boning rod is a "double" sighting rod - a tube with two cross bars (one at the top and one at the bottom, at a fixed distance) that can be moved over a stake and fixed by bolts. The two parts can move in relation to each other so that the total height of the cross bars can be adjusted. The cross bars are painted red on one side and white on the other. Besides the horizontal alignment of the drain to be installed they also indicate the level and the grade thereof.

Procedures
- Calculate the required level of the top of the boning rods (see C.17.3);
- Place pegs at intervals of 25 m in the centre of the alignment of the drain to be installed and place two pegs at 5 and 15 metres beyond the end peg (Figure C17.2);
- Place the boning rods beside the pegs and extend the cross bar to the desired height using a levelling instrument, taking into account the slope of the drain;

Observations
- Boning rods are best placed every 25 metres (or less in the case of limited visibility) in the alignment of the drain;
- The last boning rod but one is placed 5 metres further than the end of the drain. The last one is placed 15 beyond the end of the drain;

---

[1] As indicated in Chapter 5 of Part I manual depth control on trenchless machines is not practicable.

[2] In the case of manual control the presence of the sighting bar has to be specified when ordering a trencher.

- The highest point of the boning rods is a fixed height above the desired level of the drain pipe to be installed;
- The boning rods are to be placed in such a way that the red coloured cross bars are all facing the same direction, namely, either facing the driver or facing away from the driver depending on the colour that best contrasts with the background.

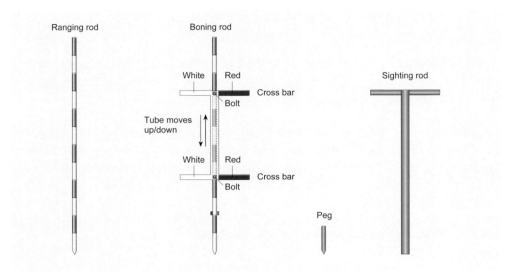

Figure C17.1   Ranging rod, boning rod, peg and sighting rod

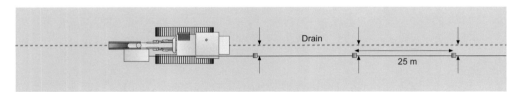

Figure C17.2   Placing of pegs

C.17.3   Determining the required level of the cross bars of the boning rod

The location and elevation of the sight bar of trenchers varies from model to model. The sighting bar must be adjusted to "eye level height" of the operator in such a way that he can sit in a comfortable upright position (Figure C17.3a).
Once the sighting bar is adjusted:
- Measure the distance from the sighting bar to the shoe (bottom) of the trench box in centimetres. The cabin must be in an exact horizontal position and the digging mechanism just touches the ground. This distance is called H_m and is a machine constant;
- The height of the first boning rod is H_t. The drain depth = D. So, the height of the first sighting stake $H_t = H_m$ - D (Figure C17.3b);
- The height of the last boning rod at the end of the drain line depends on the slope of the drain: $H_t + H_s$, H_s = height caused through slope (Figure C17.3c).

The thus created line of boning rods runs parallel to but at a level of H_t above the designed drain line. Once installation starts, the operator has to keep the sight bar level in line with the levels of the first two visible boning rods by manually adjusting the level of the trench box. Since the boning rods are installed in the line of work of the trencher, as the trencher approaches a boning rod the operator changes his sighting on the following two boning rods while at that moment the nearest boning rod is removed by the operator's assistant.
The boning rods are then to be loaded on the trenchers as soon as they have been taken way.

The accuracy of the depth of installation is determined by:
- The visibility of distance between the boning rods and the sight bar;
- The speed of installation;
- The experience and fatigue of the operator (change operators regularly to avoid fatigue factor!).

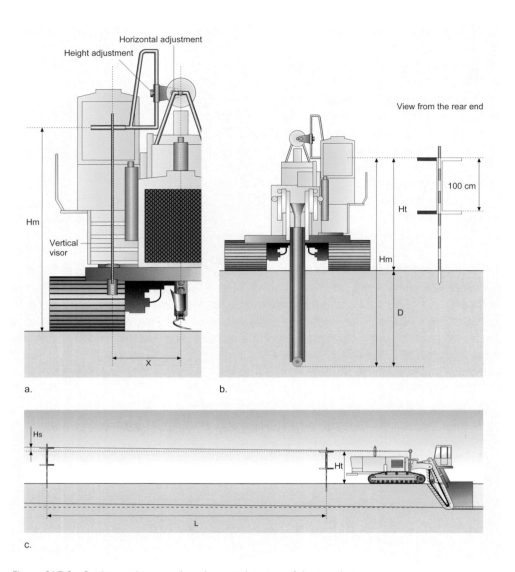

Figure C17.3   Setting up the manual grade control system of the trencher

Installation of Subsurface Drainage Systems	Machinery and Equipment *Laser equipment for grade control*	Instruction sheet C.18

Subject: **Description and maintenance of gravel trailers**

Target group: Operators, mechanics, field manager, supervisor

C.18 Description and maintenance of gravel trailers

C.18.1 General

Gravel trailers are only needed when gravel is used as an envelope material for drains. A tractor pulls the most commonly used type of gravel trailer. There are also self-propelling gravel trailers. The capacity of gravel trailers varies between 2 and 10 m^3. Gravel trailers with a capacity of 2, 4 and 6 m^3 are mounted on an undercarriage consisting of an axle and wheels. Gravel trailers with a capacity larger than 6 m^3 are provided with crawler tracks and are self-propelling.

The main elements of a commonly used gravel trailer (Figure C18.1) are:
- Undercarriage consisting of a frame with an axle and wheels;
- Hopper with a capacity of 4 m^3;
- Conveyor belt for unloading the gravel into the container on the trench box of the trencher.

The main functions are operated hydraulically by the driver of the tractor or the driver of the self-propelling unit and consist of:
- Lifting and lowering of the conveyor belt;
- Running of the conveyor belt;
- Adjusting of the outlet gate of the gravel.

The maintenance is basically only carried out weekly.

C.18.2 Weekly maintenance

On gravel trailers only "weekly" maintenance has to be done. This consists of checking:
- Tyre pressure, adjust if necessary;
- Tightness of belt (see manual), adjust if necessary;
- Bearings, add some grease if necessary;
- Hydraulic system for leakage, repair if necessary;
- Hydraulic oil.

C.18.3 Storage of the gravel trailer/winter storage

- Store the trailer preferably in a dry place;
- Protect the hydraulic hoses from strong sunlight;
- Take the weight of the tyres.

After storage: check the hydraulic oil and replace if necessary

Figure C18.1   Gravel trailer

II-C/3

Installation of pipe drainage systems

Installation of Subsurface Drainage Systems	Installation of Drain Pipes *General activities*	Instruction sheet C.19

Subject: **Preparatory activities**

Target group: Field manager, supervisor

C.19   Preparatory activities

C.19.1   General

Installation of subsurface drainage systems can start once the design is completed and approved, contracts have been signed (orders to start have been issued), materials have been ordered and the site is handed over to the contractor or to the installation unit. If the implementing authority provides the drainage materials then the drainage materials need to be on site.

The process of handing over the site to the contractor or installation unit requires:
- Verification of the site to assure that the conditions allow proper installation. This is to be carried out by the implementation authority usually represented by the supervisor or supervising engineer (the client or principal);
- Installation and/or verification of the existence and levels of benchmark, and levels at places as indicated in the specifications, terms of contract and design;
- Handing over the necessary information to the contractor or implementation unit;
- Making the necessary arrangements with other parties who have activities or rights in the area.

Most of these activities are stipulated in the contract and/or specifications or instructions to installation units.

C.19.2   Arrangements to be made by the implementation authority

These include arrangements:
- With the owners and the users of the land to secure the rights of way at the required moments;
- For removal of unforeseen and foreseen obstacles along the drain lines that have not been prescribed in the contract or instructions. The organisation responsible for removal and the unit prices as well as payment conditions are normally stipulated in the contract or the instructions to the installation unit;
- To secure permission for the removal of obstacles;
- For disposal sites for the removed obstacles and indication of the organisation responsible for the removal;

307

- For the removal of the crops either by the farmers or by the contractors in case crops are grown on the field during the approved installation period. Thus, this should be done before the work starts as well as compensation arrangements;
- For regulating the irrigation in the area. To provide workable conditions for installation, the field should not be irrigated for a period that allows proper drying of the soil before actual installation operations start. Timely and regular contacts with the farmers are required to ensure that the irrigation schedule and the construction schedule do not interfere with each other. The farmers should know the schedule of construction well in advance;
- With the design groups, if as a result of the field verification drain alignments or other parts of the designs have to be changed.

C.19.3   Right of Way

Verification that the rights of way have been secured is necessary. (The right of way is to be secured by the principal or implementation authority, not by the contractor or installation unit). The right of way should preferably be a right to the entire area affected by the drainage system to be installed, which in practice is not always possible. The minimum right of way needed is as follows:

- Along the drain pipes to be installed (a minimum of 5 metres for installation of drain pipes without envelope material or drain pipes with pre-wrapped envelope material, and 12 metres if gravel is used as envelope material);
- Access to the fields where drain lines are to be installed;
- Access to places where pumping stations/sumps/drain outlets are to be constructed;
- Places for storage of materials;
- Place(s) for building construction camp.

C.19.4   Site verification

The implementation authority and contractor/installation unit can best carry out the site verification simultaneously.

The verification consists of checking if the information provided in the designs about the site conditions are (still) correct and complete, and includes:

- General topography (topography as indicated on the maps as issued by the designers);
- Location of the existing infrastructure (such as the irrigation and drainage networks, road networks and buildings);
- Existence and location of overhead lines (electric/power/telephone lines)[1],
- Existence and location of underground pipelines or cables[2];

---

[1] Overhead lines can be too low to allow passage of the machinery and can influence the functioning of laser.

[2] Underground pipes, for example, if above or just below drain depth can get damaged during drain installation, and can damage the drain installation equipment.

- Location of other above or underground (potential) obstructions;
- Conditions of open drains, surface drain and outlet points, etc.;
- Design (layout) of the drainage system and confirmation that no unknown obstacles have to be crossed or are in the way;
- Whether or not there is enough unobstructed access along the drains to be installed (5-6 m for installation without gravel, 12 m for installation with gravel);
- Verification of the designs in the field and the correct location of all drains and ancillary works and confirmation that no (unexpected) obstructions are in the way;
- Verification of the existence of benchmarks with known height to which the systems to be installed can be related;
- Readily recognisable points (benchmarks) in the field from which the layout can be staked out in the field;
- Checking that all approvals of rights of way for the contractor/implementation unit have been obtained (see C.19.3);
- If relevant, checking that all relevant authorisations have been obtained of the utility companies (electricity, water gas) for the installation of the drainage system as designed;
- If relevant, checking whether the instructions to the contractor/implementation unit for contacting the utility companies prior to actual installation have been clearly issued.

The handing over of the field to the contractor/installation unit takes place after all parties concerned are satisfied that all above-mentioned points are in order.

Any obstructions in the field that are not on the topographic map should be removed, or in case this is not possible the layout of the drain should be adjusted accordingly. No work may commence until the utility and contractor are mutually satisfied that all requirements and safety precautions have been met.

Installation of Subsurface Drainage Systems	Installation of Drain Pipes *General activities*	Instruction sheet C.20

Subject: **Sequence of drain installation**

Target group: Field manager, supervisor, field staff

C.20 Sequence of drain installation

C.20.1 General

- All activities are designed to support the trenchers. Trenchers are the most expensive single items of machinery and should work continuously if they are to be cost effective;
- As with all drainage works, for both singular and composite systems, it is essential to start from the downstream end of the system and work towards the upstream end. In this way, water can be discharged as the system construction progresses;
- For composite systems, the field drains govern the level of the collector system. If the field drains are placed first and too deep, then the collector system will need to be deeper still and more costly than necessary. Therefore, for composite systems, *first construct the pumping station (if applicable), next the collector system, and after these have been completed, the field drains* (see C.28, C.29 and C.30);
- In case gravel is used as an envelope the supply and management of gravel is required in a specified sequence of events (see C.35). In case a pre-wrapped envelope is used, the activities for gravel application will not be relevant;
- In the case of unstable subsoil, high-speed work is essential for easy and good quality work. In reality the work must be completed before the soil has had time to collapse (see C.24).

C.20.2 Preparations shortly before installation

- Discuss activities, required labour and responsibilities with representatives of landowners;
- Have design (setting out sheet) available;
- Set out drains by placing pegs at start and end of drain (see C.21);
- Review field for obstructions, remove obstructions and if necessary smoothen alignment of collector and/or field drain (see C.22);
- Measure field level near sump, near every collector manhole and/or start of every field drain and place a reference peg (see C.29);
- Dry/drain off standing water in the field (see C.25);
- Construct a camp if necessary.

C.20.3 Preparations the day before installation

- Prepare all equipment and staff;
- Place gravel in field (when a gravel envelope is used);
- Place rolls of pipes in field;
- Place manholes and sump in field near location of the installation.

C.20.4 Installation of singular system

(See also C.26 and C.27).
1. Have design information with levels available in the field;
2. Assure that all equipment is ready (as needed: trenchers, gravel trailers, excavator, bulldozers, laser equipment);
3. Have all required drainage materials available;
4. Roll the pipe out in the field, make connections (if no prefabricated couplers are available: be sure to have (iron) wire and filter cloth or plastic!), or;
5. If pipes are delivered on rolls and the trencher is equipped with places to store the rolls and hydraulics to load the rolls on the trencher, place the rolls in the field along the drain pipe alignment at distances equal to the length of the rolls;
6. Place boning rods (red poles) in line in the field (see C.21);
7. Install laser transmitter (see C.13, C.14);
8. Determine starting level of the drain, calculate depth of pipe below reference peg (see C.26);
9. Pass the blind drain pipe through the trencher and extend it some 1.5 metres outside the trench box. Make sure the pipe remains in position over the roller at the bottom of the trench box by attaching a wire and holding it firmly;
10. Dig start hole with trencher (liftable trench box) in side slope, if required;
11. Lower the trench box into or along side slope;
12. Check level of bottom of trench box and adjust this to the required starting level;
13. (Have gravel ready);
14. Extend laser mast so that upper red light is flashing;
15. Start trencher (and gravel supply);
16. Start installing field drain;
17. (Apply gravel, manage gravel supply);
18. Control check levels of the pipe every 10 metres;
19. Control continuous pipe and envelope material for damages;
20. At end of field drain block end;
21. Install drain outlet;
Preferably a few days later when the soil from the trench is dry:
22. Backfill trench (see C.33).

C.20.5   Installation of composite (collector) systems

C.20.5.1 Installation of the Collector

1. Have design information with levels available in the field;
2. Have all machinery and equipment available in field:
   - Trencher;
   - Excavator;
   - Bulldozer;
   - (Gravel trailers);
   - Laser equipment.
3. If collector pipes are not mounted as rolls on the trencher - lay the pipes out in the field, make connections (be sure to have iron wire and plastic!);
4. Install laser transmitter with correct slope (see C.13, C.14);
5. Determine level of bottom of the sump - calculate level below the reference peg, based on the design (see C.29);
6. Determine level of the bottom of the collector at the sump connection;
7. Dig hole for sump (fast!) (if necessary stabilise soil with filter);
8. Put sump in place (see C.28);
9. Check level and straightness of the sump;
10. Make trencher ready;
11. Fill hole for sump up around sump up to the level of connection of the collector and compact (see C.28);
12. Connect collector to sump;
13. Dig start hole for trencher;
14. Put trencher at start level;
15. Determine level of bottom of trench box;
16. Calculate required length of mast and inform driver;
17. Start installing collector;
18. Finalise connection of collector to manhole (watertight);
19. Fill up hole around manhole;
20. Control levels of collector installed every 10 metres;
21. At end of collector block the end;
22. Install (temporary) pump in sump;
23. Start pumping in sump;
24. Check if collector flows;

After soil from the trench is dry:
25. Backfill trench: how and when to do this is to be determined in the field.

C.20.5.2 Installation of additional manholes in collector line

1. Determine the exact location of the manhole in the collector line;
2. Dig out a hole for placement of the manhole up to level of collector;
3. Dig out by hand around collector up to the required depth of the manhole;
4. Regularise hole to accommodate the manhole;
5. Cut a piece of the collector drain pipe. The length of the cut pipe is equal to the diameter of the manhole minus 20 cm;
6. If water is flowing out, block the now open part of the manhole using cloth or other material;
7. Bend outwards the two ends of the collector, be sure not to disturb the levels;
8. Hoist the manhole into the hole to a level just above its installation site;
9. Put the ends of the collector through the holes in the manhole;
10. Place the manhole in its permanent site;
11. Level manhole so that ends of collector do not bend up or down;
12. Secure both collector ends with cement in manhole;
13. Remove the blockage of the collector;
14. Fill in hole up to bottom level of field drain;
15. After starting field drain, complete filling up of hole.

C.20.5.3 Install field drain starting from manhole

1. Lay the pipe out in the field and make connections (be sure to have iron wire and plastic!);
2. Be sure sump is pumped so that little or no water is in the collector or manhole;
3. Dig start hole for trencher;
4. Put up laser transmitter;
5. Put trench box at the level of the hole in the manhole for the field drain;
6. (Have gravel ready);
7. Connect field drain to manhole - first length of the field drain should be "blind" (no holes);
8. Measure level field drain and compare actual level of field drain with design level;
9. Give difference between actual level and design level (if any) to operator;
10. Start trencher (gravel supply) start installing field drain;
11. Finalise manhole, filling up in layers up to the top, placing rings as necessary;
12. Put lid on manhole;
13. Continue installing field drain;
14. (Apply gravel, manage gravel supply);
15. Control check levels of the pipe every 10 metres;
16. At end of field drain block end;
Preferably a few days later when soil from trench is dry:
17. Backfill trench.

C.20.6   Check functioning of system
(See section D)

C.20.6.1 Singular system

- Check alignment of all drains (see D.4);
- If there are problems with the quality/level control of field drains, correct them immediately;
- Check whether all drains are flowing;
- If there are manholes in the drains check if the parts upstream of the manhole are flowing.

C.20.6.2 Composite systems

- Check alignment of collectors and drains (see D.4);
- If any problems with the quality/level control of field drains are discovered, correct them immediately;
- Clean out silt from all manholes/sumps by hand;
- Pump in sump;
- Check water levels in collector manholes, check if water level is logical and collectors are flowing;
- If the obstruction can be pinpointed try to remove (flusher? digging up?);
- Check water flow in field drain manholes;
- Check for obstructions and if found, remove.

Installation of Subsurface Drainage Systems	Installation of Drain Pipes *General activities*	Instruction sheet C.21

Subject: **Setting out of field**

Target group: Surveyors

C.21 Setting out of field

C.21.1 General

Setting out of the field, based on benchmarks with known levels as placed or identified by the designers and the baseline as defined by the designers, consists of setting out the:

- Reference level per field in a permanent benchmark;
- Alignment of collectors (check that there are no obstacles such as electricity posts and culverts in the alignment);
- Alignment of field drains (check that there are no obstacles such as electricity posts and culverts in the alignment);
- Location of manholes;
- Levels of manholes (only sumps and collector manholes).

C.21.2 Reference level per installation area: "benchmark"

A benchmark with a known level per installation area is to be placed in a spot that cannot be damaged by the installation. The level is based on the same reference as the design and preferably related to the national standard. This benchmark will in the future help with repairs and diagnosis of faults in the system.

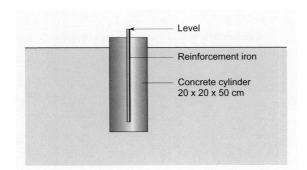

A benchmark (Figure C21.1) can be made of concrete with some reinforcement iron dug firmly into the soil (dimensions for example: 0.2 x 0.2 x 0.5 m). The best thing to do is to write the level on the benchmark.

Figure C21.1   Benchmark

C.21.3   Alignment of collectors and field drains

C.21.3.1 Alignment of collectors or baseline for the start of field drains

The alignment of the collector drain (Figure C21.2) or the downstream end locations of the field drains must be marked in the field. This alignment is usually either parallel or perpendicular to the baseline. The collector line should be marked in the field by placing pegs at the centre of the spot where the future manholes/sumps will be installed and/or where the field drains will start. Since these pegs will be destroyed during installation, it is advisable to install reference pegs in a spot adjacent to the alignment of the collector and/or start of field drains that will not be destroyed during installation. In this way one can always trace the alignment and thus locate drains and manholes if flushing becomes necessary.

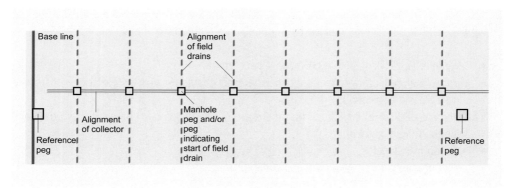

Figure C21.2   Alignment of collector

C.21.3.2 Alignment of field drains

The general alignment of the field drains is derived from the design. Once the downstream end (start end) of the drains has been marked in the field as described in C.21.3.1, the upstream end can be similarly marked (make a line perpendicular to the baseline at the top end of the field and use pegs to mark the end of the field drains). Next, a straight line is pegged out in between the start and end peg of the field drain and along this line is where the field drain will be installed (see C.21.3.3).

C.21.3.3 Staking/pegging out a straight line

Required tools
- Ranging rods/sighting rods (5);
- Spirit level (preferably).

Methodology (Figure C21.3)
1. Place ranging rods at the place of the start peg (A) and end peg (B);

2. Place the ranging rods vertically (verify by spirit level if available);
3. One person stands 3 to 5 metres behind the start ranging rod (A) and views the end ranging rod;
4. Place in the line at regular distances, which do not exceed the easy view from the previous sighting rod, the other sighting rods (maximum distance 75 m). The distance between two rods must not be too great and must not exceed the view of the workers and machine operator;
5. A second person aligns the intermediated ranging rods in the line starting 75 metres from the rod on the other end of the line;
6. Person (2) holds the rod between thumb and forefinger while person (1) sights the ranging rod in line;
7. Place a peg just behind or in front of the thus placed sighting rod.

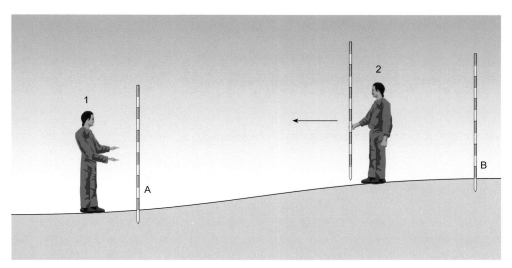

Figure C21.3   Two persons staking out a straight line

Tip: Setting out a perpendicular line

In most cases the line is situated parallel to another natural line like a canal, ditch or agriculture road. If this is not the case a line must be set out perpendicular to an existing baseline and if there are no instruments available this can be done as follows:

Using the properties of a triangle (Pythagoras law) lay a triangle of rope with sides measuring 3, 4 and 5 metres, respectively. Place an iron ring at each of the three corners and place in every ring a ranging rod. Then place one of the sides of the triangle parallel to the base or reference line. Put another ranging rod in the remaining corner. The other side of the triangle is now perpendicular to the base line.

Required tools:
- Three ranging rods;
- A rope of 12 metres;
- Three iron rings.

C.21.4   Location of manholes

If the collector and field drains are set out as given in section C.21.3, the location of the manholes will automatically be known. Since the pegs will be destroyed during drain installation, a second peg will need to be placed outside the alignment to be able to trace the centre after the drain has been installed (Figure C21.4).

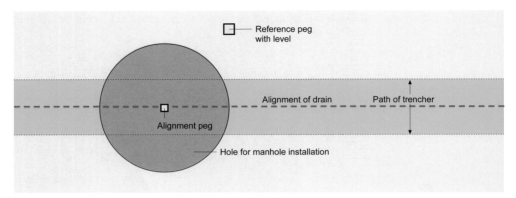

Figure C21.4   Location of the alignment peg and reference peg

C.21.5   Levels of manholes

Levels are very important for collector manhole and sump installation and to save time during the installation of the manhole a level is required close to the installation pit. The level of the reference peg outside the alignment, as mentioned under section C.21.4 can therefore best be determined and implies that the level is measured in accordance with the benchmark (see C.21.1). The best thing to do is to write the level on the peg, and if the peg is in a permanent secure place, it will also help to relocate the manhole when repairs or cleaning needs to be done (Figure C21.4).

Installation of Subsurface Drainage Systems	Installation of Drain Pipes *General activities*	Instruction sheet C.22
	Subject: **Site preparation**	
	Target group: Field manager, supervisor, field staff	

C.22   Site preparation

C.22.1   General

After the general staking out of the drain alignments the site preparation can start, which consists of:

- Removal of obstruction in the alignments, including trees, shrubs, crops and structures (if still there);
- Smoothing of the path of the trenchers with bulldozers (graders can also be used);
- Temporary filling in of ditches and removal of bunds or dykes to provide a smooth path for the trenchers;
- Temporary filling in or making bridges over ditches for access of the equipment;
- Preparation of storage places for gravel envelope, if required.

C.22.2   Smoothing of the alignments

The alignment of the drains has to be smooth to allow smooth passage of the trencher. Although trenchers can cross ditches and climb over minor bunds and so forth, this will only slow down the operation and can negatively affect the grade and depth control. The laser can of course correct the level difference within a limited range, but the reaction of the hydraulics to bumps in the field as instructed by the laser will be too slow because the hydraulic system has certain inertia (see C.23.2). Consequently, this will result in "bumps" in the level of the installed drain (Figure C22.1). This will happen if the subsoil is unstable, the float control is switched off and the laser receiver is mounted on the lifting cylinder. In stable subsoil a bump in the drain level can be avoided by driving slowly over the water course bund and keeping the float control switched on.

C.22.3   Crossing of small canals or surface drains

Whenever the drainage trencher has to cross a small canal or surface drain, these can best be levelled and smoothed by a bulldozer or excavator and reconstructed after the passage of the trencher. Getting past these obstructions, especially if this has to be done at an angle causes problems as indicated in Figure C22.2. First, one track of the machine will enter the small irrigation canal and the machine will tilt. The trench box will then get stuck in the soil, and more power will be needed to move forwards. This will cause the track to dig itself into the bottom of the small canal and will only make things worse and finally the machine could come to a complete standstill or the boom of the trench box might break.

Depending on the depth of the canal and the depth of the drain, it is often advisable to make a drain bridge (Figure C22.3) or a blind pipe (drain without holes) under the canal. In this way the irrigation water will not be able to seep into the drain. If temporarily filling in is not an option the canals/drains will have to be crossed at as large an angle as possible, preferably 90 °. In that case it would be better to place blind pipes or rigid pipes under the crossing.

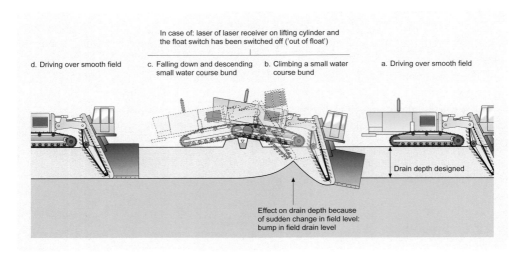

Figure C22.1   Effects of a bump in the field on the level of the field drain

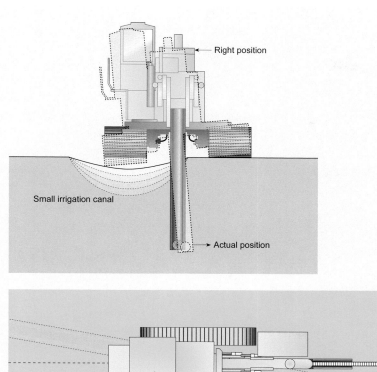

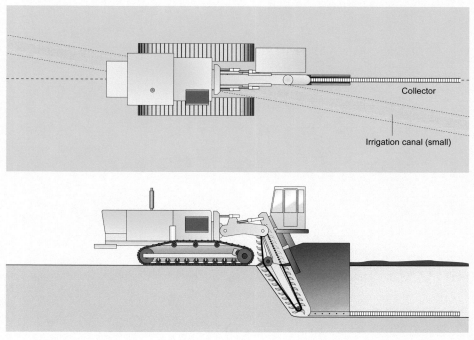

C22.2   Crossing of irrigation

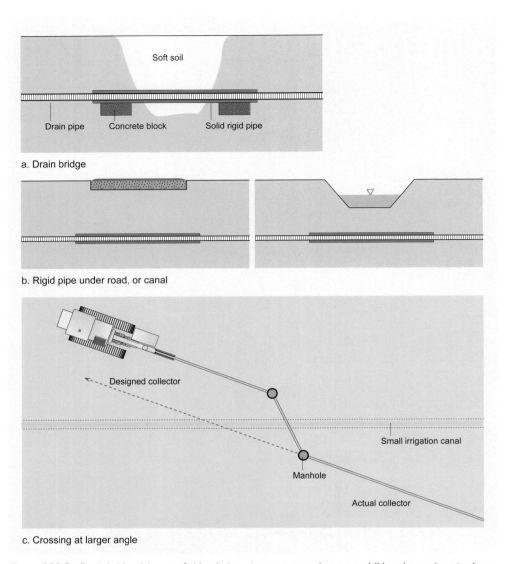

a. Drain bridge

b. Rigid pipe under road, or canal

c. Crossing at larger angle

Figure C22.3   Drain bridge (a), use of ridged pipes to cross a road or a canal (b) and crossing at a larger angle (c)

Installation of Subsurface Drainage Systems	Installation of Drain Pipes *Installation*	Instruction sheet C.23
	Subject: **Installation of drains in a straight line and with correct grade**	
	Target group: Operators, surveyors, field manager, supervisor	

C.23   Installation of drains

C.23.1   General

A subsurface drain or collector can only function correctly if installed straight, without horizontal curves, and at a correct straight grade, with minimal deviations.

C.23.2   Depth/grade control

The depth and grade of a drain line during installation can be controlled manually and automatically using a laser. Since most of the trenchers are equipped with a laser, manual control will not be further elaborated.

Laser equipment has its limitations for controlling the grade and correcting the depth of installation. A laser can very well compensate for gradual changes in field level, but not for sudden changes, because:

- One of the limitations is the speed at which the depth control is automatically corrected by the laser beam if confronted with a sudden obstruction in the field. The operator will have to slow down the speed if:
  - A sudden obstruction (small dike or dip in the field level) is encountered. (It is better before installation starts to level these using a bulldozer, for instance);
  - A hard layer in the soil is encountered. Apart from slowing down the float control will also need to be (temporarily) switched off (button 4, C.4).
- If the subsoil is unstable or if soft layers occur in the soil, the deviation of the grade over short distances can be substantial. Under these conditions the float switch will need to be switched off and the speed increased to the maximum. Even under these conditions the installation process should not be interrupted. If an interruption is really necessary, the engine and the laser will have to be kept running (see C.24).

C.23.3   Alignment control

The drain line needs to be pegged out carefully to facilitate alignment control, as described in C.21.

Ranging rods will have to be placed if there are no boning or ranging rods anymore on the line at the places of the alignment pegs. There should be at least one ranging rod at the end peg and always at least two, preferably 3 boning or ranging rods in front of the trencher (Figure C23.1).

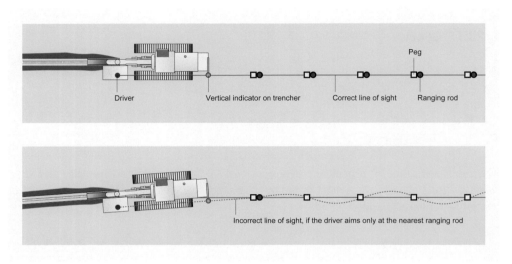

Figure C23.1   Alignment control

The trencher operator can then align the vertical indicator rod on the trencher with all the boning or ranging rods that have been set out in the field. A frequently observed mistake is that the operator only aims at the nearest boning or ranging rod. As a result the installed line will not be straight and this in turn will lead to difficulties when locating the drain in the future.

C.23.4   Handling and installation of the corrugated plastic drain pipe

The installation of corrugated plastic drain pipes if the pipes are delivered on coils and click couplers are available, is done as follows:

- Corrugated plastic drain pipes of diameters up to 200 mm can be delivered in coils. The maximum diameter up to which delivery on coils is possible depends on the manufacturer. Generally speaking field drains up to 100 or 125 mm are delivered on coils by all manufacturers. The coils can be placed on reels that are mounted on the trenchers and gradually unwound when installation starts. The pipe is guided through the trench box into the drain trench via the pipe guidance rollers;

- The press pulley at the end of the trench box has to be lowered on top of the drain pipe to keep the drain pipe in the right position at the bottom of the trench;
- During installation the free unwinding of the pipe has to be checked. One labourer is responsible for the connection of the pipes and the unobstructed unwinding and guiding of the drain pipe;
- The coils have to be connected to each other by click couplers, if these are available. Both ends of the pipes are to be put firmly in the click coupler. This has to be done in such a way that the lips of the click coupler are firmly behind the ridges of the corrugated pipe;
- Be sure that there is no undue stress on the drain during the full installation time;
- When the trencher approaches the end of the drain line the drain pipe is cut off from the coils at approximately 2.5 m before the end. The end of the drain pipe is plugged (Figure C23.2);
- The backfilling of the trenches has to be done carefully as described in C.33.

In case larger diameter corrugated drain pipes (which are often delivered in lengths of 6, 9 or 12 m), or drain pipes that are not (properly) coiled, or in case no quick couplers are available, the pipes have to be laid out in the field parallel to the drain alignment. At the downstream end of the pipe an extra length of pipe is required of some 5-7 m to allow for the for the length required to lift the pipe over the trencher at the start of the installation The pipe sections can then be connected before installation starts. Connecting drain pipe sections can be done as follows:

- The connections can be done by prefabricated plastic couplers (Figure C23.3) or the connections can be made by hand as is indicated in Figure C23.4;
- The hand-made couplers consist of 1 or 2 pieces of corrugated drain pipe of approx. 30 cm length, slit open longitudinal;
- The two ends of the drain pipes are put pushed together and then one connection piece is put over the drain pipe in such a way that it covers both sides of the remaining gap between the drain pipes. The corrugations of the connection piece fits tight into the corrugations of the drain pipe. However, the hand-made connection piece has the same diameter as the drain pipe, and there will be a small longitudinal gap, which does not hinder the proper functioning of the drain pipe. The connection will be stronger if a second connection piece is put over the first one, covering the small longitudinal slit of the first connection piece;
- The couplers should be well fitted and if necessary additional iron wire is used for securing the connection. In case there is a fear of openings in the connection which could allow soil to enter the pipe the pipe a sheet of plastic can be fastened around the pipe.

At the start of the installation the end of the pipe is lifted over the front top of the trencher and inserted into the pipe guidance system on top of the trencher. Special rollers have to be constructed on the trencher to make it possible that the pipe is smoothly guided towards the tube guidance in the trench box. The trencher drives under the pipe (see also Part I, Figure 56).

Figure C23.2   Plugged end of field drain

Figure C23.3   Prefabricated plastic coupler for the connection of large diameter drain pipe sections

C.23.5   Handling and installation of concrete/and or clay drain pipes

The concrete or clay drain pipes are loaded on a platform on the machine and then put along the chute in the trench box to the bottom of the trench. In case collector drains are installed as closed conduit-pipe, the installation requires one labourer on the platform to put the pipe in the chute and one labourer in the trench box to put cloth or other sealing around the joints (Figure C23.5)

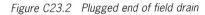

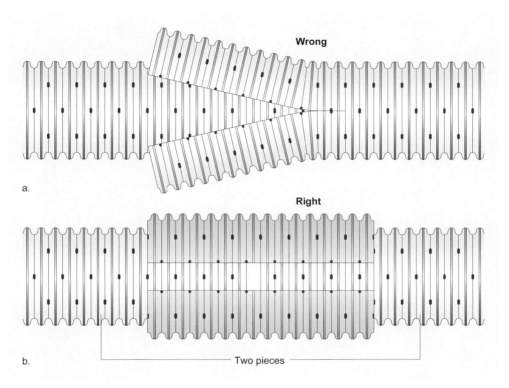

Figure C23.4   Hand made connection for small diameter drain pipes

Figure C23.5   A labourer in the trench box to put cloth around the joints

Installation of Subsurface Drainage Systems	Installation of Drain Pipes *Installation*	Instruction sheet C.24

Subject:	**Installation drains in saturated and/or unstable subsoils**
Target group:	Field staff, operators, field manager, supervisor

C.24 Installations drains in saturated and/or unstable subsoils

C.24.1 General

Installation of drains with trenchers in unstable soils that loose all cohesion and become liquid if saturated, require special installation procedures and attention of management and operators.

C.24.2 Installation methodology

The installation method that has the highest chance of success in unstable, saturated subsoils incorporates the following elements:
- Fast driving. If the trencher drives fast the drain pipe is put in its correct place quickly and can be fixed in its place, before the soil has time to become liquid or the trench collapses;
- Fixing the drain pipe quickly in its place by loading soil on the drain pipe at the moment that is leaves the trench box. This can be done by:
  - Pushing with a spade a quantity of excavated soil into the trench immediately behind the trench box, and/or by;
  - Mounting a "plough like" device on the back of the trench box that scrapes a quantity of soil from the walls of the trench, while at the same time making a "break mark" in the trench wall, which prevents dislodging of the drain pipe in case of collapse (Figure C24.1).

C.24.3 Observations

When working in this type of soil, operators should (Figure C24.2):
- Avoid to leave the trench box in the trench when the trencher stops for a longer pause (e.g. lunch or overnight), because its weight will make it sink into the ground and the level will be lost;
- If it is unavoidable and the trencher is left for a longer period with its trench box in the trench, sand and water will settle between the chain links and the sprocket and the chain will be fixed in the ground. In this case do the following:
  - Start the engine and let the chain turn a while in *first* gear before shifting to higher gears. (If you start immediately in sixth gear the engine may stall, parts may break or be damaged).

331

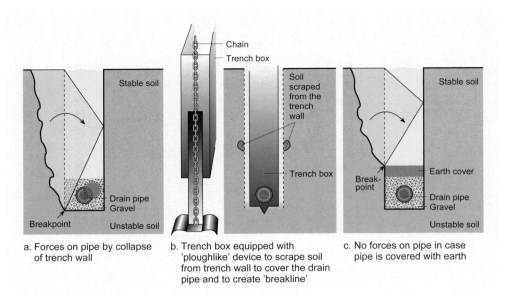

a. Forces on pipe by collapse of trench wall

b. Trench box equipped with 'ploughlike' device to scrape soil from trench wall to cover the drain pipe and to create 'breakline'

c. No forces on pipe in case pipe is covered with earth

Figure C24.1   Use of scrapers to cover the drain pipe in unstable soils

Figure C24.2   Trencher operating in unstable soil

Installation of Subsurface Drainage Systems	Installation of Drain Pipes *Installation*	Instruction sheet C.25

Subject: **Installation in fields with standing surface water**

Target group: Field staff, field manager, supervisor

C.25 Installation in fields with standing surface water

C.25.1 General

Any standing surface water on the field in the lines of installation must be removed before the installation starts. In principle, no drains should be installed under wet surface conditions. This is specifically true for field drains.

C.25.2 Effects of standing water on quality of drains

If a drain trench is made in an area with standing water, the water will immediately flow into the trench.

This water is usually mixed with mud. The muddy water will during installation flow to or fall on the drain pipe with envelope and will disturb the envelope. The effect is that muddy water will flow into the drain and fill the drain pipe with mud. Consequently the drain will not function as intended. A secondary effect is that installation will be difficult because the gravel trailers will sink or slip. In most cases, however, the trencher is capable of working under wet conditions.

C.25.3 Preventive measures

If there is standing water in the field, a shallow trench must be dug before installation commences to channel the water towards the open drain. This can be done with an excavator, a bulldozer or even a plough. It is best to do it a few days before drain installation so that the surface can dry out and if gravel is used the gravel trailers will have little or no problems.

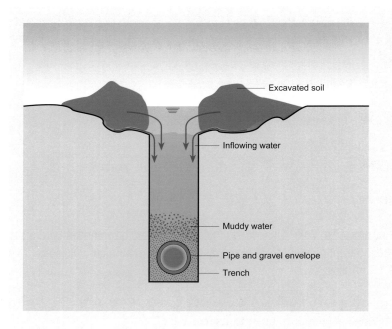

Figure C25.1   Effects of standing surface water

Installation of Subsurface Drainage Systems	Installation of Drain Pipes *Installation of Singular Systems*	Instruction sheet C.26

Subject: **Installation of field drains starting from an open ditch**

Target group: Operators, surveyors, field manager, supervisor

C.26   Installation of field drains starting from an open ditch

C.26.1   Procedures

1. Reverse the trencher until the trench box and digging chain are above the open drain taking care that the vertical direction rod is exactly in line with the ranging rods that mark the drain line (Figure C26.1a);
2. Lower the trench box and digging chain with the lifting cylinder (Button 16, C.4) until the top of the trench box is horizontal and the bottom of the trench box is at the starting level of the pipe drain (Figure C26.1b);
3. Adjust laser mast so that the top orange light is flashing (C.13);
4. Insert the drainage pipe into the trench box until it is so far out that the rigid end-pipe can be connected to it;
5. Shift the digging chain into gear and drive forwards slowly while manually adjusting the depth to keep the top orange coloured light flashing. Stop the trencher at the moment that the trench box is completely inside the side slope of the drain (Figure C26.1c);
6. Switch on slewing (C.4, no 12) and lift "float" (C.4, no.4) and set laser to "automatic";
7. When digging starts, the trench box and digging chain will automatically rise a bit until the green light flashes;
8. As the machine moves forwards the pipe should be kept in place by hand, so that the end fitted with the rigid pipe is pulled to its final position. Release the pipe when the rigid end-pipe is in the correct position and immediately fix it in this position by backfilling and carefully compacting the soil over the rigid pipe;
9. While the machine advances, the drain pipe is placed at the correct level in the trench. To prevent it from being displaced some backfilling ("blinding") can best take place instantly at regular intervals.

C.26.2   Trench box too long for width of open ditch

If the open drain is too narrow to fit the trench box and digging chain the procedure is as follows:
1. Lift the trench box with the trench box cylinder (C.4, no.16) (Figure C26.2a);
2. Lower the digging boom with its lifting cylinder (C.4, no.10) until the trench box is horizontal (Figure C26.2b);

3. Lower the digging boom further with the depth control, until the top orange laser light starts flashing;
4. Shift the digging chain into gear and move forward slowly until there is enough space to lower the trench box (Figure C26.2c). While moving forward, adjust the depth manually to keep the

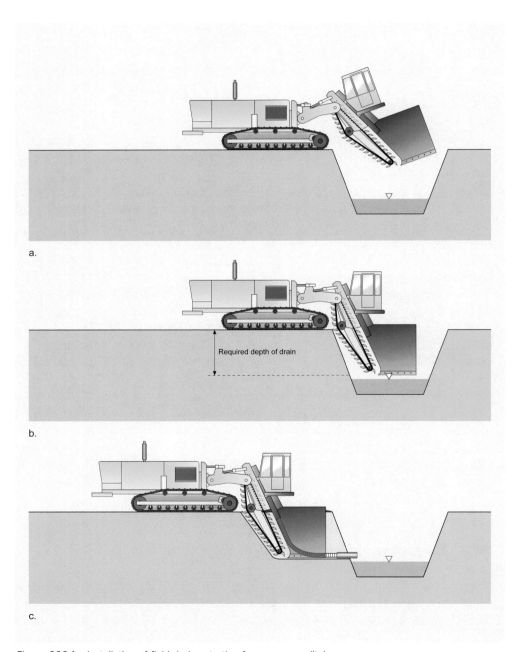

Figure C26.1   Installation of field drains starting from an open ditch

top orange coloured light flashing. Usually, it will be necessary to lift the digging chain to be able to position the trench box in the correct place;

5. *Important:* make sure that the hook between trench box and digging boom is secured properly, if not, switch on the trench box (see C.9);

6. If, during this exercise, the trench box has completely entered the side slope of the drain channel, the lift and slewing "float" can be switched on (Figure C26.2d);

7. Continue as described previously.

Important: The pipe should *never* be moved after it has been placed in position. Moving it will cause a change in bottom level so that the drain may not be able to function properly.

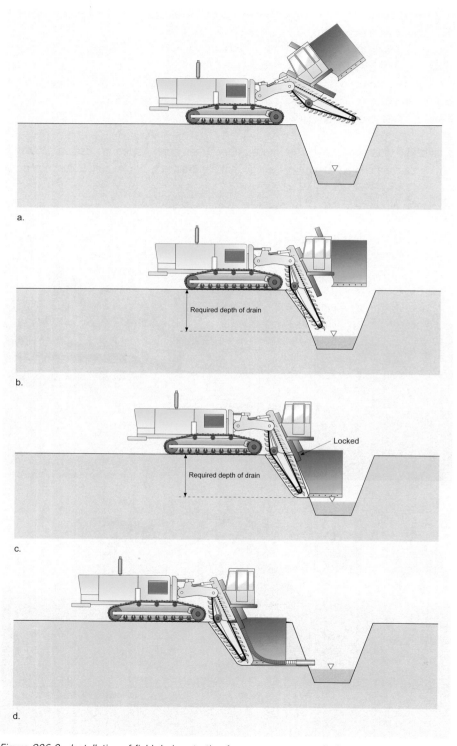

Figure C26.2   Installation of field drains starting from a narrow open ditch

Installation of Subsurface Drainage Systems	Installation of Drain Pipes *Installation of Singular Systems*	Instruction sheet C.27

Subject:	**Installation of outlets of field drains into open ditches**
Target group:	Field staff, field manager, supervisor

C.27 Installation of outlets of field drains into open ditches

If a field drain discharges into an open ditch the following provisions have to be made:

- The drain has to start with a rigid pipe of 3-5 metres in length. This length is necessary to ensure that the pipe is clearly anchored in the side slope of the drain to prevent water leaking out of the pipe and wetting and weakening the soil body of the side slope. The rigid pipe also serves to prevent the drain pipe from bending downwards after some time;
- Preferably, behind the rigid pipes are at least five metres of "blind" drain pipe (pipe without perforations). The "blind" pipe serves to prevent water from flowing out of the drain pipe into the surrounding soil causing weakening of the soil body which may lead to collapsing of the slope;
- After installation of the rigid end pipe and the blind pipe that is partially pushed into the rigid pipe, backfill the end part of the drain immediately. Backfilling should be done in layers of 30 cm and each layer should be well *compacted.* Compacting of this first section, especially around the rigid pipe, is essential to prevent the slope from collapsing and to securely anchor the pipe (Figure C27.1);
- The connection between the "blind" pipe and the rigid pipe should be as watertight as possible so that water from the open drain cannot flow into the soil of the side slope. This can be done by:
  - Tying a sheet of plastic firmly around the connection between the pipes;

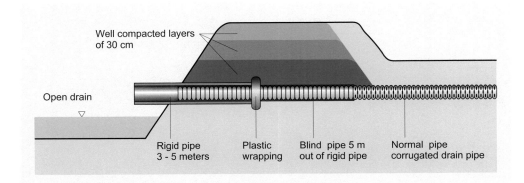

Figure C27.1   Outlet of field drain into open ditch

- Extending the "blind" pipe into the rigid pipe almost to the end (a pipe in a pipe) and wrapping a plastic sheet firmly around the connection.
- The connection between the "blind" pipe and the "normal" perforated pipe can be made just like the usual pipe joint.

Installation of Subsurface Drainage Systems	Installation of Drain Pipes *Installation of Composite Systems*	Instruction sheet C.28
	Subject: **Installation of sumps at the start of collector drains** Target group: Operators, surveyors, field staff, field manager, supervisor	

C.28 Installation of sumps at the start of collector drains

C.28.1 General

Installation of a sump at the start of a collector drain corresponds to installation of a manhole. The installation level for a sump is derived and defined by the level of the collector at the place of installation. The description of the installation of sumps is for prefabricated sumps. If the sump has to be constructed onsite in the excavated pit, the pit will need dewatering over a longer period of time.

C.28.2 Preparation

For the installation of a prefabricated sump the following preparations are to be made:
- The location of the sump will be indicated by a peg;
- The sump unit should be available near the location;
- Be sure that suction pumps are available;
- Excavator available;
- Surveyors and labourers available;
- Survey equipment available;
- Carpenters level available.

In case no prefabricated sump will be used and the sump will be constructed on site dewatering equipment is to be available.

C.28.3 Installation of prefabricated sump

1. Position the excavator (perpendicular to the drain line on the side where the field drain is planned) and start digging;
2. Excavate the hole for the sump fast and be sure no to dig too deep. If necessary remove the last layers by hand;
3. If the hole fills up with water, pump this out with the suction pump. If the hole is at the required depth and seemingly dry but muddy, throw a thin layer of gravel or course sand on the bottom;

4. When the bottom is prepared properly (right alignment, right depth, horizontal line), use the excavator to hoist the sump unit and with help of the labourers place the sump in the pit in the correct position (use carpenters level). For determining the right level see C.29;
5. After placing the sump unit prepare the connections with the collector and make connection watertight with cement. Check (carpenters level) the horizontal position of the collector connections;
6. Fill the hole with dry soil up to the level of the lower side of the holes for the collector drain in the sump's wall. Labourers compact the soil, especially immediately around the sump, and at the place of the (future) collector drain;
7. Connect now the collector pipe to the sump (see C.29).

C.28.4   Installation of sump built on site

1. If the sump has to be built onsite, install dewatering equipment (vertical well pointing), if needed, and operate pumps. Operation of the pumps should start well in advance of the digging of the hole for the construction of the sump. The groundwater table should be lowered to a level below the base of the sump;
2. Start pumping;
3. If ground water has locally be pumped out to bottom level of future sump start digging, by hand or with excavator;
4. Be sure that hole dug is 0.5-1 m wider and larger than required for sump to be built;
5. Start building sump at correct level (see C.29);
6. If sump is completed connect the collector pipe(s);
7. Fill the hole with dry soil up to the level of the lower side of the holes for the collector drain in the sump's wall. Labourers compact the soil, especially immediately around the sump, and at the place of the (future) collector drain.

C.28.5   Starting hole for collector drain.

- If there is no certainty that the collector drain will be installed immediately, then close the opening in the sump with filter sheet or plastic sheet and fill up and compact with dry soil to a higher level. In this case the starting hole will be prepared later just before installation of the collector drain. It will need a little more manual work;
- If the collector is installed immediately after the sump has been installed (which is preferable in the case of prefabricated sumps), the starting hole for the collector is dug at the same time as part of the hole for the sump.

Installation of Subsurface Drainage Systems	Installation of Drain Pipes *Installation of Composite Systems*	Instruction sheet C.29

Subject:	**Levels of manholes and starting levels for trencher for field drain installation**
Target group:	Surveyors, field manager, supervisor

C.29 Levels of manholes and starting levels for trencher for field drain installation

C.29.1 General

Sumps, collectors, manholes in collector lines and field drains have all to be installed at the correct level. To provide the correct level for installation and for checking if the levels are correct it is necessary to have a reference peg with a known level (PL) near every manhole to be installed. Moreover, the reference level must be related to the same basis as used in the design.

C.29.2 Determining the level of the levelling instrument

For determining the so called "instrument level" of the levelling instrument (Figure C29.1):
1. Install the levelling instrument in a strategic place;
2. Determine on the basis of the reference peg with known height the level of the instrument;
3. The instrument level is: IL = PL + Reading.

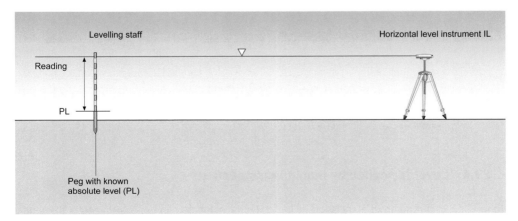

Figure C29.1   Determining the level of the levelling instrument

C.29.3 Determine the level of the sump or manhole *(Figure C29.2)*

1. Take from the design the level of the bottom of the lowest collector to be installed in the sump (DL);
2. Calculate on the basis of the design information the difference in level between the bottom of the lowest collector and the instrument level (IL-DL). The result (IL-DL) is the bottom level below the instrument level;
3. Measure with a measuring tape the distance between the bottom part of the collector entry hole and the bottom of the sump/manhole (SD = Sump Depth);
4. Add this value (SD) to the difference in level between instrument and bottom lowest collector (IL-DL);
5. The result is the installation depth of the sump/manhole below the instrument level (IDS = Installation Depth Sump).

$$\textbf{IDS = IL-(DL-SD)}$$

(Sumps, but not manholes, can better be placed 5-10 cm lower, to be on the safe side)

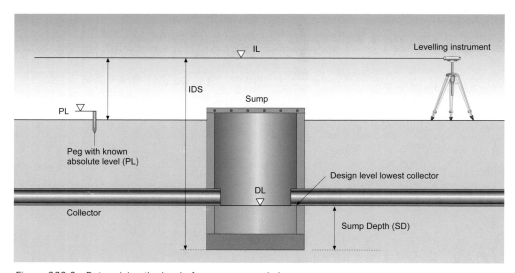

Figure C29.2   Determining the level of a sump or manhole

C.29.4 Level for collector manhole installation

Theoretically, the depth of installation of the collector manhole can be determined in the same way as the sump. In practice, however, the manhole is installed in the already installed collector line. Therefore, the level is determined in the field on the basis of the actual level of the collector. The bottom level of the manhole (BLM) is thus:

BLM = Top level collector - (Ø collector) - MD (Manhole Depth = difference between level of the bottom of the manhole and the bottom of the hole for the collector)

Be careful that the manhole is not placed too high or too deep, but at the right level. The reason why and how it differs from a sump is explained in the following drawing (if there is choice, never install too high rather a few centimetres deeper). However, if the manhole is placed too deep the downstream collector will not flow properly because the water cannot flow with the slope. This reduces the effective slope of the collector and thus the capacity.

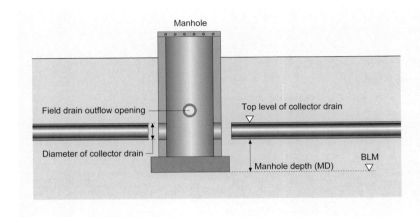

Figure C29.3   Determining the level of collector for manhole installation

The difference between a manhole and a sump is given in the following figures:
- C29.4a: A manhole should not be installed too deep because this will interrupt the flow downstream;
- C29.4b: A sump that receives water from both sides can be installed deeper, since this will only increase the slope and will not interrupt the flow towards the sump.

C.29.5   Levels for field drain manhole installation

The depth of the field drain determines the depth of installation of the field drain manhole. No other level is involved. In practice one has to align the manhole with the existing field drain. The level is thus to be determined in the field on the basis of the *actual level* of the field drain. Therefore, the bottom level of the manhole (BLM) is (Figure C29.5):

BLM = Top level field drain - Ø of field drain - MD (Manhole Depth = difference between level of the bottom of the manhole and the bottom of the hole for the field drain)

Be careful that the hole is not dug too deep, but at the right level. (See C.29.4).

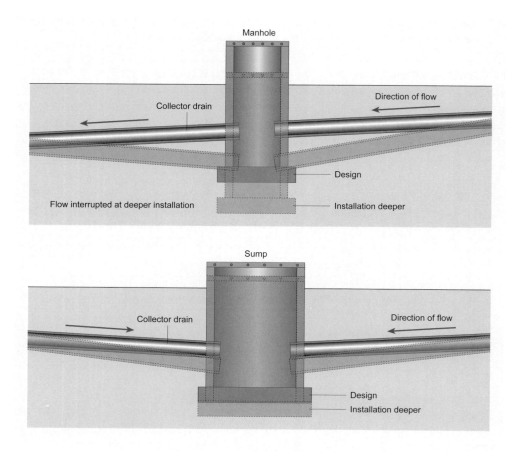

Figure C29.4   *Effects of too deep installation of a manhole and sump*

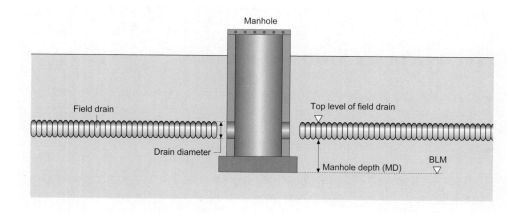

Figure C29.5   *Determining the level for field drain manhole installation*

C.29.6 Level to be given to trencher operator for collector drain at sump

After the sump has been installed and the starting hole made the following procedure needs to be followed for the installation of collectors (Figure C29.6):
1. Connect collector pipe to the sump;
2. Drive trencher forwards approximately 2 m;
3. The operator extends the laser mast until the green light appears on the display;
4. Determine the instrument level (IL) of the level instrument (see C.29.2);
5. Take the level at the top of the pipe at two places:
   • At the top of the collector pipe close to the sump;
   • At the top of the collector pipe where it comes out of the trencher.
6. Subtract from these levels the diameter of the collector;
7. Compare the values with the *design level* for the collector. If:
   • Level (2) is higher than level (1) but at or below design level, determine how much below design level and give this value to the operator. He can then, while installing slowly, raise the trench box to the desired level;
   • Level (2) is lower than level (1), determine how much (2) is below level (1) and ask operator to raise the trench box so that it is at least at level (1). Give the operator the number of centimetres the box should be raised. The operator then adjusts the mast length to come again in the green (This action will lift the collector pipe somewhat thus fill soil will need to be put under the pipe to support it).

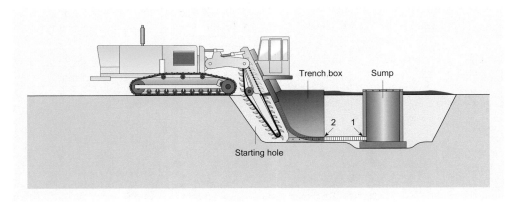

Figure C29.6   Schematic configuration of sump, collector and starting hole for trencher

C.29.7 Start Level for field drain to be given to trencher operator

After installing the collector a hole has to be dug at the place where the manhole is to be installed (Figure C29.7):
1. Dig the hole carefully so as not to disturb the pipe (see C.29.4);
2. Install the manhole at the same level as the pipes and be sure this is properly aligned (if the manhole is too high lower it, it is better that the manhole is a few centimetres too low, this is

acceptable, too high is not acceptable). Thus, the level of the openings in the manhole for the collectors is the *actual level* of the collector pipe;

3. Connect the collector pipes to the manhole and secure them;
4. Fill the manhole to a level above the collector pipes (up to the bottom opening for a field drain);
5. Dig a starting hole for the trencher;
6. Connect the field drain to the opening in the manhole;
7. Drive trencher approximately 2 m forwards;
8. The operator then extends the laser mast to the height until the green light appears on the display;
9. Determine the Instrument Level (IL) of the level instrument (see C.29.2);
10. Take the level at the top of the field drain at two places:
    - At the top of the field drain close to the sump;
    - At the top of the field drain where it comes out of the trencher;

    Subtract from these levels the diameter of the field drain;
11. Compare the values with the *design level* for the field drain. If:
    - Level (2) is higher than level (1) but at or below design level, determine how much below design level and give this value to the operator. Then, while installing slowly he will be able to raise the machine to the desired level;
    - Level (2) is lower than level (1), determine just how much this is and ask operator to raise the trench box so that it is at least at level (1). Give the operator the number of centimetres so that the box can be raised appropriately. The operator then adjusts the mast length to come again in the green (As the field drain pipe would have been lifted somewhat by this action fill soil will need to be put under the pipe to support it).

In some cases the level of the field drain will be higher than the start level at the opening in the manhole; the operator will raise the level gradually until it is at design level by gradually lowering the mast.

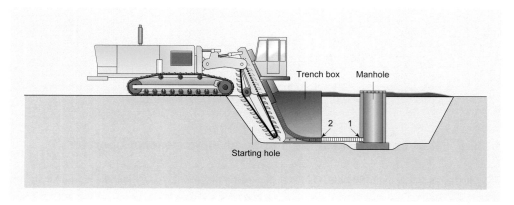

Figure C29.7   Schematic configuration of manhole, field drain and starting hole for trencher

Installation of Subsurface Drainage Systems	Installation of Drain Pipes *Installation of Composite Systems*	Instruction sheet C.30
	Subject: **Installation of manholes and starting holes for field drains**	
	Target group: Operators, surveyors, field manager, supervisor	

C.30 Installation of manholes and starting holes for field drains

C.30.1 General

The installation of a manhole in a collector or a field drain is very similar to the installation of a sump. The installation level for a manhole in a collector is derived and defined by the level of the collector at the place of installation.

C.30.2 Preparation

- The place of the manhole is pegged out;
- The manhole is at the spot;
- If necessary, the collector is pumped dry at the sump (just before installation of the manhole);
- Excavator available;
- Labourers available;
- Detection rod available. A detection rod is a rod made of concrete reinforcement steel of about 1.5 - 2 m in length with a handle (Figure C30.1);
- Carpenters level available.

C.30.3 Digging the hole and installing the manhole and collector

1. Position of excavator. For easy operation it is recommended that the excavator is positioned *perpendicular* to the collector;
2. Measure in the prefabricated manhole the distance between the bottom of the hole for the collector and the base of the manhole (see C.29 and C.29.7; SD and MD);
3. The excavator excavates a hole above the collector;

Detection rod

Figure C30.1   Detection rod

4. While excavating, a labourer timely starts to detect with a detection rod the place and the depth of the collector and gives the information to the operator. So the excavator can excavate safely the maximum quantity of soil without damaging the collector;

5. When the excavator has almost dug up the collector, the labourers dig the collector free over a length of about 1.50 m;

6. Cut out of the collector (using iron saw) a piece equal to the outside diameter of the manhole minus 40 cm;

7. When water flows from the collector the collector must be plugged instantly; (Possibility: Use a soft ball with a diameter of about 2 cm more than the inner diameter of the collector);

8. The soil to about the desired depth is excavated between both ends of the collector (see point 2 above);

9. Using the carpenters level the labourers smoothen the spot where the manhole will be installed while the manager indicates the depth of the bottom in relation to the bottom of the collector (see 2);

10. When the bottom is prepared properly (right alignment, right depth, horizontal), the excavator hoists the manhole and with help of the labourers places the manhole in the hole in the correct position (carpenters level);

11. In most cases the collector can be connected at one side of the manhole straightaway;

12. After placing the manhole prepare the collector connections and make them watertight using cement. Check (carpenters level) horizontal position of the collector connections;

13. Fill the hole with dry soil up to the level of the lower side of the holes for field drain in the manhole wall. Labourers compact the soil, especially immediately around the manhole and at the place of (future) field drain.

C.30.4   Observations

C.30.4.1 Manholes in field drains

The same working sequence as in C.30.3 applies to the installation of manholes in field drains. It is advisable to replace a part of the field drain that is connected into the manhole (approx. 1 m length) by a so-called blind pipe (pipe without perforations). Directly after the pipes are connected, the manhole can be completed by placing the top rings on the lower rings (if applicable) and the hole can be filled straightaway.

C.30.4.2 Starting hole for field drain

- If there is uncertainty about the immediate installation of the field drain following installation of the manhole, close the opening in the manhole with filter sheet and fill up and compact with dry soil to a higher level. In this case the starting hole will be prepared later just before installation of the field drain, which will require a limited amount of extra manual work;

- In case the field drain is installed immediately after the sump or collector manhole has been installed (which is preferable in the case of prefabricated sumps), the starting hole for the field drain is dug at as part of the hole for the manhole.

C.30.4.3 Inserting the trencher for field drain

As the collector and the manholes are designed and installed in such a way that the lowest field drain can discharge to the collector system, some field drains may have a higher starting level than the level of the entrance hole in the manhole to which they are connected. The procedure in that case is as follows:

- Connect the field drain to the manhole at the level of the entrance hole;
- Advance a few metres with the trencher;
- Measure the actual top level of the field drain;
- After correcting the level by subtracting the Ø of the drain pipe compare the measured level with the design level + the diameter of the drain;
- Inform the operator of the difference between the actual and the design level (in cm);
- Proceed with installation and instruct the operator to gradually shorten his laser mast with the length equal to the level difference;
- Be sure that the difference in level is corrected very gradually otherwise maintenance of the drain may become problematical.

Installation of Subsurface Drainage Systems	Installation of Drain Pipes *Installation of Composite Systems*	Instruction sheet C.31

Subject:	**Installation of pipe connections and joints**
Target group:	Field staff, field manager, supervisor

C.31 Installation of pipe connections and joints

C.31.1 General

Connections between field drains and collector drains are preferably made inside a manhole[1] as described in the pervious instruction sheets. In some cases the design prescribes direct connections. A direct connection can be made by a rectangle joint or a T-joint. The so-called T joint allows, although complicated and cumbersome, access to the field drain for a flusher. Rectangle joints do not have such provisions. This T-junction will need to be equipped with an access pipe with and end cap for the objective in mind (Figure C31.1). The access pipe should be installed in such a way that its upper part remains under plough depth (> 0.6 m depth). A reinforced concrete tile can be used to cover the end of the access pipe, which in theory can be detected underground with a metal detector in case flushing is required. However, in practice this does not always function easily.

C.31.2 Installation of connections *(Figure 31.2)*

- Joints should be installed in the starting hole dug for the field drain as soon as possible after the field drain installation has started;[2]
- If the groundwater is above the collector pipe the hole needs to be pumped out to ensure work under dry conditions;
- The joint should is to be installed on the centre line on top of the collector pipe (the starting level of the field drain is the top level of the collector drain or higher);
- A hole needs to be drilled in the collector with a diameter equal to the outer diameter of the joint;
- The joint is then inserted into the hole and fixed with iron wire or plastic wire around the collector;

---

[1] The advantage of a connection inside a manhole is that it provides relatively easy access to the field drain for cleaning and a way of inspecting the flows from field drains into collectors.

[2] This allows the field drain to flow immediately and to discharge its water into the collector. The longer the wait the higher the risk that the water starts flowing and the connection hole will be inundated, thus vastly complicating the activity.

- The lateral is then inserted firmly into the open end of the joint up to the tab stops;
- The hole is filled by hand in layers that are compacted up to just above the level of the joint, taking care that the field drain does not sag and has no reverse slopes.

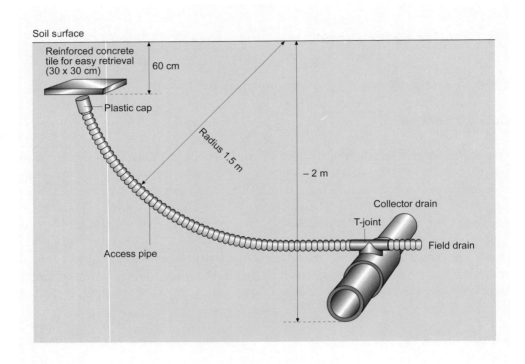

Figure C31.1   Example of T-joint with flushing provision

Figure C31.2   Installation of a lateral collector junction

Installation of Subsurface Drainage Systems	Installation of Drain Pipes *Installation of Composite Systems*	Instruction sheet C.32

Subject: **Completion of manhole/sump installation**

Target group: Field staff, field manager, supervisor

C.32 Completion of manhole/sump installation

C.32.1 General

The installation of sumps and manholes has been discussed in C.28, C.29 and C.30. Completion of the installation is discussed below.

C.32.2 Aboveground or underground manholes

Manholes can be installed aboveground as well as underground. An aboveground manhole, which is an obstruction in the field, has to be clearly marked so that a tractor is not driven over it. Also, surface water has to be prevented from freely flowing into it, so it is advisable that the top of the manhole is 0.6-1 m above ground level. Conversely, the top of underground manholes has to be at least 0.6 m below ground level so that no damage is caused to the manholes by soil cultivation activities like ploughing.

C.32.3 Backfilling methods

C.32.3.1 Background

A manhole is installed in a rather large pit. The pit is filled up later, but the soil is disturbed and has different characteristics than the original undisturbed soil. If the soil is not completely compacted then:
- It will subside in time;
- The soil will become more permeable and water will flow easily downwards towards the drain, which could cause piping and disturbance of the manhole;
- When wetted the disturbed soil will easily become muddy. If tractors work close to the manhole the soil may become boggy and disturb the manhole.

C.32.3.2 Solution

Backfilling the construction pit around the manhole can be done according to the following procedure (Figure C32.1):
- Fill up in layers of some 0.3 m;
- Compact each layer;
- Fill up the next layer and repeat the procedure;
- Continue filling up to a level above some 0.3 m of field level, so that the manhole seems to stand on a hill.

This will be minimising the risk of piping, inflow of water and muddy soil and disturbance by tractors.

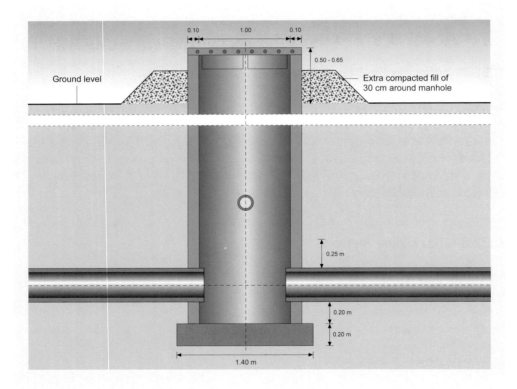

Figure C32.1   Backfilling of manhole

C.32.4   Joints of rings of manholes and joints of drain pipes with manholes

C.32.4.1 Background

The function of manholes is to provide access for inspection and cleaning of the collector and field drain pipes. Dirt (mud) should be prevented from entering the drainage system through joints of the manhole. Prefabricated manholes are often composed of rings which can be piled on top of each other to create a manhole of the desired height. If the joints of these rings are not properly sealed and watertight, muddy water may easily flow into the manhole and cause siltation of the drainage system.

C.32.4.2 Preparing water tight joints

Make the joints watertight even though the contact surfaces between rings are never perfectly level. The solution is to put cement on it repairing at the same time any damage to the rings. If available, asphalt-based joining kits are better than cement.
The rings may be off-set from the perfect alignment by side way pressure during filling or shocks with agricultural equipment. A second defence to prevent water from entering through the off set joints is to wrap a plastic sheet around the joints and fix these with iron wire. The best is agricultural (black) plastic of a minimal thickness. Agricultural plastic is both watertight and less expensive than other geotextiles.

C.32.4.3 Making joints of drain pipes with manholes watertight

The joints of the drain pipes with the manholes can be made water tight by putting (on the outside) mortar around the pipe and fill up the space in between the pipe and the manhole. If asphalt based kits are available these can also be used. As a second security some plastic sheets with iron wire can be used.

C.32.5   Lids/covers of manholes

Upon completion of the construction lids and covers of the manhole should be placed as soon as possible to avoid dirt from falling or being thrown into the manhole. The joints of the lid and top of underground manholes should be better protected using plastic sheeting as discussed in C.32.4.2, to avoid inflow of muddy water.

C.32.6   Pump house

If other than submersible pumps are used a pump house is to be installed for the protection of the pumps. For the protection of small pumps a pump box is to be installed.

For diesel driven pumps in most cases a full fledged pump house is required. The pump house is constructed either above or close to the sump. The pump house can be a simple brick building with a door that can be locked. For small drainage units a prefabricated pump house can be installed. In case submersible pumps are installed, a locked cover for the sump has to be installed.

C.32.7   Connection to the power grid system

In case of electrically driven pumps the connection to the power grid system has to be made prior to the installation of the drains, so that pumping can start already during installation of the drain pipes. The switch board for the pump operations is either put inside the pump house, or in a sturdy locked switch board box attached the electricity pole.

Installation of Subsurface Drainage Systems	Installation of Drain Pipes *Singular and Composite Systems*	Instruction sheet C.33
Subject: **Backfilling of trenches**		
Target group: Field staff, field manager, supervisor		

C.33   Backfilling of trenches

C.33.1   General

After the drain pipes have been installed (C.23) the trenches have to be backfilled.
Backfilling should be carried out according to the right methodology because if this is not done correctly it may have a negative impact on the performance of the drain, especially in the case of field drains. Ideally, all the excavated soil should be returned to the trench. If the backfilling is not correctly done there is a risk that soil lumps will form bridges in the trench and so-called "tunnels" will be formed (Figure C33.1). The formation of bridges or tunnels should be prevented at all cost because of the high risk that the muddy water will flow directly through the hollows in the trench towards the pipe and cause irreparable damage to the envelope. Figure C32.2 shows the erosion ("piping") that can occur in case of unconsolidated trench fill.

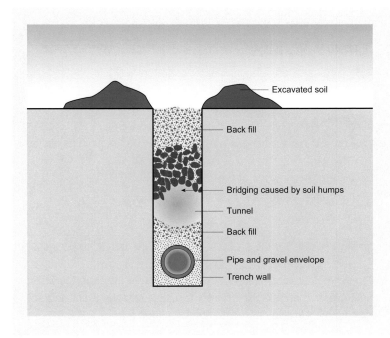

Figure C33.1   Bridges in the trench after incorrectly backfilling of the trench

Figure C33.2   Erosion ("piping") of unconsolidated trench fill

C.33.2   Backfilling methodology

Backfill of the drain trench is a three-step operation:
- Blinding;
- Backfill;
- Compaction.

Blinding
An initial backfill of 15 to 30 cm of soil is placed around and over the drain pipe. This is done to ensure that the drain pipe will remain in line when the remaining excavated material is placed in the trench.
Blinding may be done by shaving off the topsoil at the top of the trench with a spade (Figure C33.3), or with an attachment (scraping knife) to the trench box.

Backfilling
The best method for backfilling depends on the characteristics and the condition (wetness) of the soil.
- If the soil is dry, the trench can be closed almost immediately after installing the drain;
- If the soil is wet or unstable, it is preferable to wait a few days until the excavated soil is dry before commencing with backfilling.

Compaction
Compaction is required to avoid serious problems arising in irrigated areas when water moves rapidly through the unconsolidated trench fill causing severe erosion.

Figure C33.3   Blinding/backfilling the trench by hand

C.33.3   Instructions for backfilling of trench

C.33.3.1 Dry soil

- Directly after installation of the pipe the excavated soil can be pushed back into the trench using a bulldozer (or angle dozer). First the soil on one side of the trench is pushed in the trench and thereafter the soil on the other side of the trench. This will give the soil "time" to fall into the trench and thus prevents the formation of bridges. The soil can be pushed into the trench by hand, by tractor with a front end bulldozer blade, by tractor with a levelling blade, by bulldozer, by angle dozer or by grader;
- If available, a double V-shaped blade for a bulldozer can also be used. The bulldozer drives over the trench and pushes the soil deposited at both sides into the trench. The blade should be set in such a way that it does not touch the original field level. In a second go, after the soil is dried, the remaining soil can be pushed into the trench;
- After backfilling in this way the remaining ridge of soil on the trench must be pushed on top of the trench and compacted later. This compaction can be done with the wheels of a tractor that is driven over the trench.

C.33.3.2 Wet soil

In wet conditions the excavated soil is mostly wet, muddy and sticky. Collapse of drain trenches and formation of bridges are likely to have occurred during the installation of the drain.
The following procedures are recommended:
- Let the excavated soil dry before backfilling starts;
- After a few days make push with the bulldozer the excavated soil on one side of the trench, as much as possible, in the trench. After some days push the soil from the other side into the trench;

- One can harrow soil clods after drying to help the soil fall back into the trench, into the wide cracks and other hollow places.

C.33.3.3 Trenches and irrigation

It is advisable for all the remaining soil to be heaped on the trench alignment, which in time will subside and compact. At the same time a small ridge on the trench will partly prevent the direct flow of irrigation water into the trench.

Installation of Subsurface Drainage Systems	Installation of Drain Pipes *Singular and Composite Systems*	Instruction sheet C.34
	Subject: **Cleaning up of site after installation**	
	Target group: Field staff, field manager, supervisor	

C.34   Cleaning up of site after installation

The following actions need to be taken upon completion of the drain installation in an area:

- The original conditions should be restored: farm ditches, fences, roads and so forth should be able to function as before;
- Surplus soil that is not of an injurious nature should be spread over the surrounding field;
- Materials such as large stones and roots likely to damage implements or livestock, or of a size and character abnormal to material found on the surface of the field, should be removed;
- The contractor has to arrange for the removal of surplus pipe material, bands and ties, wood, glass, metal cans, and containers and other rubbish from the installation work;
- The ditches that were temporarily closed are to be opened and restored again;
- Canals that were cut by the drains are to be repaired and restored;
- The roads that were cut by the drain lines have to be restored to their original state;
- Bench marks and other permanent reference points should be protected, made clearly visible and marked correctly on the as built drawings.

Installation of Subsurface Drainage Systems	Installation of Drain Pipes *Gravel envelope*	Instruction sheet C.35

Subject: **Application of gravel**

Target group: Gravel manager, field manager, supervisor

C.35   Application of gravel

C.35.1   General

For proper performance of the drainage system the quality of the gravel envelope and the even application of a layer of about 7.5 cm of gravel around the pipe is of paramount importance. The quantity of gravel required is considerable and depending on the diameter of the pipe amounts to 4-5 m^3 per 100 m^1 of field drain.

The objective of the management of the gravel supply is to supply timely good quality gravel to the trencher so that it can work continuously and does not have to wait or slow down. A slowing or stopping of the trencher because the gravel hoppers run empty can disturb the grade of the drain. The supply should also be gradual since suddenly filling of the hoppers with gravel will add a considerable weight to the trench box. The resulting weight shock can push the trench box down so that the even grade of the drain pipe is disturbed. Best is that the degree of filling of the gravel hoppers is continuous and fluctuates between ¾ of the capacity and full capacity. This creates a constant pressure on the gravel and a regular flow of gravel in the chutes and, to some extent, prevention of clogging

The quality of the gravel itself is important. Dirt or sand or clay in the gravel will clog the chutes and prevent a regular flow, apart from the fact that the filter function will then not be optimal. Constant *quality control of the gravel* is of great importance for these two reasons and all the more because gravel is a natural product that is rather variable by nature.

Activities
Gravel supply consists of the following activities:
- Selecting storage sites;
- Quality control of the gravel upon delivery;
- Loading the gravel into gravel trailers;
- Infield transport of gravel by gravel trailers from storage site to trencher and back;
- Unloading the gravel into the trencher hoppers;
- Gravel management on the trencher.

C.35.2   Equipment and staff requirements

Equipment
- One front loader for loading the gravel at the storage sites into the gravel trailers;
- Three gravel trailers pulled by tractors.

Staff
- Operator front loader;
- Three tractor drivers;
- One gravel assistant.

C.37.3   Selecting a storage site

The location of the gravel storage in the field is important for logistic reasons. The storage site location must fulfil the following conditions:
- Sites need to be located as close as possible to the drains to be installed so that travel distances (time) are minimal;
- Cross field travel for the tractors plus gravel trailers should be minimised (slows down speed and increases travel time);
- Sites should be easily accessible to the supply trucks and gravel trailers;
- The gravel must be stored on a flat place, which if not flat should be levelled beforehand;
- A sandy place for storage free from coarse stones is preferred over a place with clay;
- Mixing of the lowest part of the gravel heap that is in contact with the soil is unavoidable and results in loss of this layer of the heap of gravel. Therefore, the surface of the storage area needs to be kept as small as possible and to achieve this the gravel should be stored in heaps as high as possible;
- Unloading of trucks arriving with gravel should be done as directed, preferably on top of an already existing heap.

Thus, to save gravel a small number of storage places with high heaps of gravel are best, but to minimise infield transport time a large number of heaps close to the drain alignments is preferable. Obviously, a compromise has to be made. If transport distances become too great and three gravel trailers cannot supply the trencher in time additional gravel trailers will have to be used.

C.35.4   Quality control

Quality control on the graduation and the cleanliness of the gravel should be carried out in the quarry before transport (see D.1.3). In the field quality control starts at the moment of reception of the transport, with a *visual check:* the gravel should not contain any coarse stones (>Ø 3-4 cm), or silt or mud. If there are doubts about the presence of mud and silt (for instance, when the gravel is dry) a simple test can be carried out. Mix a small sample with fresh, clear water. If there is mud and silt in the sample this will immediately be visible in the water. If the gravel contains dirt, too coarse stones, mud or silt, the gravel is not acceptable and should be rejected. If such problem occurs the gravel must be sieved again. If the gravel is acceptable, care should be taken to ensure that the quality of the gravel does not deteriorate while storing and loading on the site (see above for the different precautions).

C.35.5 Loading

Loading of the gravel into gravel trailers is best done by a front loader (Figure C35.1). The larger the capacity of the front loader the faster the loading and the less time lost during loading. To limit the dirt that is mixed with the gravel while loading:
- The operator of the (front) loader should take care that he keeps the bucket of the loader above the original field level to avoid loading soil as well;
- When new trucks with gravel arrive the storage manager should dictate the place of un-loading, preferably on top of already existing heaps.

Figure C35.1   Loading of gravel into the gravel trailer

C.35.6 Infield transport and unloading

The basics of the gravel transport and unloading are:
- Gravel trailer 1 has to drive alongside the trencher and unload the gravel gradual by way of the conveyor belt into the hoppers of the trenchers (Figure C35.2). The gravel as-sistant's job is to guide the process, swivel the transport belt between the front and back

hopper, manipulate the valve on the gravel trailer and indicate to the driver the required speed of unloading and the starting and the stopping thereof;
- Gravel trailer 3 has to be loaded and after loading it should be driven as fast as possible towards the trencher behind gravel trailer 1, wait until this trailer is empty and then replace it;
- Gravel trailer 2 has to travel from the trencher towards the loading place and when loaded travel to the trencher and relieve trailer 3;
- A new cycle starts.

Figure C35.2   Unloading of gravel trailer into the hoppers of the trencher

The unloading should be regular, meaning that the unloading begins when the hoppers are ¾ full (of the load supplied by the previous trailer). During the unloading (approx. 10 min) the filling grade of the hoppers should remain at the same level. Towards the end of the unloading the unloading speed is increased somewhat so that the hopper is fully filled when the trailer is empty and drives away. (The speed of unloading can be regulated by the speed of the transport belt and the valve on the gravel trailer). In the time lapse necessary for the replacement of the empty trailer with the fully loaded waiting trailer, the load of the hopper will decrease again to ¾, the starting point for the following trailer. The time required for return travel, loading and travel toward the trencher increases (or decreases) in accordance with the distance of the trencher from the gravel depot. The location of the storage site determines the travel distances and whether a continuous supply of gravel can be guaranteed with three trailers.

Trailers with a full load of gravel (> 8 tons) can only slowly travel over uneven ground. The easiest is to travel parallel to the trench, where the path is smoothed somewhat. Travelling long distances crosswise to the field is to be avoided (Figure 35.3).

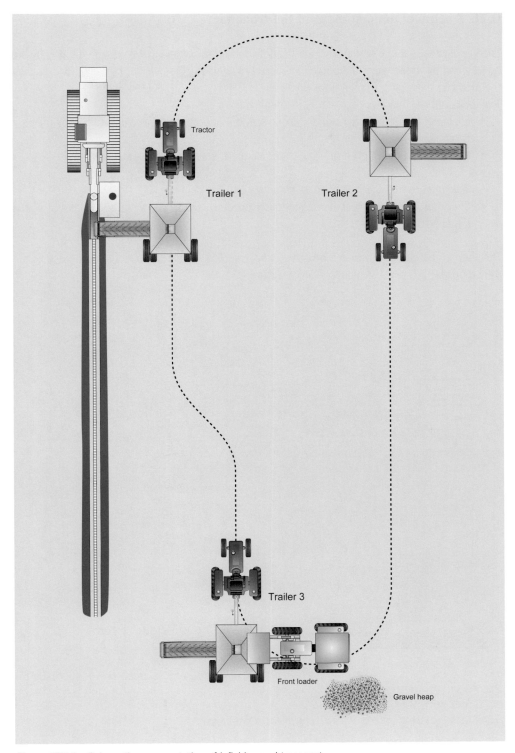

Figure C35.3   Schematic representation of infield gravel transport

C.35.7 Gravel management of the trencher

The gravel management on the trencher is partly carried out by the gravel assistant partly by the operator of the trencher or the person in charge of checking the quality of the pipe and guiding the pipe into the pipe guidance tube.

The management consists of:

- Adjusting the gate on the trench box so that the appropriate cover of gravel over the pipe is obtained;
- Assuring that the degree of filling of the hoppers stays more or less constant (3/4 full - full);
- Making sure that the gravel floats smoothly into the chutes;
- Checking that the pipe is homogeneously covered with gravel when it comes out of the trencher.

The gate at the end of the trench box should be adjusted so that the opening at the end of the trench box is: 7.5 cm + Ø pipe + 7.5 cm (Figure C35.4).

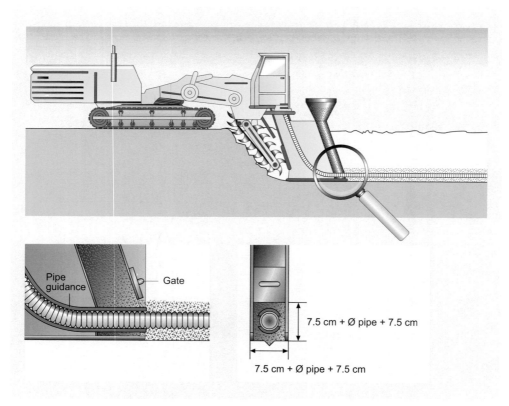

Figure C35.4 Gate at the end of trench box to adjust gravel flow

C.35.8   Possible problems

- The flow of gravel from the gravel trailer onto the conveyor belt is not regular:
  - Push the gravel with a stick and/or poke the gravel with the stick around and above the outlet of the trailer until the flowing resumes;
  - Beat with a stick against the outside of the hopper of the gravel trailer. (Not a very elegant solution).
- The gravel in the hopper of the trencher is sticky and/or does not flow down the chute towards the pipe, or obstructions have formed in the chute:
  - Push the gravel with a stick into the chute until the regular flow is re-established;
  - Beat with a stick against the side of the hopper;
  - If serious, stop the trencher and remove the gravel so that a possible obstruction can be removed.
- If the supply by the gravel trailers stagnates and the hoppers run the risk of running dry an undesirable situation occurs. To make the best of it one can do the following:
  - Stop the trencher when the hoppers are still ½ full;
  - Put the float control lock on just before the trencher stops;
  - Be sure the laser is in the green;
  - When a full gravel trailer is available again, bring it into position;
  - Start the trencher engine and manipulate the trench box height manually so that the laser is in the green;
  - Start filling the hoppers very slowly;
  - Start driving with the trencher;
  - Gradually fill the hoppers up to the normal level.

Installation of Subsurface Drainage Systems	Installation of Drain Pipes *Manual Installation of drains and envelope materials*	Instruction sheet C.36

Subject: **Manual installation of drains**

Target group: Field staff, field manager, supervisor

C.36   Manual installation of drains

C.36.1   General

Installation of drain pipes with trenchers is in most cases the most cost effective and quality secure method. Even in low labour cost countries, especially in large-scale projects, the total cost of mechanical installation often turns out to be less than the cost of manual installation. However, there may be situations where equipment is not available, where it is not economically justified to invest in equipment or where the equipment cannot access the site. Under these circumstances manual installation may be the only option. So, for the sake of completeness, an instruction for manual installation is given below.

C.36.2   Procedure and method for manual installation

The procedure for installing pipe drains manually consists of the following steps:
- Setting out alignments and levels;
- Excavating the trenches;
- Placing the drain pipes and envelopes;
- Backfilling of the trenches.

C.36.3   Setting out alignments and levels

Setting out the alignment and the levels of the drains is to be done as follows:
1. Mark the start or downstream end of the drain by placing a peg at the designated place of the outlet or at the connection point with a collector drain;
2. Then, mark the centre line of each drain by placing a peg at the upstream end (Figure C36.1a) of the drain;
3. These pegs are placed in such a way that the level of the top of the peg is at a fixed height above the planned trench bed, whereby the slope of the drain line is implicitly indicated (Figure C36.1b);
4. Draw a chalk line between the two pegs to mark the centre line of the future drain and place a row of sighting rods on the line at 10 m intervals. Next, fix a rope along the sighting rods at the level of the start peg and the end peg. This rope shows the slope of the proposed drain,

not at its actual level but at a fixed height above the design level (e.g., drain depth + the height of the top of the pegs above trench bottom).

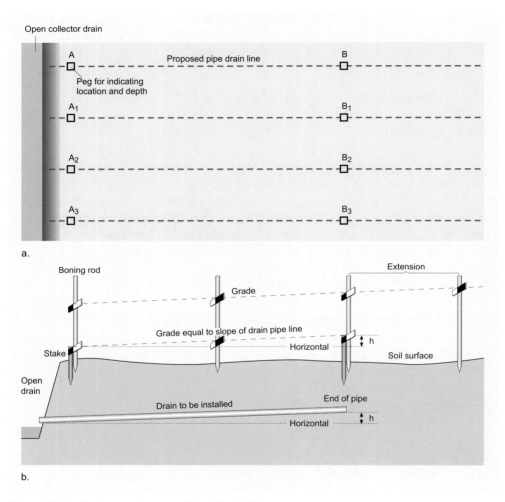

Figure C36.1   Setting out alignments (a) and levels (b)

C.36.4   Manual excavation of the trench

Tools
Special tools have been developed for manual installation of pipe drains. These tools can facilitate the work considerably. The tools consist of (Figure C36.2):
- Normal and long-blade spades. The blade of the long-blade spade is concave and approximately 70 cm long;
- Drain scoop to smoothen the trench bottom;

- A laying hook to place clay or concrete pipes (only if these are used);
- Auxiliary tools:
  - Correction hook (to correct the alignment of the pipes, only for concrete or clay pipes);
  - Pipe tongs (to remove broken concrete or clay pipes);
  - Soil pincer (to remove earth or debris from the trench bottom);
  - A hoe (to remove hard soil lenses/layers).

If these tools are not available, installation will require some more work, but installation with normal digging spades if the drains are not deep (50-80 cm) is quite possible.

Figure C36.2 Tools used for manual installation of pipe drains

Excavation

Excavation starts from the downstream end so that excess rain or groundwater can be discharged immediately. Excavation should preferably be carried out under dry conditions so that a smooth trench bottom with a uniform gradient can be made. It may be advantageous to wait a few days for favourable weather conditions rather than to install the pipes in muddy soil.

The top part of the trench up to a depth of about 0.5 m can be dug using a normal spade. Best would be a width of about 0.3 to 0.4 m for this upper part of the trench so that a man can stand in the trench to dig the remaining part. The excavated topsoil must to be placed at least 0.5 m away from the trench. This is because this soil often contains organic matter (remains of the crop, roots, etc.) and using it for backfilling immediately on top of the installed drain pipe should be avoided.

The long-blade spade can be used to dig this remaining part of the trench up to the design depth, thereby reducing the amount of earth moving (Figure C36.3). The last 5 cm or so should be removed with care to ensure that the pipes will be laid at the exact slope. If, by accident, part of the trench has been excavated too deep, it should be backfilled and compacted before the pipes are installed. The excavated soil from below 0.4 m must be kept separately from the excavated soil from the upper part. Special care needs to be taken to ensure that the trench bottom is dug at the correct grade, so that the pipe can be installed at the correct grade.

Figure C36.3   Digging a drain trench by hand

C.36.5   Manual installation of drain pipes

Concrete or clay drain pipe installation
If available, a drain scoop and a laying hook can be used to place the drain pipes (length +/- 30 cm) correctly on the bottom of the trench. The other auxiliary tools can also be very useful in this process. Clay or concrete pipes should be laid in such way that they are in line with no gaps left between the pipes.

Plastic pipe installation (pre-wrapped or without envelope)
- Roll the plastic pipes out parallel to the trench;
- Fix the downstream end of the pipe (roll) in the trench by putting some soil on it and hold in place preferably manually - one person;
- A second person carefully puts the pipe in the trench while walking backwards through the trench and keeping a limited tension on the pipe, taking care that the pipe is not twisted or over stressed;

- To fix the pipe in place at regular intervals (10 m) put some soil on it;
- At the end of each working day, the upstream open end of the installed drain pipe should be protected so that no debris or rodents can enter the pipe overnight.

During installation of pre-wrapped pipes the pipe should be lifted in its totality and not lifted by grabbing the envelope to avoid tearing the envelope.

Application of gravel envelope
If a gravel envelope is to be installed the trench needs to be over-excavated (made deeper) equal to the thickness of the envelope (7-10 cm).

- After excavation put a layer of gravel on the trench bottom. The thickness of this layer should be in accordance with the design thickness;
- Then, install the pipes on top of the gravel bed as described above, taking care not to disturb the envelope;
- Finally, put a second layer of gravel equal the design thickness along the sides and on top of the pipes to cover the pipes.

C.36.6   Manual backfill of the trench

To avoid damage it is preferable not to leave open trenches overnight, instead, immediately backfill the drain or the part of the drain that has been dug and installed. Before backfilling starts the elevation, grade, alignment, thickness of envelope and joints must be verified and broken or cracked pipes replaced.

Start backfilling with a layer of about 25 cm to secure the pipe using dry and friable soil. Care should be taken to ensure that the drain pipe is not disturbed by the backfill soil either vertically or horizontally. For the remainder of the backfill the trench is filled in layers of about 25 cm, with light compaction (spreading the backfill and walking over it) in between. Use the topsoil that was laid aside during the excavation of the trench for backfilling the last (top) 0.5 m. All debris that is not used for backfilling such as larger stones, boulders, plant and root remains must be removed from the site.

Backfill and compaction can also be done mechanically by using a tractor, in which case for compaction it is sufficient to drive over the trench a number of times with the wheels of a tractor.

Installation of Subsurface Drainage Systems	Installation of Drain Pipes *Manual Installation of drains and envelope materials*	Instruction sheet C.37

Subject:	**Manual installation in trenches dug by excavators**
Target group:	Field staff, field manager, supervisor

C.37 Manual installation in trenches dug by excavators

C.37.1 General

Installation of drain pipes with trenchers is generally considered to be the most cost effective and quality secure installation method. There may, however, be situations where trenching equipment is not available or where large diameter collector drains need to be installed that cannot accommodate the available trenchers. Under such circumstances manual installation of the drain pipes in trenches dug by excavators can be a functional alternative.

C.37.2 Procedure and method for manual installation in trenches dug by excavators

The procedure to install pipe drains manually in trenches dug by excavators consists of the following steps:
1. Setting out alignments and levels;
2. Excavating the trenches with excavators;
3. Placing the drain pipes and envelopes in the trench;
4. Backfill of the trenches.

C.37.3 Required equipment and material

The following equipment and material is required:
- Excavator with the capacity to dig to the required depth;
- Digging buckets for the excavator with widths suitable for the diameter of pipes to be installed;
- Measuring equipment (measuring tapes 50 or 100 m, measuring tapes 5 m, levelling instrument with staff gauge);
- Pump (suction pump preferable);
- Ranging rods and pegs;
- Hand tools (spades, etc.);
- Hoist material if heavy concrete pipes are to be installed;

- Drain pipes, joints, caps, etc.;
- Drain scoop and laying hook, correction hook, pipe tongs and soil pincer if small diameter, 30 cm long concrete or clay pipes are to be installed (Figure C36.2).

C.37.4 Setting out alignment and levels

Setting out of the location and alignment of the drain lines takes place as follows:
1. Ranging rods are placed at the start (downstream) and at the end (upstream) of the alignment of the drain and the locations of the ranging rods secured with pegs;
2. Pegs are placed in the centre line every 10 - 25 m in between the two extreme ranging rods, with the aid of other ranging rods;
3. A second row of pegs spaced around 25 m (or less) is placed parallel to the centre line at a distance of about 10 m from the centre line, either to the left or right;
4. Place a marker peg or benchmark near the downstream end of the drain and determine the level thereof in centimetres in relation to the base level used in the design;
5. Calculate the level difference between the top of the marker peg (or bench mark) and the design level of the bottom of the trench (= depth of the drain) at the downstream point (start point) of the drain line;
6. Determine the level of the top of the pegs in a line parallel to the centre line;
7. Calculate the required bottom depth of the trench below the head of each peg;

{Level peg head (cm)-level of benchmark (cm)}- {level of drain trench at start (cm) + [Distance between peg and start of drain line (m) x required slope (cm/m)]

8. Clearly note the level (cm below top of peg) of the trench bottom near each peg. (It is also possible to place all the pegs on the parallel line at a prefixed level, for instance, 2 m above the desired bottom of the trench. This requires a considerable amount of work that can be avoided if a levelling instrument is available during construction.[1])

C.37.5 Organisation of the process

The installation process is to be organised in such a way that the installation of a drain or a part thereof is completed in one day, meaning that the excavation, installation and backfilling are all completed in the same day. If the full drain line is not completed in one day, the installed drain pipe must be capped so that no dirt or water can enter it.

---

[1] If laser equipment is available a laser reception mast can be mounted on the bucket of the excavator. The operator of the excavator can monitor the digging depth, in which case the laser transmitter has to be set at the appropriate slope and the mast on the bucket extended so that when the bottom of the bucket is at the required depth of bottom of the trench a green light lights up on console of the laser.

C.37.6 Excavation of the trench

1. Select the required digging bucket (width as close as possible to diameter of drain + 10-20 cm);
2. Make arrangements so that water flowing in the trench can be removed, either through an outlet by gravity flow or by pumping (if groundwater is expected);
3. Place the excavator at the *downstream side of the drain line* in the centre line so that it can be driven backwards to excavate the trench;
4. Place a levelling instrument in the parallel line of the pegs and regularly check to see that the trench is at the required depth making use of the levels of the pegs in the parallel line;
5. Start digging: deposit the excavated soil of +/- the top 40 cm on one side of the trench and the remainder on the other side of the trench;
6. Removal of the bottom layers is to be done carefully to avoid over excavation;
7. If water starts flowing let it flow out of the trench immediately or pump it out;
8. Move the excavator backwards to dig the next part and repeat the process;
9. Verify with the levelling instrument the level of the trench bottom every 5 m or more often;
10. If by error the trench bottom is over excavated, the over excavated part must be filled up again to the right level with dry soil in thin layers that are carefully compacted.

C.37.7 Manual installation of drain pipes

Installation of small diameter 30 cm concrete or clay field drain pipes
The installation must be commenced from the downstream end and the first part of the drain directly connected to the outlet, be it a direct outlet, a manhole that connects to a collector drain or a sump.
The drain scoop and laying hook, if available, are used to place the drain pipes in the trench. If available, auxiliary tools can be used like: (i) a correction hook to correct the alignment of the pipes; (ii) pipe tongs to remove broken pipes; and (iii) a soil pincer to remove earth or debris from the trench bottom. Clay or concrete pipes should be laid in the trench in such way that they are in one straight line with no gaps left between the pipes.

Installation of plastic field drain pipes installation (pre-wrapped or without envelope)
1. Roll the plastic pipes out parallel to the trench;
2. Fix the downstream end of the pipe (roll) in the trench by putting some soil on it and preferably manually hold it in place - one person for the job;
3. A second person carefully puts the pipe in the trench while walking backwards through the trench and keeping a limited tension on the pipe, taking care that the pipe is not twisted or over stressed;
4. Put some soil on the pipe at regular intervals (10 m) to keep it in place;
5. At the end of each working day, the upstream open end of the installed drain pipe should be protected so that no debris or rodents can enter the pipe overnight.

During installation of pre-wrapped pipes the pipe should be lifted in its totality and not lifted by grabbing the envelope so as to avoid tearing the envelope.

C.37.8   Installation of large diameter concrete collector pipes

Larger concrete collectors in lengths of 0.8-1.0 m are also installed starting from the downstream end in an upstream direction.
- The bottom of the trench should be nominally dry and stable. If the bottom is muddy first place a layer of 5 cm of gravel or sand on the bottom of the trench;
- If the pipes cannot be manually handled they need to be hoisted with a hoist on the digging bucket of the excavator and lowered into the trench. When this is being done a person needs to stand in the trench to guide the pipe to the right spot;
- If the pipes are equipped with spigot and groove joints, the pipes should be firmly pushed together. If an asphalt based kit is available this could applied in the grooves before the pipes are pushed together;
- If there is no special provision at the joints and to avoid leakage, a burlap or jute cloth can be put over the joint and fixed with asphalt;
- Immediately after installation partly backfill the trench by carefully filling up the bottom part and thus fixing the pipes in place.

C.37.9   Application of gravel envelope

If a gravel envelope is to be installed the trench should be over excavated (made deeper) equal to the thickness of the envelope (7-10 cm).
1. After excavation put a layer of gravel on the trench bottom. The thickness of this layer needs to be the design thickness;
2. Pipes are installed on top of the gravel bed as described above, taking care that the envelope is not disturbed;
3. Put a second layer of gravel applied along the sides and on top of the pipes so that there is a cover over the pipes equal to the design thickness.

C.37.10 Backfilling and compaction

The trench can only be backfilled after verification that the levels, grade, alignment, joints and thickness of the envelope comply with the norms and/or specifications. Moreover, a check is to be done to see that there are no broken or cracked pipes.

Quality of backfill soil

Backfilling can best be done by dry, friable soil. Stones, wood, trunks or soil clogs in the excavated soil should not be used for backfilling and can best be removed from the site. Start the backfilling with the soil that came from the bottom part of the trench that was kept separate. Once all this soil has been used up finish the backfill with the soil excavated from the upper surface.

Backfill method

Backfilling can be done both mechanically and manually. In the case of large collector drains the first part of the backfilling up to the top level of the pipe should be done manually. Initially, the bottom sides of the pipes have to be filled, carefully avoiding the displacement of the pipe.

For all pipes

- The initial backfilling is considered to be backfill up to 30 - 50 cm above the pipe. This backfill needs to be placed in thin layers (15 cm) that are carefully compacted by hand, while avoiding the displacement of the pipe or damage/disturbance to the envelope;
- Backfilling of the top part starts 30 - 50 cm above the top of the pipe. The top part can be backfilled mechanically preferably also in layers of 15 - 20 cm that are individually compacted. The wheels of a tractor driven over the trench can do compaction of the last layer.

All available soil (suitable) is to be used for backfilling. Overfill of the trench resulting in a small bund or hill on top of the drain line will compensate for the inevitable subsidence that will eventually occur.

Installation of Subsurface Drainage Systems	Installation of Drain Pipes *Manual Installation of drains and envelope materials*	Instruction sheet C.38
	Subject: **Wrapping a synthetic sheet envelope around the pipes in the field**	
	Target group: Field staff, field manager, supervisor	

C.38 Wrapping a synthetic sheet envelope around the pipes in the field

C.38.1 General

If synthetic envelopes are used, these are usually pre-wrapped in the factory. If the need arises (experimental fields) and the so-called "nylon sock envelopes" can be used, these can be wrapped around the drain pipes with simple tools in the field. If the envelope is in the form of sheets, these can be folded around the pipe with a longitudinal overlap of at least 15 cm and later sown or fixed by thread.

C.38.2 Wrapping at the site

The wrapping of around synthetic fabric material around the pipe in the field is done as follows (Figure C38.1):
- Check the fabric material visually for any cuts, tears or other damage;
- Testing of envelope material is required periodically in the laboratory to make sure it complies with the specifications. A record should be maintained of the brand name, nominal weight per square metre and date and time of receiving. Tests for other specifications are expensive and require specialised equipment that may not be available locally but should, however, be performed for each supply received;
- The seam of non-woven fabric should be lapped, folded and stitched properly with polyester thread;
- The fabric should be loose enough around the pipe to avoid stretch, yet tight enough to ensure it does not restrict pipe travel through the installation equipment;
- Before pulling the fabric around the pipe check the pipe for damages. If necessary remove the damaged parts of the pipe;
- The actual hand wrapping is to be done by pushing the sock over the pipe, not by pulling it. Pulling can cause excessive stretching and consequently damage of the sock. In the process the pipe is to be properly fixed;
- *Fabric should not be installed on non-perforated or damaged pipe.*

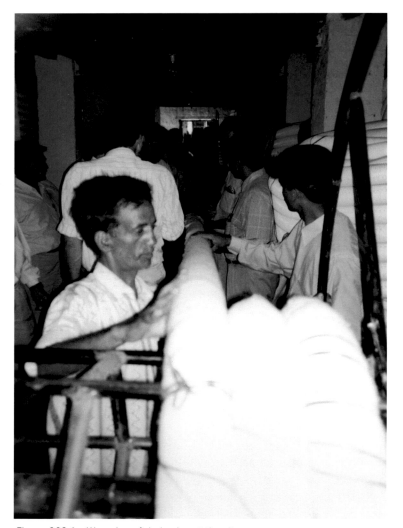

Figure C38.1   Wrapping of drain pipe at the site

II-D

Practical aspects of quality control

General

The practical aspects of quality control during and directly after the installation process are discussed in the following sections. It includes what needs to be checked, when to check and the consequences if deficiencies turn up. The sections have been written under the assumption that the supervisors directly or indirectly carry out the checks passively or actively. The responsibilities of all persons involved in the quality control process is not dealt with here but in Part I, Chapter 8 of this handbook.

Quality Control	Instruction sheet D.1

Subject: **Quality control of drainage materials**

Target group: Field manager, supervisor

D.1 Quality control of drainage materials

D.1.1 Quality control of corrugated plastic drain and collector pipes

Quality control of corrugated drain and collector pipes consists of at least 5 checks during the installation process:

Check	Where	What to check	Consequence if deficient
1	In factory before transport (note)	a) Pipes against norms b) Pipes stored in shade c) Supply conform order	a) Reject total lot b) Reject total lot c) Reject bad pipes only
2	On site in depot after transport	Damage during transport Storage in shade	Take out damaged pipes return to factory or repair immediately
3	In the field after distribution	Damage during transport	Take out damaged pipes or repair small damages
4	Just before installation on machine	Small damage, and strength at the connections	Stop machine, repair or replace
5	After installation in trench	Small damage Lose connectors	Dig up and repair damage or connection

Note: The check in the factory consists of:
- Checking whether the pipes have been produced according to the specified norms (ISO, NEN, DIN, ASTM or other) and if a certificate of an independent entity is available. If there are no independent entities find out who can professionally do the checking and issue certificates, and check the internal production quality control reports of the factory;
- Verification during the production that the checks and tests are carried out according to the norms may be called for. Detailed descriptions of the checking procedures are given in the norms (see Part I, Chapter 4).

A visual check in the factory of the produced pipes can consist of:
- Evenness of thickness (discolorations);
- Perforations;
- Dimensions;
- Stiffness/flexibility;
- The production date of the pipes (not older than approx. 3 months);
- Storage of pipes after production away from sunlight;
- Check lot against order (quantity, length of perforated, non-perforated pipes, etc.).

D.1.2 Quality control of cement or clay drain and collector pipes

Quality control of cement or clay drain and collector pipes consists of at least 5 checks during the installation process:

Check	Where	What to check	Consequence if deficient
1	In factory before transport or on the site after production (note)	a) Pipes against norms b) Pipes not broken or chipped c) Supply conform order	a) Reject total lot b) Reject damaged pipes c) Instruct to correct before acceptance
2	On site in depot after transport	Damage during transport	Take out and destroy damaged pipes or return to factory
3	In the field after distribution	Damage during transport	Take out damaged pipes
4	Just before installation on machine	Small damages	Take out damaged pipes
5	After installation in trench	Damage Loose connections	Dig up and correct connections Replace damaged pipes

Note: The check in factory consists of:
- Checking to see if the pipes have been produced according to the specified norms (ISO, NEN, DIN, ASTM or other) and if a certificate of an independent entity is available. If there are no independent entities find out who can professionally do the checking and issue certificates.

The following checks are required during production process:
- For cement pipes: the dosage, the mixing/vibration process and the curing process;
- For clay pipes: mixing and wetting of the clay, extrusion of the clay, cutting of the ends of pipes (straight!), baking process time and temperatures. Detailed descriptions of the checking procedures are given in the norms.

A visual check in the factory of the produced pipes can consist of:
- Evenness of thickness of pipes;
- Round form of pipe (not oval!)
- Straightness and smoothness of the ends;
- Dimensions;
- Breakage, cracks and chippings;
- Check lot against order (quantity, packing, etc.).

D.1.3 Quality control of gravel envelope

Quality control of the gravel envelope material consists of at least 3 checks during the installation process:

Check	Where	What to check	Consequence if deficient
1	In quarry before transport	a) Grading (note 2) b) Quantity c) Cleanliness	a) Grading: reject until re-graded b) Quantity: correct, or pay less c) Cleanliness: reject until cleaned
2	On site in depot	a) Unloading & storage b) Cleanliness (note 6) c) Grading (note 1,3) d) Quantity (note 4) e) Loading (note 5)	a) Correct (note 5) b) Clean, remove dirt c) Remix and try to correct d) Note and report adjust payment
3	In the field on trailer before application	Cleanliness	Remove dirt

Notes:

1. *General.* The grading of the gravel is extremely important. The mixing of the gravel may be undone by vibration during transport (larger particles separate from smaller particles). This may be corrected by remixing the gravel.

2. *Inspection at quarry*
   - *General inspection*
     - Check the results of the quality control (sieving curves) of the supplier.
   - *Visual inspection on all loads before transport*
     - If particles larger than the maximum allowed or smaller than the minimum allowed (dust) are present, the loads should be sieved again;
     - Check cleanliness of the loads.
   - *Detailed inspection at random*
     - Take a 1 kg sample of each 100 m^3 of gravel (approximately 25 truckloads), and carry out a sieve analysis in the laboratory;
     - Compare the gradation curves against the given specifications;
     - If grades do not comply with specifications sieving of the gravel should be done again before transport.

3. *Inspection at field depot*
   - *General inspection on all gravel*
     - Inspect visually before unloading. If visually not according to standards (cleanliness) reject the load;
     - After unloading inspect that all gravel is graded as when loaded in the quarry (no clear separation in coarse and fines as a result of transport) this can be checked by eye;
     - Cleanliness of gravel should be inspected to see:
       * Whether contaminated by dust (If so, change transport procedures and clean affected loads);

  ∗ Whether clay or organic material has entered (clean this by hand).
  - Quantity of gravel by: number of trucks and filling level of the trucks.
- *Detailed inspection*
  - For analysis in the laboratory, take samples randomly over time approximately 1 sample every 100 m^3 after normal deposit procedures, and two samples in bottom and top of deposited pile;
  - Compare grading of the two samples;
  - If there are discrepancies in consistency, improve field-mixing procedures.

4. *Quantity*. The quantity of gravel loaded in the quarry and the quantity on arrival needs to be checked and recorded. This can be done by counting truckloads and by measuring the contents of the truck. Payment should be either:
   - Against quantity loaded in the quarry, client is responsible for transport, or;
   - Against quantity received in the field, if supplier is responsible for transport.

5. *Cleanliness*. If there is a doubt about the presence of mud and silt (for instance, when the gravel is dry) a simple test can be carried out: mix a small sample with fresh, clear water. If there is mud and silt in the sample, this will float on the water and will be visible immediately.

D.1.4 Quality control of synthetic envelopes

Quality control of synthetic envelopes should take place simultaneously with the control of the pipes. The quality control is to be carried out with at least 5 checks during the installation process:

Check	Where	What to check	Consequence if deficient
1	In factory before transport (note 1)	a) Material used complies with specifications/norms b) Enveloping is done according to norms with specified thread c) Supply against order	a) Reject total lot b) Reject total lot c) Reject total lot or insist on correction
2	On site in depot after transport (note 2)	Damage during transport	Take out pipes with damaged envelop, return to factory or cut out damaged parts
3	In the field after distribution	Damages during transport	Take out pipes with damaged envelopes, or cut out damaged parts
4	Just before installation on machine	Small damage	Stop machine, repair or replace
5	After installation in trench	Damage	Dig up and correct or repair damage

Notes:

1. The check in the factory consists of: Checking whether the manufactured envelope and the enveloping process comply with the specified norms (See Part I, Chapter 4) and if a certi-

ficate of an independent entity is available. If there are no independent entities that can professionally do the checking and issue certificates, then check:

- The specifications of the material and the guarantees of the producers of the base material;
- The specifications of the fixing thread and the guarantees of the producers of the thread;
- Evenness of thickness of the envelop;
- Tightness of the fixing thread;
- The date of enveloping the pipes (not older than approx. 3 months);
- Storage of pipes after enveloping away from sunlight;
- Check lot against order.

2. Check whether storage in the field is done in the shade.

D.1.5   Quality control for prefabricated structures

Quality control of prefabricated structures should consist of at least 3 checks during the installation process:

Check	Where	What to check	Consequence if deficient
1	In factory before transport	a) Dimensions (note 1) b) Concrete quality (note 2) c) Chipping/broken	a) Reject b) Reject c) Reject
2	On site at arrival	a) Breakages b) Chippings	a) Return or refuse to accept b) Small chippings acceptable
3	After installation	a) Breakages b) Chippings	a) Remove and install other b) See if repair is possible, repair with cement

Notes:
1. Dimensions: Includes checking of dimensions, holes made for field drain and collector pipes. Compare against specifications and orders;
2. Compare quality with specifications.

Quality Control	Instruction sheet D.2
Subject: **Quality control of installation of** **pipe drainage systems** Target group: Field manager, supervisor, surveyors	

D.2   Quality control of installation of pipe drainage systems

D.2.1   Field layout and levels

What to control

Before installation, check that pegs have been placed at the start and end of the drain lines (field drains and collectors) in accordance with the design. Pegs with known levels should be placed at crucial points (downstream end of field drains and collectors). These level pegs form the basis for the design start levels of the drains. The location of the future drains and the levels must both be checked.

How to check

The check can be carried out by verifying if the staked out layout is in agreement with the design and by checking the levels.

Observation

If discrepancies are observed (drains not located in logical places) and levels do not turn out to be realistic, corrections must be made immediately and before construction starts, preferably together with or by the design group. It is better to double-check the corrections to ascertain that the result does not interfere with the logic of the design or the design criteria.

D.2.2   Installation of plastic field and collector pipes

What to control and norms

Quality control of the installation of field drains and collector pipes consists of control of:
- Levels: check starting levels (downstream) of the pipes against the design allowing for minimal deviations. This is especially important for composite systems since a mistake in one level can have repercussions on the levels of the whole system;
- Grade: the grade set at the laser must agree with the design;
- Connections: pipe sections must be properly connected for obvious reasons. During installation if too much tension is exerted on the pipe and/or if the connections are not properly made, the connections may become undone;
- Alignments: must be in accordance with the design, small deviations do not normally cause much problems;

- Horizontal straightness: the pipes should not zigzag in the trench as this will hinder flow and entrance of the flusher for cleaning;
- Vertical grades and levels: should be conform the design with a maximum deviation from the straight line of approx. 0.25 x the pipe diameter and no negative slopes;
- If a gravel envelope is used: check correct application of gravel around the pipe/adequate coverage on top of the pipe;
- For synthetic envelopes: check for damage to envelope during installation.

How to control

During installation: A thorough check during installation is the most effective. All discrepancies can then be seen and corrections can still be made relatively easily. After installation the only way of correction is mostly by reinstalling the drain. The simplest and most practical control during installation is to check:

- The levels (starting level) using a levelling instrument just before the trencher starts installation;
- By hand the strength of the connections of the pipe sections;
- The alignment and the horizontal straightness visually (Figure D2.1a):
  - Alignment by verifying the start and end from the maps or specifications;
  - Horizontal straightness during installation by checking if the pegs have been properly placed and that the operator follows the staked line. After installation check the straightness of the trench.
- The vertical grades and levels by measuring the elevation of the installed pipe every 5-10 m with a levelling instrument, directly behind the trencher[1] (see D.4, and Figure D2.1b);
- The gravel envelope application visually, by direct observation in the trench of the outflow of gravel and the coverage of the pipe and, indirectly, to see if there is a regular flow of gravel from the hopper;
- Synthetic envelope application visually in the trench, looking for damage.

Corrective measures and prevention

- Horizontal straightness: If (plastic) drain pipes meander in the trench this can be caused by:
  - Not enough stress on the pipe during installation. More stress must be maintained on the plastic pipe during installation because horizontal straightness cannot be corrected once pipe is installed;
  - Quality of the pipe (extensibility, straightness: if during production process pipe is not cooled enough before it is coiled or stored). Improve quality control of pipe. No correction possible.
- Vertical grade: If excessive deviation of the prescribed grade is noted the only solution is to dig up the section and correct it manually. To prevent deviations:
  - Adjust digging chain/trench box;

---

[1] Can only be done if trenchers are used.

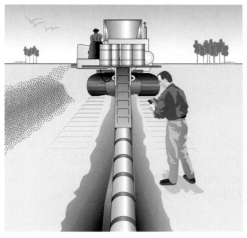 

a.   b.

Figure D2.1   Visual inspection and checking of drain level

- - Adjust slip clutch;
  - Laser management (closer spacing of the transmitter, prevention of wind impact on transmitter);
  - Operator management (adjust speed of installation in case of hard layers, unevenness of field, gravel supply. No stopping during installation).
- • Gravel envelope: Correct inadequate application of gravel around the pipe by digging up and applying gravel by hand. If there is too much gravel around the pipe, adjust the gates for the gravel supply (above and below the drain). To prevent problems with gravel application:
  - Correct adjustment of gravel gates depending on size of gravel and speed of installation;
  - Improve cleanliness of gravel;
  - Improve regular supply of gravel to hoppers.

D.2.3   Installation of concrete collectors

Quality control for the installation of concrete collectors is basically the same as for plastic collectors, with the following adjustments:

Levels
Since the pipe sections are prepared in lengths of 0.75-1.0 m, the control of the levels needs to be intensified, meaning that the level needs to be measured at both sides of each pipe section using a levelling instrument.

Alignment

Since with concrete pipes the number of joints per drain line is considerably larger than with plastic pipes, the alignment of the pipes must be checked carefully with regard to water tightness of the joints. This can be checked visually to ascertain whether the top levels of the end of the earlier section and the start of the new section are the same. The visual check should also focus on the underside of the pipes.

Stability of the pipe sections

Concrete pipes are heavier and require stable bedding in the alignment otherwise the individual pipe sections can easily become dislocated during backfilling. Check this visually and do a second check during backfilling after the backfilling has been completed up to half the Ø of the pipe, to be sure that no dislocation of the pipes had occurred as a result of backfilling.

D.2.4   Backfilling of trenches

What to control:

Check if all the trenches are properly closed and if there is some extra soil heaped on the alignment of the trenches to allow for subsidence.

How to control:

Visual control and testing of compaction by pushing a testing rod or ranging rod into the trench.

Corrective measures:

Extra compacting with extra soil on top of former trench, very slow application of irrigation water, especially during the first irrigation.

D.2.5   Quality control installation of prefabricated manholes and sumps

What to control

- The levels of the entry holes for collector and drain pipes
  Norms: Maximum deviation from design 1-2 cm - measure with levelling instrument.
  Correction: Dig under the manhole or pushing down the manhole with the excavator. If the manhole is too low: push soil or gravel under the manhole (lift first the manhole with the excavator).
- The level of the manholes/sumps
  Norms: Maximum deviation on the ring: 1-2 cm - measure with carpenters level.
  Correction: Dig under the manhole or push down with excavator.
- The integrity of the manholes/sumps (no breakage, no excessive chipping)
  Norms: No breakage allowed, chippings should not threaten structural strength or expose reinforcement steel - visual inspection.
  Corrections: Repair with cement or replace.

- Water tightness of the connections of field drains/collectors to manholes/sumps
  Norms: No water may enter the manholes otherwise than through the collector pipes/field drains. Check: (i) Visual check for flow; (ii) indirect: check if silt on top of pipes; (iii) manholes fill up with water if field drains are not running.
  Correction: Repair with sleeve of cement around pipe. Try first to repair on the inside if it does not work, dig out and repair on the outside with cement sleeve.
- Water tightness of the joints of rings of concrete manholes/sumps
  Norms: No water may enter through joints. Check: (i) visually for flow; (ii) indirectly to see if much silt is in manhole/sump; (iii) to see if manhole fills up with water if field drains are not running.
  Correction: Make watertight using cement.
  Prevention: During installation, place sheet of plastic around joint and tighten with iron wire.
- Aboveground manhole/sump placed well above field level
  Norm: > 50-60 cm above field level - visual inspection.
  Correction: Increase level with one ring - keep rings of approx. 50 cm height in stock.
- Belowground manhole placed well below field level
  Norm: Below at least the ploughing depth (as per specification) below field level - visual inspection.
  Correction: Remove rings or replace rings with rings of less height.
- Protective soil hill above ground around manhole/sump (Figure D2.2)
  Norm: A soil hillock around manhole/sump to prevent damage by tractors - visual check.
  Correction: Add soil.
- Cover in place and not broken
  Norm: Cover to be in place and stably installed - visual check.
  Correction: Place, repair or replace cover.
- End of plastic collector/drain pipes inside manhole/sump smoothened and cut off at acceptable length
  Norm: Length op pipes inside manhole approx. 10 cm and smooth to prevent cutting of hose while flushing - visual check (Figure D2.2).
  Correction: Cut to length and smoothen by filing.
- Manhole clean, no silt
  Norm: Clean and no silt inside.
  Correction: Clean out.

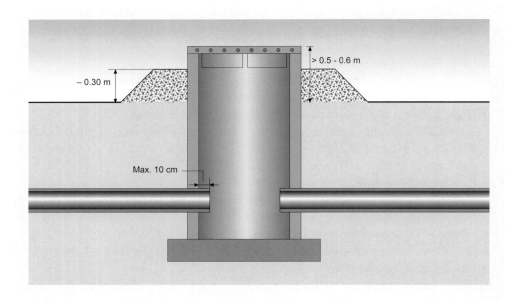

Figure D2. 2   Ideal layout of manhole

D.2.6   Quality control of installation of pumps

Quality control of the installation pumps depends very much on the quality norms of the manufacturer. Items needing attention too are:
- Pump installation level;
- Electric connection protected against water;
- Electric lines safely installed;
- Switches in place and well adjusted;
- Outlet protected.

Quality Control	Instruction sheet D.3

Subject: **Checking the functionality of composite drainage systems**

Target group: Field manager, supervisor, surveyors

D.3   Checking the functionality of composite drainage systems

D.3.1   What to Check

Once a composite drainage system has been installed in its entirety including the whole system of field drains, collector drains, manholes and sumps and pumps, its functioning requires to be checked as soon as possible. The methodology for the checking is described in the sections below.

D.3.2   Principles of the checks

In first instance one has to check in the manholes if all the collector drains and field drains are flowing at capacity[1]. If there is no flow or only a limited flow, first check the quality control of drain installation to verify that the grade of the drains have been installed at the correct grade. If not, first repair the location where the grade is not acceptable. When done and corrected:
- Check if there is a silt build-up in the sumps;
- Check water levels in manholes (Figure D3.1). If the water is high in a manhole and not in the manhole situated downstream of it, there must be an obstruction in the stretch downstream of the manhole where there is no flow. Then,
  - If the water is high in the field drain manhole and the water is flowing at the end of the field drain, there is an obstruction in the field drain between the collector and the field drain manhole, in which case flush out the field drain;
  - If no water is running from the field drain in the collector manhole or the field drain manhole and there is a high groundwater table, flush out the upstream end of the field drain first and later the bottom end.

---

[1] If groundwater is below drain level there will generally be no flow. Verify if the groundwater level is below drain level. If this is the case the check should be done during the following irrigation season or wait for rain.

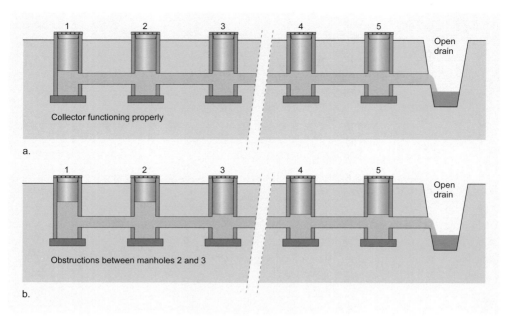

Figure D3.1   Principles of checking functioning collector system

D.3.3   Methodology for checking the functionality of collectors

Checking procedures
1. Open all collector manholes and the sump (in case of a pumped outlet);
2. If not yet installed, put a pump in the sump and start pumping (if the drains are flowing start pumping the day before). In case of a gravity outlet be sure that the outlet can flow freely.

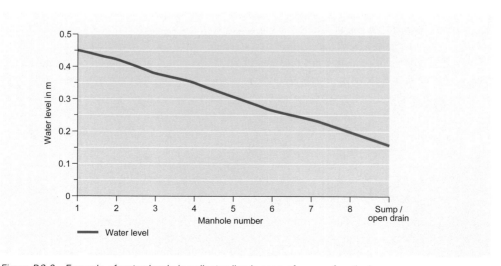

Figure D3.2   Example of water levels in collector line in case of proper functioning

3. Wait till the water is in balance (if pumping, then keep pumping);
4. Measure in each manhole the bottom level of each collector pipe (top level minus outside diameter of the collector pipe);
5. Check if the bottom levels of the collector pipes are in a regular line. The slope of the line should approximate the design slope of the collector;
6. Measure the water levels in each manhole;
7. Plot the water levels and the pipe levels in the manholes as absolute levels:
   • If the field drains are flowing and the water level is as indicated in Figure D3.2 there are no problems and the system is functioning properly;
   • If the water level is as indicated in Figure D3.3, there is an obstruction between manhole 2 and 3.

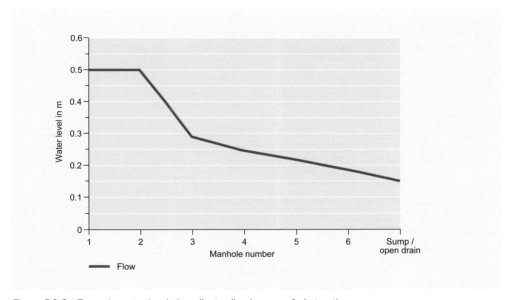

Figure D3.3   Example water levels in collector line in case of obstructions.

If there is *no water flowing from the field drains:*
   • And the water level is almost horizontal or in line with the slope of the collector, most likely there is no obstruction in that part of the line;
   • And the water level shows a discontinuity it also implies that there is an obstruction upstream of this discontinuity.

Correction of collectors
If there is an obstruction:
1. Flush upstream with the flusher from the downstream manhole and clean the collector pipe. If the flusher hose cannot proceed, then you know where the obstruction is. If it cannot be cleared by flushing, mark the location (measure the length of hose in the collector pipe);
2. The only solution now is to dig up the collector and try to remove the obstruction by hand.

D.3.4   Checking field drains

Observations
1. Open the manholes (field drain manhole and collector manhole);
2. Start pumping (in case of a pumped outlet). In case of a gravity flow outlet be sure that the outlet can flow freely;
3. Wait till the water is in balance (if pumping, then keep pumping);
4. Measure in each manhole the top level of each field drain pipe;
5. Check if the bottom levels of the field drain pipes show a regular line. The slope of the line should approximate the design slope of the drain;
6. Measure the water level in each manhole;
7. Plot the water levels and the pipe levels in the manholes as absolute levels.

Interpretations
Interpretation of the observations for field drains is similar to the methodology for collector drains.

Corrections
If there is an obstruction:
1. Flush upstream with the flusher from the downstream collector manhole and clean the drain pipe. If the flusher hose cannot proceed, then you know where the obstruction is. If it cannot be cleared by flushing, mark the location (measure the length of hose in the field drain pipe);
2. Repeat the activity stream upwards from the field drain manhole;
3. If the flusher cannot clean out the drain and/or clear the obstruction, the only solution is to dig up the drain and try to remove the obstruction by hand.

Note:
In case there are no field drain manholes, only the flow of those field drains discharging into the collector manholes can be checked visually. If no water is running from the field drain into the collector manhole and there is a high groundwater table, flush out the field drain.

D.3.5   Final field check before completion

All is complete only after a final field check has been performed and includes checking that:
- All trenches are properly closed and soil of starting holes levelled;
- All remaining materials have been removed from field (pipes, manholes, broken manholes etc.);
- Functioning of the field drains have been checked;
- Functioning of the collector system have been checked;
- All manholes cleaned and closed;
- Pump functioning and well adjusted;
- Farmers instructed in maintenance.

Quality Control	Instruction sheet D.4
Subject: **Methodology for checking the grade of installed drain and collector pipes during installation**	
Target group: Field manager, supervisor, surveyors	

D.4 Methodology for checking the grade of installed drain and collector pipes during installation

D.4.1 General

The field drain and collector pipes are installed with the trenchers using laser control for assuring the design slope/grade of the pipes. Installing the drain pipes at the right grade is essential to assure a correct functioning drainage system. Deviations from the grade may result in reduced or no flow in pipes, air locks and so forth.

Based on extensive research the maximum acceptable deviation from the design grade has been determined as follows:
- $+\frac{1}{4}$ or $-\frac{1}{4}$ of the diameter of the drain pipe;
- No negative slopes.

Should there be faults outside the tolerances stated above, repairs have to be carried out only if:
- Deviation is more than $\frac{1}{4}$ of the diameter (thus $> +20$ or -20 mm of the design grade in case of an 80 mm Ø pipe);
- Negative slope shows a deviation of more than $\frac{1}{2}$ of the Ø (thus $+40$ mm of the design grade in case of an 80 mm Ø pipe).

From the point of view of flow it can be stated that the pipe is functional:
- As long as the pipe has an average slope that is at or higher than the design slope;
- If there are no negative deviations of more than $\frac{1}{4}$ of the Ø of the pipe.

Since the laser is an aid and does not provide absolute security and the installation may be less than ideal especially in unstable subsoils, a continuous check on the grade and slope of the pipe is recommended. If, as a result of the check, it turns out that there is a serious problem, corrective measures need to be taken immediately. If the problem is not detected at an early stage, it will be considerably more troublesome to correct later when the drain will need to be dug up.

D.4.2   Methodology

D.4.2.1   General

Quality control on drain slopes is carried out during or immediately after installation by measuring the level of the top of the drain every 5 m. This means that the surveyor's measurements are done directly behind the trencher.

D.4.2.2   Placing of the levelling staff

If the drain pipe is covered with gravel measuring on top of the gravel may give uneven results. Digging with the levelling staff in the gravel may leave the surface of the pipe at that particular spot uncovered by gravel, which can cause inflow of silt into the pipe later on. To avoid this fit the bottom of the levelling staff to a special shoe (Figure D4.1). In this way the gravel cannot be disturbed.

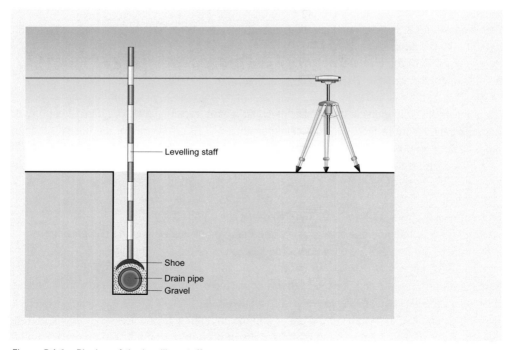

Figure D4.1   Placing of the levelling staff

In the case of trenchless drain installation a detection probe can be used (Figure D4.2). The levelling staff is put on top of this drain probe.

Detection rod

Figure D4.2   Detection probe

Placement of levelling instrument
The levelling instrument should be placed as close to the trench as possible and measurements taken first backwards then forwards (Figure D4.3). When the levelling staff is out of sight replace the instrument forwards and maintain, in the meantime, the level with the levelling staff.

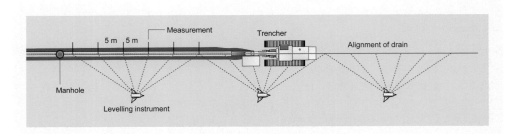

Figure D4.3   Placement of the levelling instrument

Measuring at every 5 or 10 m
This can be done by measuring with the levelling staff.

Reporting
A reporting form model is attached (Table D.4-1)

Table D.4-1   Reporting form

Level control field drain								
Field:			Date:			Surveyor:		
Drain no:			Drain machine			Page	1/2/3/	
Start from: Manhole/sump			Driver:					
Level at:	Reading	Level	Level at:	Reading	Level	Level at:	Reading	Level
0 m+			100m+			200 m+		
5			5			5		
10			10			10		
15			15			15		
20			20			20		
25			25			25		
30			30			30		
35			35			35		
40			40			40		
45			45			45		
50			50			50		
55			55			55		
60			60			60		
65			65			65		
70			70			70		
75			75			75		
80			80			80		
85			85			85		
90			90			90		

Processing of data

Process the results the same day in a spread sheet and make a graph, marking on it the design slope and the upward and downward deviations. In this way one can see directly if the drain has been properly installed. A sample of the results of quality checking of the grade of drains is presented in Figure D4.4. The graph shows that the drain level fluctuates up to 200 m from the start within the acceptable range. After 200 m the slope becomes steeper but there is no negative slope and the flow will not be interrupted. However, the drain depth is 5 cm less than designed. The drain is of acceptable quality. The operator must take care in the futures no to start lifting the trench box too early and only during the last 10 m or so of the drain.

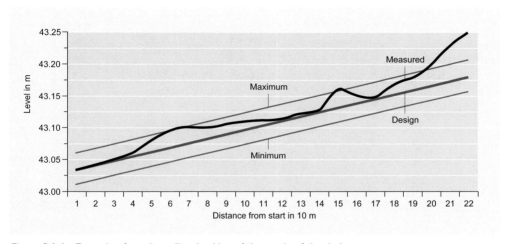

Figure D4.4   Example of result quality checking of the grade of the drains

Quality Control	Instruction sheet D.5
Subject: **Post construction verification of drain pipes**	
Target group: Field manager, supervisor	

D.5   Post construction verification of drain pipes

D.5.1   Introduction

Once a drain is installed and covered with backfill, no visual inspections are possible. The same is true for drain pipes installed with trenchless drainage machines. The two techniques developed for checking the correct installation of drains under these conditions are *Rodding, Continuous depth recording* and *Video inspection.* As described in Part I Chapter 7.5 these checking methods are rather complicated and time-consuming and more suited for research purposes and pilot projects than for routine installation. Instructions for the rodding and continuous depth recording are given in the sections below.

D.5.2   Rodding

D.5.2.1   General

Rodding is a technique to check whether there are abrupt disturbances in the drain line, such as broken pipes, loose couplings and sharp changes in the slope. Besides checking for problems with functioning of the drain, the technique can also be used to determine if the drain will be accessible for flushing. The rodding method cannot be used to check the grade of the drain line. Rodding was developed to test drains in a singular drainage system, but the technique can also be used in composite systems with special arrangements for access to the field drain (Figure D5.1).

D.5.2.2   Testing protocol

In principle, every single drain can be tested, but this will be rather expensive. Hence, it is advisable to randomly test only a limited number of drains, for example, 10% of the drains. Testing can be increased if the number of drains that fail the test exceed a prescribed percentage. The number of drains to be tested, the method and whether or not the malfunctioning drains have to be replaced can be specified in the contract or instructions.

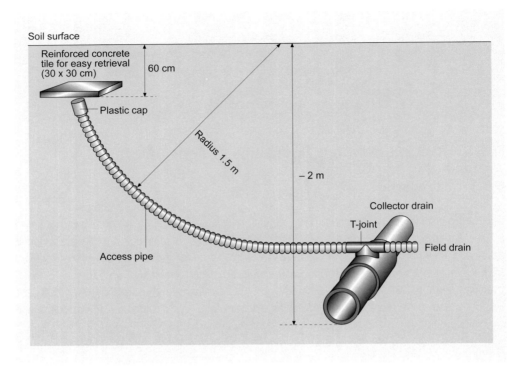

Figure D5.1   Access of rodding equipment in composite systems

D.5.2.3   The rodding equipment

The rodding systems consist of a steel rod with a torpedo shaped tip. The steel rod is screwed to a long fibreglass rod. The length of the fibreglass rod is 300 - 400 m. A probe for radio detection can be attached to the tip of the steel rod. The fibreglass rod is winded on a reel. The reel can be transported, attached to a tractor or it can be rolled over the ground surface on the outer ring of the cage with the coiled rod (Figures D5.2).

Use:
- The reel should be put in the correct position at the beginning of the drain line which will be checked;
- The top end of the fibre-glass rod is put through the white plastic rings;
- During transportation of the reel by rolling, the rodding head and/or probe cannot be attached to the fibreglass rod, and the rod should be out of the white plastic rings;
- A piece of metal pipe with screw-thread is attached to the tip of the fibreglass rod;
- Torpedo-shaped tips of different diameter can be attached to the rod;
- The screw-thread should be clean and not damaged;
- The torpedo-shaped tips have screw-thread on both sides;
- The screw-thread at one side can be used for attaching a probe for radio detection;

- The rod is pushed manually into the drain pipe over its entire length starting at the outlet (Figure D5.2a).

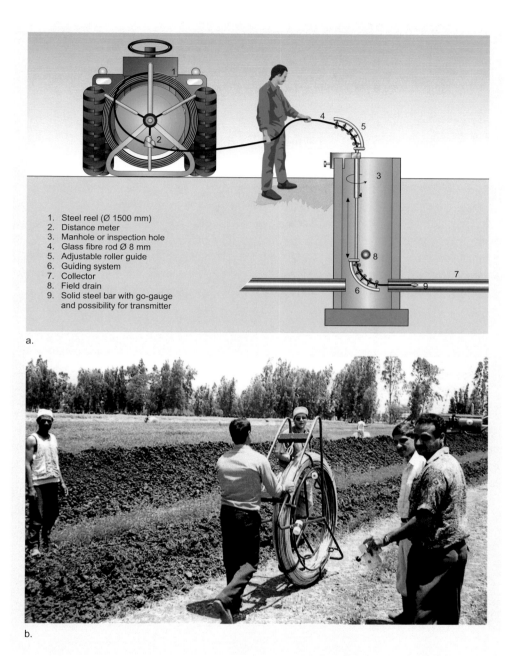

1. Steel reel (Ø 1500 mm)
2. Distance meter
3. Manhole or inspection hole
4. Glass fibre rod Ø 8 mm
5. Adjustable roller guide
6. Guiding system
7. Collector
8. Field drain
9. Solid steel bar with go-gauge and possibility for transmitter

a.

b.

Figure D5.2   Rodding equipment attached to the tractor (a) and transported in the field by hand (b)

Location of a disturbance

Locating aboveground the spot where the rodding head came up against an abrupt disturbance can be done by:

- Fitting a counter on the fibreglass rod for distance measurement, or;
- Fitting a probe to the rodding head when the location of the probe can be measured directly via a radio detection device.

The site of the disturbance has to be marked in the field and/or on a map. Its location can then be traced later on for the purpose of excavation and repair.

D.5.2.4 Functioning of the rodding systems

If the drain has been correctly installed, the rod can pass unhindered but the required pushing force increases slightly with the length of the drain. If the drain spirals, however, the required pushing force increases considerably with the length of the drain. The required force should not exceed a pre-set limit[1] (Table D.5-1), because the misalignment of the drain will mean that cleaning the drain using a flusher will not be possible (Figure D5.3). Consequently, the quality of the drain installation will not be acceptable and the drain will need to be reinstalled. The same applies if the rod cannot pass a particular point in the drain because there is a fault in the installation, when the drain will have to be excavated at this point. The maximum drain length that can be checked by rodding is *400 m.*

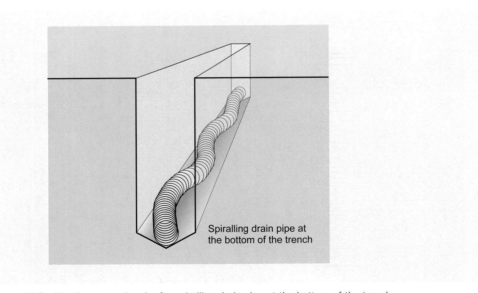

Spiralling drain pipe at the bottom of the trench

Figure D5.3   Misalignment: sketch of a spiralling drain pipe at the bottom of the trench

---

[1] The norms have been developed for singular drainage systems. For composite drainage systems no norms have been developed, and rodding is used to check abrupt disturbances in the drain line.

Table D.5-1   Maximum permissible forces for rodding

Distance from outlet (m)	Maximum permissible force (N) With drain discharge	Without drain discharge
0 - 100	20 - 30	20 - 40
100 - 200	30 - 60	40 - 80
200 - 300	60 - 90	- -
300 - 400	90 - 120	- -

D.5.3   Continuous depth recording

D.5.3.1   General

Continuous depth recording provides a good picture of the actual alignment of the drain line. It enables more accurate checking of the quality of different installation methods than by using traditional levelling. The equipment is very useful for measuring the grade of drains installed by trenchless drainage machines. It can be used to check whether the quality standards set for drain installation have been achieved.

D.5.3.2   The equipment

Collins at the Leichtweiss Institute of the University of Brunswick, Germany has developed a method for continuous depth recording based on a water level gauge. One end of a hose is connected to a special open container, the water surface of which serves as a reference level (Figure D5.4). A pressure transducer is fitted to the other end of the hose. This transducer transforms the hydrostatic pressure into an electric signal, which is proportional to the hydrostatic pressure over the reference level.

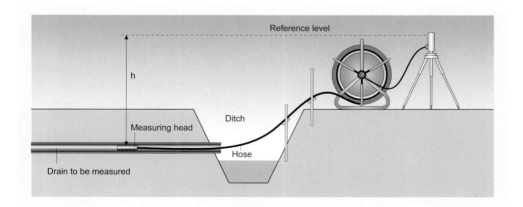

Figure D5.4   Level recording instrument for continuous depth recording

D.5.3.3 The use

- The hose with the pressure transducer is pushed into the drain. The transducer can be inserted into the drain to a *maximum length of 200 m;*
- The hose is withdrawn at a constant speed;
- Measuring takes place while the hose is being withdrawn from the pipe. The hydrostatic pressure can be measured with an accuracy of less than 2 mm;
- The data can be recorded in digital form and plotted graphically (Figure D4.4).

D.5.3.4 Comments

This method is quite costly (the cost per metre amounts in the Netherlands to about 50% of the total costs of pipe drainage system). Because of it limitation of length and cost the system can only be used in exceptional cases and for pilot areas or research. The equipment should only be used for random checks on a limited number of drains, for instance, 1-2 % of the drains.

II-E

Maintenance of drainage systems

Operation and Maintenance	Instruction sheet E.1
Subject: **Checking the functioning of subsurface drainage systems** Target group: Maintenance staff, farmers	

E.1 Checking the functioning of subsurface drainage systems

E.1.1 General

A subsurface drainage system can have a singular (Figure E1.1) or composite layout (Figure E1.2).

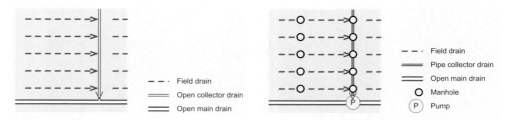

Figure E1.1 *Singular drainage system discharging into an open drain*

Figure E1.2 *Composite drainage system*

The components of the systems are:
- Singular system: field drains, in some cases manholes and outlet pipes;
- Composite system: field drains, collector drains, manholes and sumps (possibly with pumps) and outlets.

Regular checking of the system is required to see if the system functions and/or if repairs and/or maintenance is required. The methodology for the routine checking of the system and the techniques for cleaning and repairing parts of the system is given in the following sheets.

E.1.2 Checking the functioning of a singular system and minor repairs

Activity I: Visual checks
Visual checks that can be routinely carried out (Figure E1.3):
- Flow of drains;
- Flow of drains into manholes (if any);
- Condition of outlets;

- Adequate depth of open drain;
- Silt in manholes;
- Silt flowing out of the pipe.

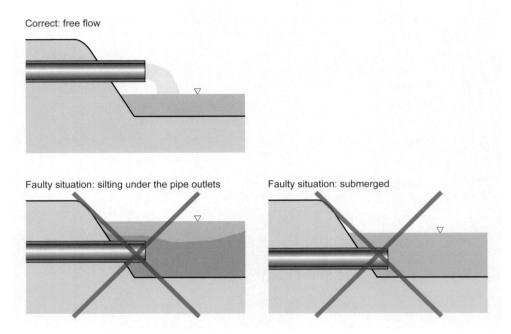

Figure E1.3   Possible conditions of outlet of a singular system: (a) free flow; (b) siltation and (c) submerged conditions

Activity 2: Carry out minor repairs and cleaning
- Outlets: replace or rearrange outlet pipes. If required, remove the silt around the outlet;
- Manholes (if applicable): remove silt from the manholes.

Activity 3: Reporting
If problems surpass the capacity of the farmers to correct them, the problems should be reported to the responsible entity so that they can take action. In all cases reporting is necessary if:
- A drain does not flow while the other drains are flowing;
- The open drain is too shallow;
- Drain outlets are under water or silted up;
- The drain flow of one or more pipes has been slowly decreasing over the years;
- Drain water is muddy;
- There is a high water level in the manholes (if there are manholes).

E.1.3   Checking the functioning of composite systems and minor repairs

Activity I: Visual checks of functionality
The following visual checks can be routinely carried out (easily done by the farmers):
- Is there a flow from outlet or pump;
- Is there a flow from the field drains into the manholes;
- Water level in manholes above field drains or below field drains;
- Is there a silt built-up in the manholes;
- Is there a leakage from outside water into manholes;
- Flow of field drain into field drain manholes (if any);
- Condition of outlets;
- Silt in manholes.

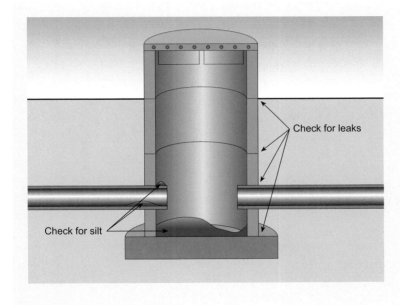

Figure E1.4   Checking for leaks in a manhole

Activity 2: Carry out minor repairs and cleaning
- Outlets: Rearrange outlet pipe of pump or gravity flow;
- Manholes: Close covers and/or repair covers or manholes (restore ground cover);
- Manholes: Remove silt from the manholes;
- Manholes: If possible repair leaks in the manholes.

Activity 3: reporting
If problems surpass the capacity of the farmers to repair them, the problems should be reported to the responsible entity so that they can take action. In all cases reporting is necessary if:
- A drain does not flow while the other drains are flowing;
- There is a sudden build-up of silt in the manholes;
- The drain flow of one or more pipes has been slowly decreasing over time;
- The drain flow of the entire system is getting less and less;
- The drain water is muddy;
- There is a high water level in the manholes;
- The pumps are not functioning.

E.1.4   Checking the functioning of a composite system *(Figure E1.5)*

E.1.4.1   Detailed monitoring to pinpoint location of obstruction in composite systems

If there is no flow in part of the collector the location of the obstruction or damage to pipes has to be pinpointed, this can be done in the following way:
1. Open all collector manholes and the sump (in case of a pumped outlet);
2. Start pumping (if the drains are flowing start pumping the day before) or in case of a gravity outlet be sure the outlet can flow freely;

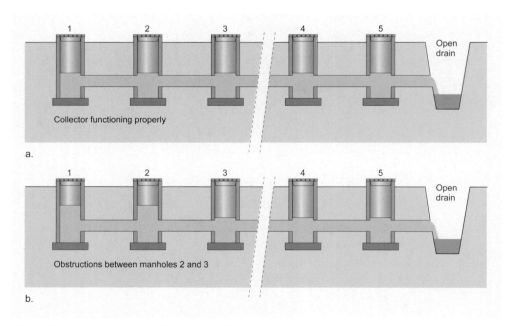

Figure E1.5   Schematic layout of collector drain

3. Wait till the water is in balance (if pumping, then keep pumping);
4. Measure in each manhole with the levelling instrument the bottom level of each collector pipe (top level minus the outer diameter of the collector pipe);
5. Check if the bottom levels of the collector pipes are in a regular line. The slope of the line should approximate the design slope of the collector;
6. Measure the water levels in each manholes;
7. Plot the water levels and the pipe levels in the manholes as absolute levels.

Under normal conditions the water level plot should look as is given in Figure E1.6. If the water levels are as indicated in Figure E1.7, there is an obstruction between manhole 2 and 3. If there is an obstruction:
1. Flush upstream with the flusher from the downstream manhole and clean the collector pipe. If the flusher hose cannot proceed, then you know where the obstruction is. If it cannot be cleared by flushing, mark the location (measure the length of hose in the collector pipe);
2. The only solution now is to dig up the collector and try to remove the obstruction by hand.

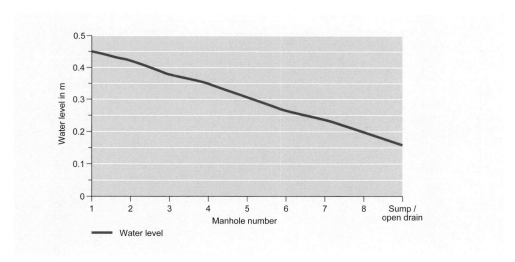

Figure E1.6   Water levels in a properly functioning collector drain

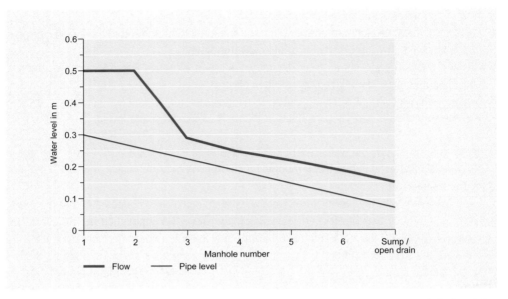

Figure E1.7   Water levels in a collector line with an obstruction in the section between manhole 2 and 3

Operation and Maintenance	Instruction sheet E.2
Subject: **Principles of flushing of subsurface drains**	
Target group: Maintenance staff, farmers	

E.2 Principles of flushing of subsurface drains

E.2.1 General

Maintenance of subsurface drainage systems consists of the removal of silt from the field and collector drains by flusher. Silt removal from manholes is done manually.

A flusher basically consists of a pump, reel, hose and a "jet head" at the end of the hose. Water is pumped into the hose and leaves the hose through the jet head. The hose with jet head can be pushed into the drain pipe to a maximum distance of some 300 m for "high-pressure flushers". Once the hose has reached the end it is pulled back and rewound on the reel. On the basis of the pressure developed by the pump three types of flushing units can be distinguished:
- Low-pressure: up to 20 bar;
- Medium-pressure: 20-50 bar;
- High-pressure: 50-100 bar.

The differences between the first two types and the high-pressure flushing unit are:
- High-pressure flushing units are mounted on a chassis with wheels and pulled by a tractor. The hose reel is driven from the tractor with Power Take Off (PTO) or engine when fitted on the chassis;
- Medium and low-pressure flushing units are directly connected to the PTO of an agricultural tractor and is attached on a frame to the tractor;
- The hose of the high-pressure unit moves into the pipe through the reaction force of the backward directed jets coming out of the nozzle;
- The hose of low-or medium-pressure flushing units needs to be pushed into the drain pipe;
- Length of drains to be flushed by medium and low-pressure flushing units is limited as the hose can only be pushed to a limited length (approximately 150 m);
- Length of drain that can be flushed by a high-pressure unit is 300 m.

As discussed in Part I the pressure of a high pressure flushing unit can be reduced be reducing the speed of the engine. In any case the loss of pressure in the longer hoses of the high pressure flushers reduces the pressure at the jet head already considerably (with a pressure of 85 bar at the pump and a hose of 300 m length, the pressure at the jet head is some 30 bar). In the following paragraphs the flushing with a high pressure unit is described. The high and medium-pressure flushing units are presented in Figure E2.1.

Figure E2.1   A high (left) and medium (right) pressure flushing machine

E.2.2   Required equipment

For flushing one requires:
- One flusher;
- One tractor (about 75 HP) with Power Take Off (PTO);
- If no water is available: one tractor plus tanker (4 m^3) - for flushing one drain of 500 m one needs about 3 m^3 of water thus an almost full tank.

If flushing is done from a manhole or sump, additionally requirements are as follows:
- One hose guidance for manhole;
- One mud pump with a capacity of at least 100 litres/min (for pumping out the return flow from the manhole and to fill the tank).

The hose guidance equipment (ladder) can be made locally. The hose guidance (ladder) (Figure E2.2a) is made of angular steel 1 x 1 inch of some 3.5 or 4 metres in length with steps 50 cm apart. In the lowest metre of the "ladder" holes are made at intervals of 10 cm to fix a system with a moveable roller. The top roller is fixed near the top. The diameter of the roller is at least 0.40 m. The movable roller is similar in size. The hose guide (ladder) is placed inclined in the manhole. Another more sophisticated type of hose guidance is presented in Figure E2.2b.

E.2.3   Cleaning

The cleaning action of the jet head at the end of the hose is achieved through the outlet holes, three directed backwards and one forward (Figure E2.3). The backward force of the three high-velocity waterholes in the jet head combined with the pulsation of the pressure make the jet head and hose move or jump forward into the drain pipe. This force is sufficient to penetrate into the drain over a length of some 300 metres. The cleaning consists of:

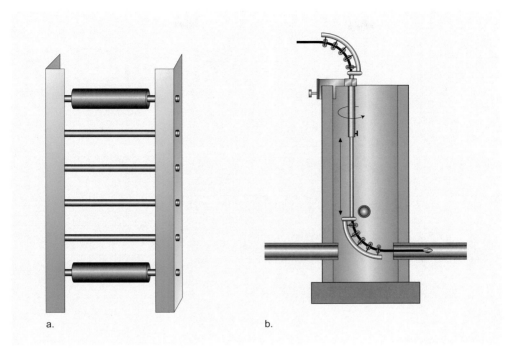

a.   b.

Figure E2.2   Two types of hose guidance for use in a manhole

- The hose is first pushed into the drain pipe from the downstream end by the force of the water pressure directed backwards. During this inward movement of the hose with jet head, the dirt and sediments are loosened up and partly flushed out;
- When the end of the drain or drain section is reached the pumping is continued but the pulsation is stopped and the hose is pulled backwards. During the pulling back action the backward holes act as a sweeper and sweep the loosened sediments towards the downstream end of the pipe. The hose is pulled back by the pulling power of the then activated reel on which the hose is rewound.

During the inward movement the coupling in the driveline should be disengaged. During the pulling out action the hose reel can be activated from the cardan shaft via the pump's gear case. The hose is then automatically rolled on the reel and pulled out from the drain pipe (the driveline to the hose reel is engaged when the hose is pulled out, and disengaged when the hose pushes itself into the drain).

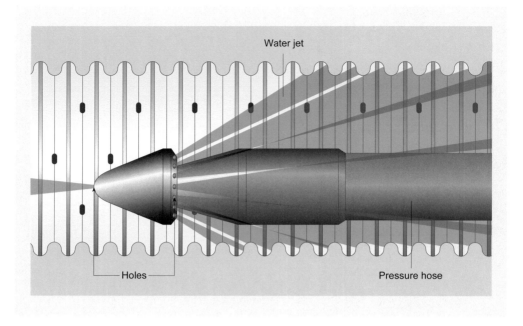

Figure E2.3   Jet head

E.2.4   Conditions for flushing

Flushing is not a solution to correct badly installed drains, because the flushing action may cause damage to the pipe and filter.
The following rules apply:
- Only flush drains when they are giving real problems or are not flowing;
- Starts flushing only if field drains are flowing. If a dry drain is cleaned the envelope will be damaged;
- Do not enter a (field) drain with the flusher twice during one cleaning session because this may damage the filter;
- Flushing of field drains should be done preferably at about 12-15 bar at the jet head. Higher pressure will damage the filter. In case the hose cannot enter the drain pipe, the pressure may be increased temporarily. For un-perforated collector drain flushing there is no limit to the amount of pressure you can use;
- Flushing must always be done downstream in an upstream direction. In case of a collector or field drain consisting of several sections, the flushing starts in the downstream part (in upstream direction) of the most upstream section;
- For collector systems the sequence of flushing is:
  - In the case of dirty collector drains: first collector drains, next field drains and then a second cleaning of the collector drains to remove any silt that has entered from the cleaning action of the field drain;
  - In the case of slightly dirty collector drains: first field drains and then collector drains.

E.2.5   Flushing water

For flushing, use water from a nearby drain or canal. If no open water is available a tank with approx. 4 m^3 of water will be required.

E.2.6   Flushing methods

Depending on the local conditions flushing can be done according to the following methods:
- Flushing of collector drains;
- Flushing of field drains from an open ditch;
- Flushing of field drains from a manhole.

The details of the methods are given in instructing sheets for maintenance: E.3, E.4, and E.5.

E.2.7   Possible problems with flushing

Flushing may not be possible and the jet head may be lost if the installed drain:
- Is not straight;
- Not at a proper grade;
- Is damaged or pipes have got flattened.

If a drain is broken the jet head will sometimes leave the drain pipe and penetrate into the surrounding soil. If the jet head has left the drain pipe to either side of it or downward it will be almost impossible to recover the hose and jet head.

If a drain has not been installed in a straight line or the pipe has got flattened, the jet head may get stuck in the bends of the drain against the corrugations. Often the only way to recover the jet head is to estimate the place where the jet head is stuck from the length of hose that has entered the drain, then dig up the drain, cut it and recover the head by cutting it off from the hose.

If the drain has not been installed straight or at a straight grade, it may happen that the jet head still passes, but because the resistance is so great the jet head and hose will only partly penetrate. Withdrawing the hose will be troublesome and the jet head may get stuck.

431

Operation and Maintenance	Instruction sheet E.3
Subject: **Management, maintenance and repair of high pressure flushers**	
Target group: Operators and field staff	

E.3 Management, maintenance and repair of high pressure flushers

E.3.1 General

The flusher referred to in the following sections is a high-pressure flusher produced by a specific manufacturer. Similar rules apply to other flushers, but the details have to be checked with the relevant instruction manual of the manufacturer.

E.3.2 Safety rules

The flusher is entirely safe when used properly. For the safety of the personnel read the instructions below first.
- The chief operator has the responsibility for the safety of the individuals around the flushing machine;
- Check - every day after use - the rubber hose and nipples for external damage and repair any damage before use;
- Check daily if the pressure relief valve is properly adjusted;
- Check steel cable of hose guide wheel for signs of damage and deterioration and if damage is detected replace immediately before use;
- Do not drive over the hoses of the flusher with any vehicle, especially the suction hose, because this will damage the hoses;
- Always have at least two persons available for the operation of the flusher;
- When connecting flusher to the tractor, the hinge-pin should be secured firmly so that it cannot loosen during transport.

E.3.3 Preventive maintenance

- Change the oil in the pump crankcase every 1000 working hours or every 6 months.

E.3.4 Regular maintenance

E.3.4.1 Weekly maintenance

Actual maintenance only needs to be done once a week though continuous checks should be made during operation.

- Grease nipples;
- Grease the bearing and the spiders of the cardan shaft every week during operating periods;
- Check for loosened bolts (tighten);
- Check oil in the sump of the pump;
- Check tyre pressure and adjust if necessary.

E.3.4.2   Verification during operation

- Check and if necessary clean suction filter;
- Pressure valve should be adjusted to a maximum of 80-85 bar at the pump. If the pressure increases to over 80-85 bar, it means that one of holes in the jet head is blocked. Stop pumping and clean the jet head immediately;
- Prevent pump from running without water;
- Water leaking out of pump through holes behind pistons indicates that seals are rotten. Replace seals;
- Protect the hose from the sun.

E.3.5   Repair of the hose repair using hose clamp device

1. Cut out the damaged part of the hose with a hacksaw;
2. Slide the hose clamp into the hose;
3. Position the hose over the connector pipe;
4. Put the complete assembly in the clamp device (pay attention that the proper size of clamp elements is used);
5. Position the clamp rings properly over the hose ends and tighten the clamp elements again. Repeat this over the total hose circumference and in the same way for the other rings;
6. Open the clamp device and remove the hose.

E.3.6   Storage of the flusher/winter storage

- Store the flusher in a place preferably free from frost;
- Drain water from pump cylinder body by opening the two plugs;
- Remove the 3 pump valve covers and lift the ball valves to release the water from the cylinders;
- Take the hose off the reel connection and blow the water out of the hose using a compressor;
- Grease the ball valves of the pump and its seating when extended storage is expected;
- Protect the hose from strong sunlight;
- Take weight off the tyres.

Operation and Maintenance	Instruction sheet E.4
Subject: **Flushing of collector drains**	
Target group: Operators and field staff	

E.4 Flushing of collector drains

E.4.1 General

Flushing of a collector drain is always done from a manhole, usually requiring specific equipment for the job and a water tank.

E.4.2 Required equipment

For flushing one requires:
- One flusher;
- One tractor (about 75 HP) with Power Take Off (PTO);
- If no water is available: one tractor plus tanker (4 m^3) - for flushing one drain of 500 m one needs about 3 m^3 of water thus an almost full tank.

Since flushing is done from a manhole or sump, additionally one needs to have:
- One hose guidance for manhole;
- One suction pump capacity of at least 100 litre/min (for pumping out the return flow from the manhole and to fill the tank).

E.4.3 Sequence of flushing

E.4.3.1 General

For the flushing of collector drains there are no limits to pressure and time, which means that flushing can also be done when there is no natural drain flow.

E.4.3.2 Sequence

The sequence of cleaning is as follows (Figure E4.1):
1. Clean out the mud from all the manholes, if necessary with a mud pump;
2. Start cleaning at the downstream end of the upstream section side of the collector. Be sure that in each manhole the downstream pipe is closed off.

Be sure that the field drain pipe is closed off;
3. Flush out with the highest possible pressure.

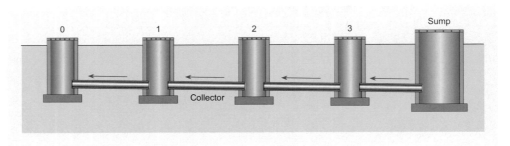

Figure E4.1   Sequence of cleaning

E.4.4   Flushing water

- If there is an open drain or canal nearby that has clean water at least 20 - 25 cm deep, one can use water from the drain or canal for cleaning. In that case:
  - Dig a hole in the open drain and put a bucket or other metal container in the hole. The rim of the bucket should be at least 10 cm above the bottom of the drain and the water level should be about 10 cm above the rim of the bucket;
  - Put the suction valve of the pump in the bucket.
- If no water is available in the drain, one can use a tank, in which case put the suction part of the flusher in the tank.

E.4.5   Flushing action

E.4.5.1   General

- Flushing is done from the sump or a manhole;
- Flushing is always done in an upstream direction;
- Be sure there is always plenty of water;
- Never leave the hose in the drain without pumping, the head may get stuck and it may be lost!;
- During the pulling back action the pumping (flushing) has to continue otherwise the jet head may get stuck.

E.4.5.2   Entering the hose into the collector drain

1. Put the flushing machine downstream of the manhole or near the end pipe so that one can guide the hose straight into the drain;

2. Close off all the inlets/outlets to the manhole or sump, with the exception of the part to be cleaned, with a cloth plastic ball or other material;

3. Install the mud pump close by and put the suction of the mud pump into the manhole/sump. Start the engine of the mud pump as soon as the manhole fills up with water;

4. Put the suction hose of the flusher into the water of the ditch or into the tank;

5. Use hose guidance to protect the hose from wear on the edges of the manholes (Figure E4.2);

6. Check the tightness of the jet head on the high-pressure hose;

7. Insert the hose by hand about 2-3 metres into the collector pipe;

8. Start the engine of the tractor and run the pump at low speed. Open the relief valve on the pressure side so that the water runs off of the bottom of valve (this relief valve opens automatically when its pressure is released);

9. Open the valve fitted on the first cylinder (this valve should always be in the open position when pulling out the cleaning hose);

10. Open the valve fitted under the pressure gauge;

11. Now close the relief valve by pulling lever upwards. The pressure will now build up in the pressure line;

12. Increase the engine speed until pressure gauge on the pump indicates the pressure at which the hose is entering the drain pipe (for collectors 65 up to 85 bar). Close the pressure gauge valve to protect the gauge. During normal operation check the delivery pressure twice per day;

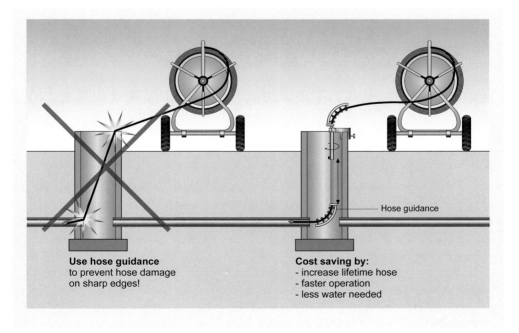

Figure E4.2   Correct (right) and faulty (left) way of entering the hose pipe through a manhole

13. During the first fifty metres of penetration, the cleaning hose will tend to run too fast into the pipe due to low friction. Thus, decrease the speed of the penetration by decreasing the engine speed of the tractor so that the entry speed is no more than 30 m/min.
14. Continue with the flushing until the jet head has reached the upstream manhole.

E.4.5.3 Withdrawing the hose from the collector drain and rewinding it onto the reel

During the pulling back action the pumping (flushing) has to continue otherwise the jet head may get stuck), thus:
1. Decrease the engine speed to half speed;
2. Close the valve on the first cylinder;
3. Move the engaging lever of the reel drive system to the right so that the V-belt drive is engaged and the hose reel starts to turn. Pulling out of the hose is to be done at moderate speed (20- 25 m/min) to achieve the extra benefit of the second cleaning;
4. Keep pumping with the mud pump;
5. Take care that the hose is properly rewound on the reel. Cross winding of the hose might lead to disconnection of the hose connections. The last metres of the hose should be pulled out very carefully and at low engine speed of the tractor to prevent the hose from swinging dangerously. The hose filled with water should always be wound on the reel;
6. When the jet head is about to leave the drainage pipe the relief valve should be operated by hand in order to relieve the water pressure as soon as the jet head leaves the drain pipe. Open the valve on the first cylinder again before closing the relief valve and increasing the engine speed of the tractor;
7. Pump out with the mud pump all the remaining water and clean out all the silt from the manhole by hand (if necessary);
8. Remove all the closures of other inlet and outlets.

E.4.6   What to do in the case of damaged pipes or faulty drainage system

To follow the progress and/or to detect the location of a problem in the drain, it is recommended marking off every 20 m of the drain, so that at all times one knows how far the hose has penetrated.

If there is a damaged drain the jet head will sometimes leave the drain pipe and penetrate into the surrounding soil when a considerable amount of cleaning water will be injected into the surrounding soil. This problem will be indicated by a decrease of the out flowing cleaning water, and the out coming water will suddenly carry a lot more dirt. The place where the jet head has left the drain pipe may be deduced from the measurement marks on the length of the hose. If the jet head left the drain pipe to either side of it or downwards, it will be almost impossible to recover the hose and jet head. When a drain has not been installed in a straight line the jet head may get stuck in the bends of the drain against the corrugations. Often the only way to recover the jet head is to estimate the place where the jet head is stuck from the lengths of hose which has entered the drain, dig up the drain, cut the drain and recover the head by cutting it from the hose.

Operation and Maintenance	Instruction sheet E.5

Subject: **Flushing of field drains from a ditch**

Target group: Operators and field staff

E.5 Flushing of field drains from a ditch

E.5.1 Required equipment

For flushing one requires:
- One flusher;
- One tractor (about 75 HP) with Power Take Off (PTO);
- If no water available: one tractor plus tanker (4 m^3) plus pump for filling the tank - it will take 3 m^3 of water thus an almost full tank to flush one drain of 500 m.

E.5.2 Conditions for flushing

- Only flush drains when they give real problems or are not flowing;
- Start flushing only if *field drains* are flowing. If a dry drain is cleaned the envelope will be damaged;
- Do not enter a (field) drain with the flusher twice during one cleaning, this may damage the filter;
- Flushing of field drains should be done preferably at about 12-15 bar at the jet head. With the high-pressure flusher the pressure at the pump (see on the pressure meter) should be no more than 50 bar. Higher pressure will damage the filter. If the hose is unable to enter the drain pipe, the pressure may be increased temporarily;
- Flushing must always be done downstream in an upstream direction.

E.5.3 Flushing water

- If there is an open drain or canal nearby which has clean water and where the water depth is at least 20 - 25 cm, one can use water from the drain for cleaning. In that case:
  - Dig a hole in the open drain and put a bucket or other metal container in the hole. The rim of the bucket should be at least 10 cm above the bottom of the drain and the water level should be about 10 cm above the rim of the bucket;
  - Put the suction valve of the pump in the bucket.
- If no water is available in the drain, one can use a tank, in which case put the suction part of the flusher in the tank.

E.5.4   Flushing action

E.5.4.1   Entry of flusher hose into the drain

1. Put the tractor and the flusher on the opposite bank of the open drain. In this way the hose can enter the drain very easily and runs smoothly off or on the drum over its entire width (Figure E5.1a);
2. If the flusher cannot be positioned on the bank opposite the drain the reverse roller can be used (Figure E5.1b). In that case position the flusher in such way that the hose runs off from the bottom side of the drum. Lower the reverse roller far enough into the ditch so that the hose running off the drum can move in a straight line into the drain pipe;
3. Put the suction hose into the water of the ditch or tank as described above;
4. If necessary protect the hose from wear on the edges of the pipe;
5. Check the tightness of the jet head on the high-pressure hose;
6. Insert the hose by hand about 2-3 metres into the drain pipe;
7. Start the engine of the tractor and run the pump at low speed. Open the relief valve on the pressure side so that the water runs off of the bottom of valve (this relief valve opens automatically when its pressure) is released;
8. Open the valve fitted onto the first cylinder (this valve should always be in an open position during pulling out of the cleaning hose).
9. Open the valve fitted under the pressure gauge;
10. Now close the relief valve by pulling lever upwards to let the pressure build up in the pressure line;
11. Increase the engine speed until pressure gauge on the pump indicates the pressure at which the hose is entering the drain pipe (preferably not exceeding 50 bar, but if necessary 65 up to 85 bar). Close the pressure gauge valve for protection of the gauge. During normal operation check the delivery pressure twice per day;
12. During the first fifty metres of penetration, friction will tend to cause the cleaning hose to run too fast into the pipe. Therefore, decrease the speed of the penetration by decreasing the engine speed of the tractor. Speed should be limited to 30 m/min;
13. Continue with the flushing until the jet head has reached the end of the pipe.

E.5.4.2   Withdrawing the hose from the drain and rewinding it onto the reel

During the pulling back action the pumping (flushing) has to continue otherwise the jet head may get stuck.
1. Decrease the engine speed to half speed;
2. Close the valve on the first cylinder;
3. Move the engaging lever of the reel drive system to the right so that the V-belt drive is engaged and the hose drum starts to turn. Pulling out of the hose is to be done at a moderate speed (20- 25 m/min) to achieve the extra benefit from the second cleaning;
4. Ensure that the hose is properly rewound on the reel. Cross winding of the hose might lead to disconnecting of the hose connections. The last metres of the hose should be pulled out

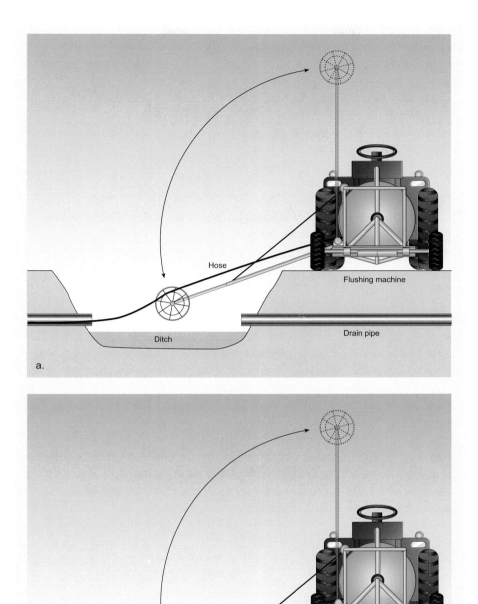

Figure E5.1   Tractor with flusher cleaning from an open drain

very carefully and at low engine speed of the tractor to prevent the hose from swinging dangerously. The hose filled with water should always be wound on the reel;

5. When the jet head is about to leave the drainage pipe the relief valve should be operated by hand in order to relieve the water pressure as soon as the jet head leaves the drain pipe. Open the valve on the first cylinder again before closing the relief valve and increasing the engine speed of the tractor;

6. Pump out with the mud pump all the remaining water and clean out all the silt from the manhole by hand (if necessary);

7. Remove all the closures of other inlet and outlets.

E.5.5   What to do in case of damaged pipes or faulty drain system

To follow the progress and/or to detect the location of a problem in the drain, we recommended marking off every 20 m of the drain, so that at all times one knows how far the hose has penetrated.

If there is a damaged drain the jet head will sometimes leave the drain pipe and penetrate into the surrounding soil when a considerable amount of cleaning water will be injected into the surrounding soil. This problem will be indicated by a decrease of the out flowing cleaning water, and the out coming water will suddenly carry a lot more dirt. The place where the jet head has left the drain pipe may be deduced from the measurement marks on the length of the hose. If the jet head left the drain pipe to either side of it or downwards, it will be almost impossible to recover the hose and jet head.

When a drain has not been installed in a straight line the jet head may get stuck in the bends of the drain against the corrugations. Often the only way to recover the jet head is to estimate the place where the jet head is stuck from the lengths of hose which has entered the drain, dig up the drain, cut the drain and recover the head by cutting it from the hose.

Operation and Maintenance	Instruction sheet E.6
Subject: **Flushing of field drains from a manhole** Target group: Operators and field staff	

E.6 Flushing of field drains from a manhole

E.6.1 Required equipment

To flush a field drain from a manhole one requires:
- One flusher;
- One tractor (about 75 HP) with Power Take Off (PTO);
- One tractor plus tanker (4 m^3) - for flushing one drain of 500 m one needs about 3 m^3 of water thus an almost full tank;
- One hose guidance for manhole;
- One mud pump capacity of at least 100 litre/min (for pumping out the return flow from the manhole and to fill the tank).

E.6.2 Conditions for flushing

- Only flush drains when they give real problems or are not flowing;
- Start flushing only if *field drains* are flowing. If a dry drain is cleaned the envelope will be damaged;
- Do not enter a (field) drain with the flusher twice during one cleaning, this may damage the filter;
- Flushing of field drains should be done preferably at about 12-15 bar at the jet head. With the high-pressure flusher the pressure at the pump (see on the pressure meter) should be no more than 50 bar. Higher pressure will damage the filter. If the hose is unable to enter the drain pipe, the pressure may be increased temporarily;
- Flushing must always be done downstream in an upstream direction.

E.6.3 Flushing sequence

Flushing a field drain from manhole may only be done in an upstream direction! Thus, if there are field drain manholes start in the downstream field drain manhole, clean the upstream field drain and after that the next one, then the next and so forth.

E.6.4   Flushing water

- If there is an open drain or canal nearby which has clean water that is at least 20 - 25 cm deep, one can use water from the drain for cleaning. In that case:
  - Dig a hole in the open drain and put a bucket or other metal container in the hole. The rim of the bucket should be at least 10 cm above the bottom of the drain and the water level should be about 10 cm above the rim of the bucket;
  - Put the suction valve of the pump in the bucket.
- If no water is available in the drain, one can use a tank, in which case put the suction part of the flusher in the tank.

A tank is almost always required for flushing from manholes.

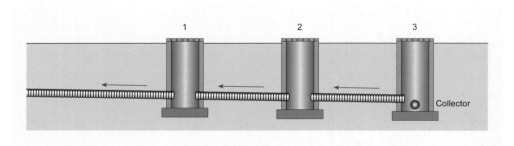

Figure E6.1   Direction and sequence of flushing of a field drain from a manhole

E.6.5   Flushing action

Flush only in an upstream direction (otherwise the out coming dirt which flows downstream through the still dirty drain can clog up the drain!!).

E.6.5.1   Preparation

1. Put the flushing machine downstream of the manhole or near to the end pipe so that one can guide the hose straight into the drain;
2. Open the manhole;
3. Cleanout the silt of the manhole by hand;
4. Close off all the downstream outlets of the manhole with a cloth, plastic ball or other material;
5. Install the mud pump close by and put the suction of the mud pump into the manhole/sump and start the engine of the mud pump if the manhole fills up with water;
6. Install the hose guidance to prevent damage to the pipe.

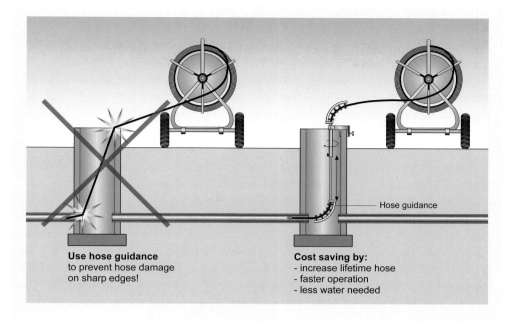

Figure E6.2   Correct (right) and faulty (left) way of entering the hose pipe through a manhole

E.6.5.2   The entry of the flushing hose into the field drain

1. Put the suction hose of the flusher into the water of the ditch or into the tank;
2. If necessary protect the hose from wear on the edges of the pipe;
3. Check the tightness of the jet head on the high pressure hose;
4. Insert the hose by hand about 2-3 metres into the drain pipe;
5. Start the engine of the tractor and run the pump at low speed. Open the relief valve on the pressure side so that the water runs off of the bottom of valve (this relief valve opens automatically when its pressure is released);
6. Open the valve fitted on the first cylinder (this valve should always be in open position during pulling of the cleaning hose);
7. Open the valve fitted under the pressure gauge;
8. Now close the relief valve by pulling the lever upwards when the pressure will build up in the pressure line;
9. Increase the engine speed until pressure gauge on the pump indicates the pressure at which the hose is entering the drain pipe (preferably not exceeding 50 bar, but if necessary temporarily 65 up to 85 bar). Close the pressure gauge valve for protection of the gauge. During normal operation check the delivery pressure twice per day;
10. During the first fifty metres of penetration, friction will tend to cause the cleaning hose to run too fast into the pipe. Therefore, decrease the speed of the penetration by decreasing the engine speed of the tractor the entry speed should not be more than 30 m/min;
11. Continue with the flushing until the jet head has reached the upstream or the end of the drain.

E.6.5.3   Withdrawing the hose from the drain and rewinding it on the reel

During the pulling back action the pumping (flushing) has to continue otherwise the jet head may get stuck.

Actions
1. Decrease the engine speed to half speed;
2. Close the valve on the first cylinder;
3. Move the engaging lever of the reel drive system to the right so that the V-belt drive is engaged and the hose reel starts to turn. Pulling out of the hose is to be done at a moderate speed (20- 25 m/min) to achieve the higher benefit of the second cleaning;
4. Take care that the hose is properly rewound on the reel. Cross winding of the hose might lead to disconnecting of the hose connections. The last metres of the hose should be pulled out very carefully and at low engine speed of the tractor to prevent the hose from swinging dangerously. The hose filled with water must always be wound on the reel;
5. When the jet head is about to leave the drainage pipe the relief valve should be operated by hand in order to relieve the water pressure as soon as the jet head leaves the drain pipe. Open the valve on the first cylinder again before closing the relief valve and increasing the engine speed of the tractor;
6. Pump out with the mud pump all the remaining water and clean out all the silt from the manhole by hand (if necessary);
7. Remove the closures of other outlets.

E.6.6   What to do in the case of damaged pipes or faulty drain installation

To follow the progress and/or to detect the location of a problem in the drain, we recommended marking off every 20 m of the drain, so that at all times one knows how far the hose has penetrated.

If there is a damaged drain the jet head will sometimes leave the drain pipe and penetrate into the surrounding soil when a considerable amount of cleaning water will be injected into the surrounding soil. This problem will be indicated by a decrease of the out flowing cleaning water, and the out coming water will suddenly carry a lot more dirt. The place where the jet head has left the drain pipe may be deduced from the measurement marks on the length of the hose. If the jet head left the drain pipe to either side of it or downwards, it will be almost impossible to recover the hose and jet head.

When a drain has not been installed in a straight line the jet head may get stuck in the bends of the drain against the corrugations. Often the only way to recover the jet head is to estimate the place where the jet head is stuck from the lengths of hose which has entered the drain, dig up the drain, cut the drain and recover the head by cutting it from the hose.

PART III

CASE STUDIES

Preamble

Part III presents salient features of the history, development and present practices of the implementation of subsurface drainage in China, Egypt, India, The Netherlands and Pakistan. Although subsurface drainage is practised in many more countries a selection of only these five countries has been made on the basis of availability of up to date information. Furthermore these five countries are considered to be representative for various climate regions and institutional settings. The most relevant experiences in the countries have already been used to compile Part I and Part II. These practices are not repeated in the case studies, the presented information is to highlight that each country has its specific physical and institutional conditions. For each and every country, technical and organisational arrangements have to be tailor-made to fit for the specific local conditions, straightaway copying practices and experiences from one country to another is no option. Thus the case studies are presented as a reference for the reader and are considered useful for those who want to start subsurface drainage on a local or national scale.

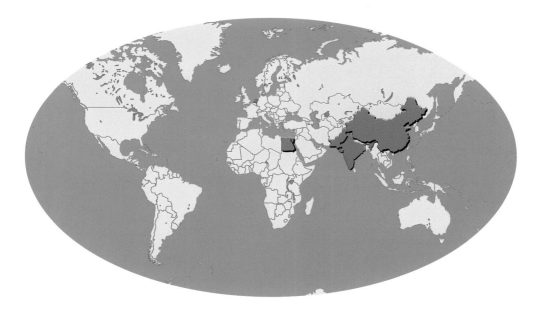

Countries were pipe drainage is or has been practised

Algeria	France	Poland	Syria
Australia	Germany	Portugal	Taiwan
Belgium	Hungary	Turkey	Czech Republic
Chili	India	The Netherlands	Tunisia
Canada	Iraq	Pakistan	United States of America
China	Iran	Peru	Uzbekistan
Colombia	Italy	Rumania	United Kingdom
Denmark	Jordan	Russia	Yugoslavia (former)
Egypt	Korea (South)	Senegal	
Ethiopia	Mexico	Slovakia	
Finland	Morocco	Spain	

Case Study - China

Case Study - China[1]

1   Introduction

More than half of the cultivated land in China is affected by either waterlogging and/or salinity. Consequently waterlogging and salinity are important issues in China, even more so since the natural conditions of the country are such that only one third of the land is suitable for agriculture. Salinity problems occur in 13 to 14 million ha or 14% of the total cultivated land (around 97 million ha) and waterlogging in 24 million ha or 25% of the cultivated areas[2]. In the northern parts of China, which has a rainfall deficit, about 50% of the cultivated lands are irrigated. Irrigation induced salinity occurs in more than 11 million ha or 23 % of these irrigated lands.

Modern drainage techniques in combination with traditional methods can potentially solve most of the waterlogging and salinity problems at field level. Since the 1960's major improvements have been realised by implementing large scale open drainage systems, (tube)well drainage systems and intensifying research and experiments with pipe drainage on pilot and practical scale.

2   Distribution of areas with drainage problems

The distribution over the country of the areas suffering from drainage problems can be summarised as follows (Figure 1 and 2):
- No obvious drainage problems occur in the western part of China: the mountainous areas of and around the Qinghai-Tibet plateau;
- The plateaus and plains and river valleys in the arid and semi arid north and northwest have considerable salinity problems often combined with alkalinity;
- The river plains in the North East that form a delta area (Three River or Sanjiang Plain) have high groundwater tables but no significant salinity;
- The North China Plain, located in the east (Huang-Huai-Hai Rivers Plain) is affected by a combination of high groundwater tables, saline groundwater and consequently soil salinity, in some areas combined with alkalinity. Large areas in the Yellow River Delta, an economically important part of the North China Plain, are either in direct or indirect contact with the sea and hence have saline groundwater and suffer from saline soils;

---

[1] This chapter has been written in close cooperation with Prof Fang Sheng of the Hebei Institute of Hydrotechnics, dr. Ding Kunlun of the IWHR, Engineer Lin Chi, retired from the CAAERP, and Mr. Zhuang Huijiang of Municipal Government of Dongying Shandong. Use has been made of the Chinese publications of En. Yang Cheng Qu retired from the Xinjiang Agricultural Industrial and Trade Corporation (XAITC) and the experience of Mr.He Gang formerly of the (XAITC) and Mr. Zheng Cunhu of the Kingchuan Company Dong Ying Shandong.

[2] Irrigation and Drainage in China, Ministry of Water Resources and Electric Power, 1987.

- The Yangtze Delta and the Pearl River Delta suffer from waterlogging and salinity problems. Salinity is more prevalent in the coastal areas, but because of the high rainfall it is less serious than in the North China Plain. Water logging is more prominent land inwards;
- The inland river plains of the huge Yangtze River basin have considerable, sometimes seasonal, waterlogging problems;
- The river plains of the Pearl River basin have the same considerable, sometimes seasonal, waterlogging problems. Since most of the areas in this basin are traditional rice growing areas, waterlogging does not always seriously impede crop growth.

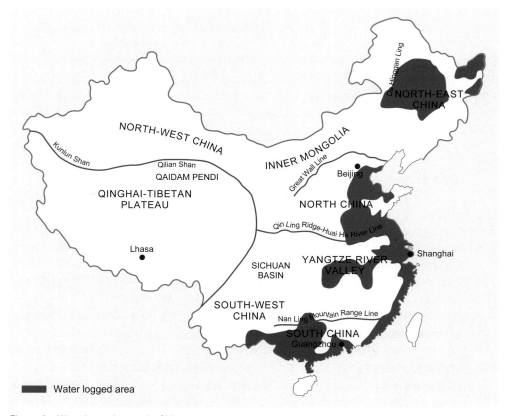

Figure 1   Waterlogged areas in China

3   Historical developments

3.1   Drainage in ancient times

The Chinese population has been struggling with waterlogging and salinity control throughout its history. The earliest records of a search for solutions date from around 1000 years B.C. Over the years ingenious solutions have been found to control waterlogging and salinity, among which

Figure 2   Saline-alkali areas in China

of course is leaching through rice growing. Open drains have been built to convey the surplus water to rivers and seas. In inland areas drainage canals have been built and rivers have been deepened to allow disposal of drainage water and consequently lowering of water tables.

Salt management has been practiced by traditional methods, for example:
- Building up the soil level by so called "warping". Warping is a technique consisting of filling manmade basins with silt-loaded irrigation water and then draining off the water once the silt has settled. In this way a new salt-alkali free soil layer is deposited on top of the salinised land, which allows temporarily cultivation in a relatively salt free environment;
- "Stone mulching" to reduce capillary rise and to prevent secondary salinisation to some extend;
- Land forming/levelling, a method to concentrate the capillary rise of saline groundwater in predetermined areas, so that crops can be planted in areas where no or limited secondary salinzation occurs;
- Crop rotations, where rice crops are alternated with dry-foot crops, thereby allowing leaching of salts accumulated in the soil during the growing season of the dry-foot crops and percolation of water from the rice crops;

- So-called winter irrigation. Winter irrigation is in fact a leaching of fields after harvest before the inset of frost at a moment when there is limited demand on the available irrigation water. The salts accumulated during the growing season are (partly) leached;
- Biological control, which involves planting trees on strategic places for the purpose of lowering groundwater levels and to limit secondary salinisation.

3.2 Drainage in China after the creation of the Peoples Republic

Construction of irrigation and drainage
After the Chinese revolution impressive efforts were made to bring large areas under irrigation. Within 20 years about 32 million ha, often located in remote areas, were provided with irrigation systems. The newly reclaimed and irrigated areas were equipped with open drainage systems. Well drainage systems, often in conjunction with groundwater exploitation, were installed in 17 provinces and municipalities in Northern China (2 980 000 wells!). Moreover some experiments were conducted with pipe drains.

In the 1960s and 1970s impressive successes with lowering groundwater tables and reducing salinity were obtained by improving the main drainage systems and the drain outlets towards the Bohai Sea in the North China Plain. These improvements increased the drainage capacity four to six fold making it possible to evacuate the salt out of the area with floods and the summer rains. This prevented the recirculation and accumulation of salts in soil and groundwater. It resulted in reducing the area affected with salinity/alkalinity problem in the North China plain with 50%.

The extensive well drainage in the North China Plain and where possible reusing the pumped water for irrigation has caused a serious overdraft of the shallow and deep aquifers that has resulted in regional lowering of the groundwater table, land subsidence and sea water intrusion into the aquifers.

Research
Considerable research efforts have been carried out since 1949 in the field of drainage and salinity control. On national level, the China Institute of Water Resources and Hydropower Research (IWHR) and the Chinese Academy of Agricultural Engineering Research and Planning (CAAERP) conducted and guided many local research activities both in basic research on soil plant water relationship and on applied research on drainage methods and materials. At field level pilot areas were equipped with pipe drainage and well drainage systems (for instance, pipe drainage in Tianjin, in the Yellow River Delta, and well drainage in the Yellow River Delta and in the Ningxia Autonomous Region).

Field research was also conducted in Hebei (Nanpi) to develop methods for comprehensive control of draught, waterlogging, salinity and groundwater salinity by making use of open drainage and well drainage/irrigation. In the Houying Pilot Area (Hebei Province) similar experiments were conducted by making use of open drainage system. Part of the experiments focussed on growing crops by irrigation consecutively with fresh and saline water.

Increased need for artificial drainage in China

The impressive intensification of agricultural, the expansion and consolidation of the irrigated areas and the progressive irrigation induced salinisation of part of the areas brought under irrigation in the last 50 years, as well as the reclamation of coastal areas for agricultural use will undoubtedly require some form of large-scale artificial drainage. And, there is the added complication of the scarcity of water for irrigation, which will reduce the automatic leaching and consequently worsen the salt balance.

4 Pipe drainage in China

4.1 Introduction

In theory all three drainage methods, i.e. open, pipe and tubewell drainage, can be used to fulfil the drainage needs in China's agricultural lands. Well drainage will only be practical and feasible in limited areas where there is fresh groundwater that can be recycled for irrigation. The most common drainage method is open ditch drainage, a traditional and well-known technique in China. Open drainage has some disadvantages like considerable land loss and high maintenance costs.

The intensification of agriculture, coupled with the population pressure and the fast growing mechanisation results in an increasing interest in pipe drainage, because with pipe drainage there is almost zero land loss, there are less obstructions in the field and maintenance is expected to be limited. Added to this is the fact that the soil profiles in the arid north and northwest of China and in the North China plain show often unstable subsoils. Maintenance of the deep open drains that are required for the salinity control in these soils is either impossible or extremely cumbersome and thus expensive. Part of these problems can be avoided by limiting the length of (deep) open drains and replacing the up stream parts of the drainage systems with pipe drains.

4.2 Objectives of pipe drainage in China

In general terms pipe drainage in China is and can be used to realize the following objectives:
- Lowering groundwater levels for water logging control in coastal areas and inland river plains. The advantage over open drains is a limited or zero land loss and fewer obstructions for mechanised agriculture;
- Facilitating fast lowering of watertable in the more humid southern areas after the monsoon period. A fast lowering of the groundwater after a rice crop creates additional time in the crop calendar, time to grow of a third crop. Drainage systems have in that case to be "controlled drainage" systems so that they can be closed during the rice growing period;
- Lowering groundwater tables for salinity control, in some cases combined with water-logging control. In the North China Plain and in North and North-West China this form of

drainage has mainly as objective to prevent secondary salinisation. In unstable soils, pipe drainage can control the watertable with limited land loss and minimal maintenance (Figure 3). In most cases pumping is required. In this way secondary salinisation can be reduced to harmless proportions;

- Timely lowering of watertables in North Eastern river plains. The cropping season in the cold and humid North East is extremely short. If summer rains are abundant or late, the heavy soils prevent a timely drainage of the water resulting in high watertables and ponding water. This hampers the timely (mechanised) harvesting of crops. Moreover a high ground-watertable at the moment the frost sets in, may result the following spring in ponding water above the frozen deeper soil layers. This can prevent timely soil cultivation in spring. Pipe drainage systems alone, or in combination with mole drainage and in some places soil ripping, can improve the drainage during and after the summer rain and thus create conditions for timely harvesting of the crops and creating soil water conditions that allow soil cultivation in the spring;
- Increase efficiency of the reclamation of salinised areas: A pipe drainage system can increase the efficiency of the initial leaching process considerably. This will save time and more important scarce water. The system can after reclamation be used to control the secondary salinisation.

Figure 3
In the unstable soils of North and North-West China open drains are not very sustainable

5   Development of pipe drainage in China

Since ancient times, pipe drainage has been practised in China by using underground bamboo sticks with holes. Modern pipe drainage technology was introduced starting in the nineteen seventies in the following way:

- A tractor drawn Chinese trencher was designed and produced in the 1970's. The trencher is still successfully used in southern China where shallow drainage for waterlogging control is practiced. Because of its light weight and manoeuvrability it is very well suited for the small plots in southern China;

- The first integrated self propelled trencher with hydraulic depth control and a horizontal chain was imported in 1979 in Tianjin. The objective was to determine if under coastal conditions in North China pipe drainage could be installed for waterlogging and eventually salinity control. The installation was carried out with tile drains. With this machine, large areas in the Tianjin municipality were drained;

- In the end of the 1970's trials were conducted with hand installed subsurface drains in Shandong, (Dayuzhang irrigation district) with the objective to determine the technical viability of controlling watertables with piped drains;

- In 1985 a pilot area was set up in Shandong Yucheng County, for testing pipe drainage system as an effective method for salinity control. The installation was carried out with a 350 HP trencher with a vertical chain that was introduced as part of a Sino-Dutch cooperation project (Figure 4). This model was at that time the most advanced and is basically still the same as the models that are presently produced. In the pilot area the machine installation under North China plain conditions was tested out. A large variety of drain envelopes, gravel as well as pre-wrapped synthetic envelopes around locally pro- duced corrugated PVC drain pipes were tested;

- In the early eighties a modern western corrugated plastic drain pipe drain production line (PVC) was started up in Shanghai. This line has produced large quantities of pipes for drainage and other purposes. Simultaneously a number of PE pipe producing plants were inaugurated in provincial capitals;

- Starting in the eighties in large parts of humid southern China singular pipe drainage system were installed by hand or by Chinese made trenchers at shallow depth. Many of the systems were installed in rice growing areas. The systems are blocked during the wet season when rice is grown and opened at the end of the season for fast drying out of the soil, to facilitate ripening and to allow the timely soil cultivation for sowing of a dry-foot crop;

- In 1987 in Southern Xinjiang, a pipe drainage project for salinity control was started on a state farm. The objective was to control secondary salinisation with relative deep pipe drains installed in the unstable sub soils, to replace the deep open field drains that were extremely maintenance intensive. A secondary objective was to reduce water use for leaching of the built up salinity. The systems were installed with two laser guided trenchers of 350 HP that could install both field drains and collector drains up to a maximum depth of 3 m. Because of the remoteness of the area a special PVC corrugated drain pipe producing plant was installed on the farm. The drain envelope consisted of a locally found and sieved gravel;

- In the late nineteen eighties and the early nineteen nineties the installation of modern pipe drainage systems started in Ningxia Autonomous region. Initially several singular systems were installed by hand on an experimental scale and various pre-wrapped envelopes were tested. Towards the end of the nineties with assistance of a European Union sponsored project and somewhat later a Sino-Dutch cooperation project the large scale implementation of pipe drainage systems was started. The installation is done with three laser guided trenchers. Initially imported PVC corrugated plastic pipes were used, later locally made PE pipes. A Chinese produced thin typar is used as envelope and trials with other envelopes have been started. The planning is to install pipe drainage in 23 500 ha in five years;
- In 1992 as an indirect follow up of the experiments in the eighties in Shandong, a detailed plan was prepared for applying large scale pipe drainage in the Yellow River delta. In 2000 a specialised private company was set up to design and install pipe drainage in the Yellow River Delta (Figure 4). The company is fully trained and is equipped with two trenchers and has the capacity to install 400-600 km of drains per year. Chinese made corrugated PVC drain pipes are used and gravel envelopes are applied. The majority of the gravel trailers are produced in China. The company has installed 6000 ha in the period 2000-2002.

Figure 4   Trencher machine installing a plastic collector drain in North-West China

6   Technical aspects of pipe drainage systems in China

6.1   Drainage systems

Drainage in China is can be divided into the drainage for waterlogging and into drainage for salinity control and/or waterlogging.

Drainage for waterlogging control
Drains for waterlogging control are mainly installed at relative shallow depth (0.5-1.0 m) in singular systems that discharge into open drains. Drain depth is determined by the water levels in the open drains and is often around 1 m. The length of the field drains is variable depending on the field lengths. Drain spacing is rather variable, spacing of 20 m have been noticed. Where controlled drainage is applied this is done by simply capping the outlets of the drains, or with more sophisticated structure. Installation is done by hand, or by tractor drawn Chinese trencher. Envelopes are not commonly used.

Drainage for salinity and waterlogging control
Drainage for salinity control and waterlogging in the North China plain and the North and North-West of the country is done by deep drainage (>2 m). Pumped composite drainage systems are therefore the most economic solution seen from a national or regional view point. Some of these systems have been installed in Xingjiang, Ningxia and Shandong (Figure 5). On local level

Figure 5   Pipe drainage for the reclamation of saline soils in the Yellow River Delta (only the manhole cover
is visible)

understandably the simpler gravity singular systems are preferred that discharge onto existing open drains. The actual water level in the existing open drains, dug into the unstable sub soils, is in most cases not more than 1-1.5 m below field level. The result is that the field drains cannot control the water level at the required depth of around 2 m for optimal salinity control. The result is consequently an only partial functioning system that solves in most cases the visible waterlogging problems, but does not fully limit the secondary salinisation during the critical spring and autumn periods.

Composite systems

The composite systems are mainly systems with extended field drains of up to 1000 m length. The field drains discharge into collector drains with maximum length around 1000 m. Slopes of field and collector drains are 0.7‰. This layout fit generally quite well into the existing field layouts. Because of the length of the laterals, in some cases every 300 m manholes for cleaning access are placed. Field drain spacing varies generally between 50 and 100 m in these areas. Since the systems are often installed in flat areas, the subsequent slopes of the field drains and collector drains result in outlet levels of 2.5-3 m below field level. These levels are much lower than the water levels in the existing open drains and consequently pumping is required. Therefore at the end of the system is sump is installed from where the water can be pumped by an electric underwater pump into the open drainage system.

Singular systems

The singular systems discharge directly in to open drains. Spacing of field drains vary between 50 and 100 m, slopes vary between 1‰ and 0.5‰. The drain depth at outlet is in theory above the water level in the open drainage system, in practise (temporary) submergence is allowed. The resulting average depth of the systems is often not more than 1 m in flat areas.

6.2   Installation

The installation in South China of shallow drainage systems is either done by hand or by Chinese built small tractor drawn trenchers. A considerable amount of these Chinese drawn trenchers are used mainly in southern China. The deeper installation in the often unstable subsoils in Shandong, Yellow River Delta and Xinjiang has been carried out with modern self propelled laser guided trenchers of about 300-350 HP with the capacity to install drains at depth of 2- 3 m (Figure 6). There are (in 2003) half a dozen imported modern trenchers in the country. Trenchless drainage is not yet tested out in a systematic way although a sample machine is in the country. Where gravel envelopes are applied this is done with tractor drawn hydraulically driven gravel trailers. Gravel trailers have been imported into the country, but starting 2000 Chinese produced trailers have been introduced. The drain installation in areas with unstable subsoils, that are quite common in the North and Northwest China, is possible in most cases with modern trenchers but it requires special skills.

Figure 6   Installation of a collector pipe in North-West China

6.3   Drainage materials

Drain pipes
There are a fair number corrugated pipe producing factories in China both for PE and PVC pipes, quality is variable but this more a question of management than of the quality of the production equipment. The factories that can produce the larger diameter pipes for collector drains are relatively scarce. The maximum diameter is Ø 200 mm.

Envelopes
There is no universal functional pre-wrapped envelope available yet, although research is on-going. Locally gravel is used as well as pre-wrapped envelopes made of Bidim, Typar and other geo-textiles. Extensive laboratory trials are done on pre-wrapped envelopes. Post installation observations and evaluations of the functionality of these envelopes at field level are rare. The

relative uniform particle distribution in the loess soils makes the selection of a suitable envelope rather complicated.

7 Challenges for the further development of pipe drainage in China

7.1 General

It is realised by many parties that pipe drainage is can contribute significantly to waterlogging and salinity control in North China and to waterlogging control in Southern and North East China. The waterlogging control in Southern China has reached proportions that it is undergoing most likely a self propelled development. Although the development of pipe drainage for salinity control has started in Northern China and North West China, it has not yet reached the status of a self sustained momentum. One of the reasons is that the investments in equipment and production of drainage materials are considerable and only justified if long term use is envisaged. The scattered initiatives for the implementation of pipe drainage at this moment do not lead yet to the required economy of scale. A regional approach for which specialised entities are created either private or governmental can in time overcome this problem. Besides this there are some additional temporary institutional complications. Large-scale drainage implementation requires a close cooperation between the government authorities and the private sector for implementation and for production of drainage materials. Privatisation is presently going steadily ahead in China, but is not fully completed and engrained. It will require some time before the situation is fully settled. The first positive developments into that direction are already visible in Shandong and Ningxia.

7.2 Technical aspects

There are some technical hurdles that have to be taken to facilitate the universal application and acceptance of pipe drainage in Northern China. These are:

Development of a pre-wrapped envelope
The only known envelope that can technically be relied on as universally applicable is the graded gravel envelope, designed on the basis of the local soil texture. Gravel envelopes are besides being cumbersome and logistically complicated, in many regions expensive because of long transport distances. Although laboratory test and some field test with pre-wrapped synthetic envelopes have started, no universally or regional functional pre-wrapped envelopes have been identified so far. This will require systematic research and multi local field tests. Once suitable envelopes are identified, the industrial production and the wrapping of the envelope in or near the pipe production plants has to be organised.

Development of small drainage pumping systems
The nature of the drainage problems on the valleys, plains and plateaus of North and North-West China is such that relative deep drainage is required. Such drainage system discharge at levels

of around 2.5 m below field level. The discharge can generally not be gravity discharge. Somewhere in the system pumping to lift the drairage water is required. Cost wise and technically this should not be a major problem. The costs are easily off set by the considerable savings in maintenance of deep open drains. Moreover China's rural areas are relatively well electrified, so that electric pumps can be used and no cumbersome diesel engines and fuel supply are required. A solution with a small, automatically on and off switching under water pumps, for each collector system, looks in theory simple. In practise this solution is however considered rather complicated and not universally accepted. There is a preference for larger central pumping units that are manually operated for both security reasons and presumed saving of energy. The challenge is to develop simple small electrically driven pumping units (under water pumps) that are salt resistant and require a minimum of maintenance and are acceptable under the rural conditions.

Development of smaller size self propelled trenchers
The self propelled trenches of 300 HP and mare than 20 tons are too heavy and too large for use in the smaller plots and the road/bridge infrastructure in large parts of the waterlogged southern part of China. A smaller size machine with proper depth control could very well increase installation speed and efficiency in these areas.

Case Study - Egypt

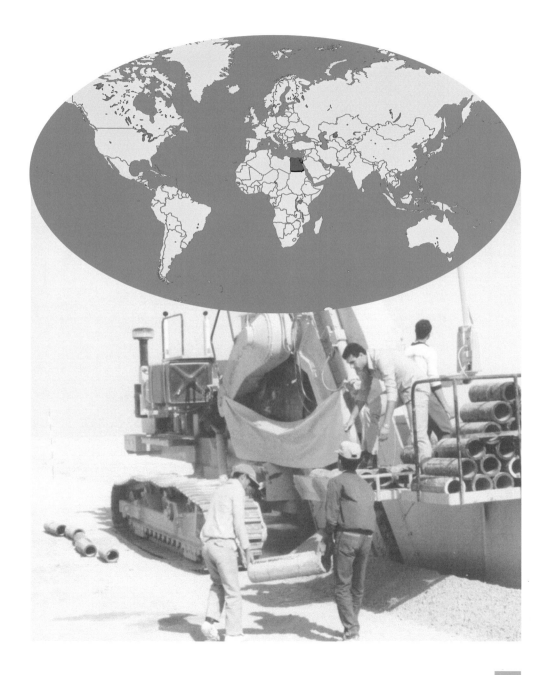

Case Study - Egypt

1   Background

Egypt's Nile Valley and Delta, one of the oldest agricultural areas in the world, has been under continuous cultivation for at least 5000 years. Egypt has an arid climate, characterised by high evaporation rates (1500-2400 mm/year) and little rainfall (5-200 mm/year), thus agriculture depends almost entirely on irrigation from the river Nile (Figure 1). From ancient times onwards, irrigated agriculture in the Nile Valley and Delta depended on the annual floods of the River Nile. The receding floods also drained and leached the cultivated areas. The construction of the Aswan High Dam in 1964 ended the annual flooding but made irrigation water available throughout the year. Since then, two to three crops can be grown each year, resulting in a practical continuous growing season.

These developments had as a secondary effect that the natural annual drainage and leaching ceased to exist. The absence of this natural drainage and leaching, in combination with the intensification of agriculture, made it necessary to provide the Nile Valley and Delta with an artificial drainage system to control water logging and salinity. Although the quality of the water from the River Nile is good (EC = 0.3 dS/m), salinity control is needed; otherwise over the years salt will be accumulated in the root zone. Therefore, in the 1960's, the Egyptian Government started an ambitious programme to drain all of Egypt's agricultural land (approximately 2.5 million ha). This programme is expected to be completed around 2012. Since the 1960, organisational reforms, the local production of drainage materials, mechanisation of the installation together with the necessary basic and operational research has resulted in a drainage organisation and drainage industry that has an annual implementation capacity of about 75 000 ha.

The drainage systems in Egypt consist of a network of piped field drainage systems and open main drains (Figure 2). The field drainage system consists of subsurface field (lateral) and collector pipes that runs by gravity. The pipe collectors discharge into open main drains from where the drainage water is pumped into large open gravity drains which eventually discharge into the River Nile or the sea. Pumping is necessary almost everywhere in the Delta and the Valley, expect in some areas in Upper Egypt, where there is enough gradient to dispose of the effluent freely by gravity.

The implementation of drainage systems involves the following steps:
- Construction of open main drains or the remodelling of the existing main drains;
- Construction of drainage pumping stations to keep the water level in the open main drainage system at 2.5 m below field level so that the pipe systems can discharge by gravity in these main drains;
- Construction of pipe field drainage systems consisting of field drains (named laterals in Egypt) and pipe collector drains.

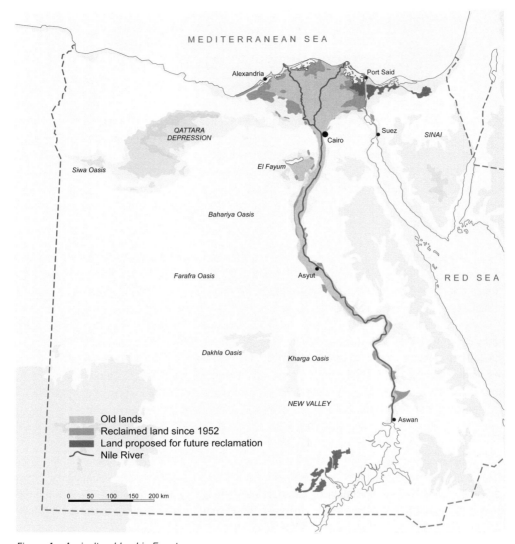

Figure 1   Agricultural land in Egypt

2   Organisation

2.1   Role of the Government

The Egyptian Government has been closely involved in the development of land drainage in Egypt right from the start. This is reflected in the early creation of a specialised authority for the implementation of the national drainage programmes. Moreover the prevailing fragmented land use and land ownership practically precluded the construction of private pipe drainage systems.

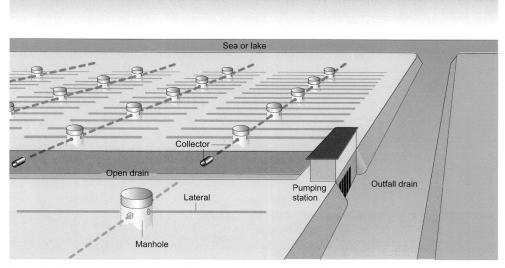

Figure 2   Schematic representation of the drainage system used in Egypt

In the 1930's, well before the construction of the Aswan High Dam, the Irrigation Department started to construct open drainage system and the pumping stations, while the installation of the field drainage system was left to the initiative of the individual farmer. This practice was modified in 1949, when Law No. 35 was issued, decreeing that the State should undertake the implementation of subsurface drainage projects on all agricultural land and that farmers would be accountable for the costs thereof. The total area provided with pipe drainage systems in the years 1942/43 up to 1952/53 was about 20 000 ha.

In 1958, a new drainage policy stipulated that the construction of new pumping stations on newly reclaimed lands, the rehabilitation of deteriorated drainage systems in the "old" land and the renewal of existing pumping stations to meet the required water level in the main drainage system, i.e. 2.5 m below field level.

In 1978, the drainage policy was revised again to include long-term planning up to the year 2000 and to guarantee sufficient flexibility of its implementation. The basis for the new policy was:
- To provide, in the long run, all cultivated lands with pipe drainage networks at a depth suitable to the prevailing crops grown in the area. The construction of open field drains and soil amelioration works were recommended in areas north of latitude 31 in the Nile Delta where dark alkali clay soils and summer rice prevail. However, these plans required assessment to permit the future conversion to pipe drainage. The farmers had to repay the costs of the field drains in 20-year interest-free annual instalments;
- To accommodate the widespread use of drainage machinery and plastic pipes for the implementation of the pipe drainage systems. This to assure higher implementation rates and the proper functioning of the drains;
- To enable the use of appropriate envelope material dictated by the texture of the soil;

- To introduce an irrigation and drainage extension service to demonstrate and advice on water management techniques.

This policy changes resulted in large-scale implementation of subsurface drainage projects using mechanical installation methods (Figure 3). For the management of these projects, several institutions were established within the Ministry Water Resources and Irrigation (MWRI). First, in 1969, the Nile Delta Authority for Tile Drainage projects (NDDA) was established with executive responsibility for the construction of drainage projects in the Nile Delta. Then, in 1971, the newly established Egyptian General Authority for Drainage (EGAD) became responsible for the drainage projects in Upper Egypt. In 1973, NDAA and EGAD were merged in the Egyptian Public Authority for Drainage Projects (EPADP) under the authority of MWRI, by Presidential Decree No. 158.

Figure 3   Mechanical installation of subsurface drainage was introduced in Egypt in the 1960's

In 1975, the Egyptian-Dutch Advisory Panel on Land Drainage (APP) was established to assist the Egyptian Government in its efforts to accelerate the implementation of drainage projects. The main objective of the Panel was to assist the Ministry of Water Resources and Irrigation in carrying out its responsibilities towards managing the quality and quantity of Egypt's freshwater resources more efficiently and effectively.

The General Authority for Reclamation Projects and Agricultural Development (GARPAD) and the Egyptian Authority for Land Improvement Projects (EALIP), both under the Ministry of Agriculture, are in charge of the newly reclaimed areas. Land reclamation companies are responsible for the construction of land reclamation projects, designed and prepared by GARPAD. The sole concern of activities related to drainage at field level is the construction of shallow drains and the addition of gypsum to reclaim alkali soils.

2.2 The Egyptian Public Authority for Drainage Projects

The Egyptian Public Authority for Drainage Projects (EPADP) has been implementing subsurface drainage systems ever since it was established in 1973. EPADP still has comprehensive responsibility for the field drainage works, including the planning of projects, data collection, preparation of designs, contracting and supervising the installation of subsurface drains, monitoring of the impact of drainage, budgeting, and operating project accounts (Figure 4). In addition, EPADP is charged with any remodelling of open drains receiving drainage water from subsurface pipe drains, and also new pumping stations that may be required for the open drains. In 1992, EPADP was also given the responsibility for the maintenance of all open drains.

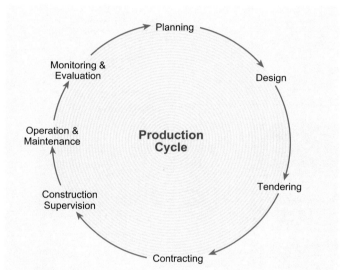

Figure 4
Production cycle of EPADP

Much emphasis was placed on the execution of the drainage projects from 1973 until the mid-1980s. After their construction and formal acceptance by the contractors, the project works were handed over to Department of the MWRI, who then became responsible for all operations and maintenance. The first Department of Drainage Maintenance was established within EPADP in 1978. An additional important task since the late 1980s has been the rehabilitation of subsurface drainage systems that had been previously installed whose function was impaired or maintenance had become excessively costly. A new organisational set-up was needed to cope with the increasing responsibilities in terms of rehabilitation and maintenance (Figure 5). The main change concerned a division of the organisation into five geographically based regions (Figure 6). EPADP is a semi-autonomous authority, headed by a Chairman with the rank of First Under-Secretary directly responsible to the Minister of Water Resources and Irrigation. EPADP has one Vice-Chairman supported by five regional Departments, each headed by an Under-Secretary. At present EPADP employs about 4000 permanent staff at its headquarters and directorates and about 3000 casual labourers who mainly work in the maintenance of drainage systems.

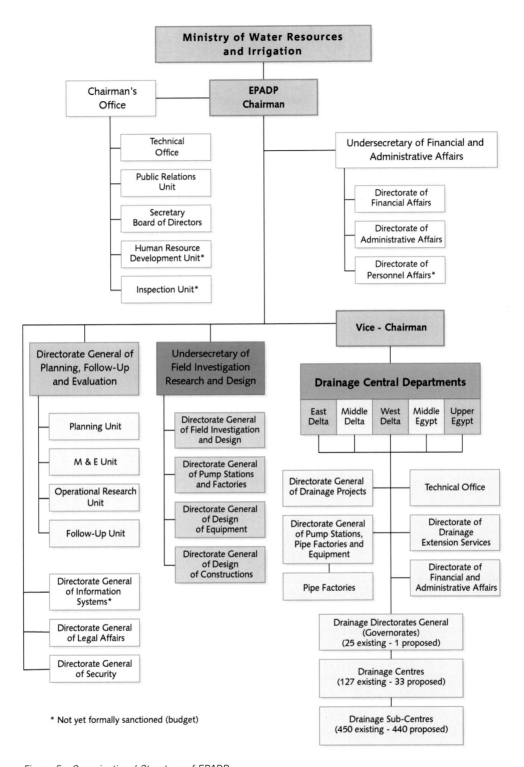

Figure 5   Organisational Structure of EPADP

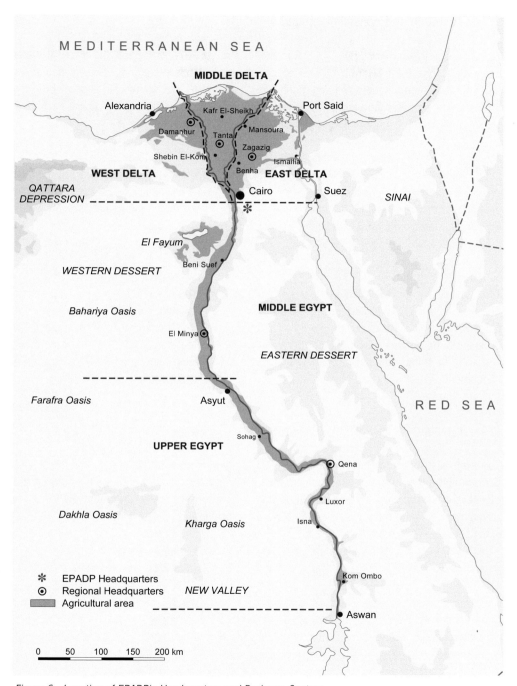

Figure 6   Location of EPADP's Headquarters and Drainage Sectors

2.3   Research and consulting institutions

The Drainage Research Institute (DRI) was established in 1976 as part of the National Water Research Centre (NWRC) of MWRI to conduct applied research, monitoring, testing, and evaluation of drainage methodologies and techniques. Its activities are intended to support EPADP's implementation programme and to solve their technical problems. DRI employs about 72 professional staff and 150 supporting and administrative staff.

The Research Institute for Ground Water (RIGW), another research institute of the NWRC, carries out groundwater surveys and groundwater development studies. This institute also provides the drainage implementation programme with significant research input. It has investigated the seepage from the new land schemes located at higher elevations, which has caused waterlogging and salinisation problems in the old lands. RIGW has implemented studies on the technical and economic feasibility of vertical drainage in these zones, known as the fringe zones of the Nile Valley.

The Soils, Water, and Environment Research Institute (SWERI) is one of the Agricultural Research Centre Institutes of the Ministry of Agriculture and Land Reclamation (MALR). Its main function is to carry out soil surveys on irrigated land. SWERI has conducted extensive research on the drainage of heavy clay soils in the northern part of the Middle Delta. SWERI has also undertaken research on concurrent applications of gypsum and subsoiling and its effect on drainage enhancement.

2.4   Egyptian-Dutch Advisory Panel on Water Management

Following the establishment of EPADP in 1973, the Egyptian Government and the Dutch Government agreed on the establishment of a joint (Egyptian-Dutch) Panel. Initially, the Panel's objective was to assist the Egyptian Government in its effort to control waterlogging and salinity through accelerating the implementation of drainage projects. This was done under the following initial set-up:
*   Twice-yearly Panel Meetings (once in Egypt, once in the Netherlands);
*   Appointment of a Resident Drainage Engineer, stationed at the Drainage Research Institute (DRI);
*   Appointment of various Associate Experts guided by the Resident Engineer;
*   Allocation of a budget for: (i) Applied Research on drainage design and implementation; (ii) Consultants (national and international), and (iii) Training, both local and international, through participation in ILRI's International Course on Land Drainage.

A few of the "early drainage issues" dealt with by the Panel are:
*   Development of new drainage technology;
*   Selection of pilot areas for the investigation of various land drainage problems;
*   Study of water management in drained and non-drained rice areas;
*   Economic evaluation of land drainage;

- Reuse of drainage water for irrigation;
- Maintenance of drainage systems;
- Drainage design in rice fields;
- Economic evaluation of drainage.

The Advisory Panel Project developed over time. During the first stage (1976-1982), the Panel was a separate and independent project whose activities were solely directed towards different technical aspects of drainage. After 1982, when the technical activities of the Panel increased, the decision was made to separate the activities into different project identities with the Panel as umbrella. It was during this stage (1983-1990) that the Panel started to guide the activities of the Dutch "water" projects and to advise on some "water policy" issues. An evaluation of the Panel's performance preceded the third stage (1992-2004) during which the Panel's role became primarily one of advising on policy issues and coordinating the ongoing Dutch projects.

The Panel is chaired by the Egyptian Minister of WRI and is co-chaired by a Dutch Panel member. The other members of the panel are: six Egyptian and six Dutch members with scientific and administrative experience in drainage, land reclamation, and water resources development and management and include representatives from both the Egyptian and Netherlands Governments. The Panel secretariat services are rendered by MWRI and Alterra-ILRI. A World Bank representative, provider of the necessary funds for the unprecedented drainage implementation, also attended the first Panel meetings. The technical assistance required for this World Bank programme is supplied through the Egyptian-Netherlands bilateral cooperation.
Some selected achievements:

- Solutions were found to many technical problems;
- Policy was formulated or assistance was given to policy formulation;
- The capability of the staff involved (both Egyptian and Netherlands) was greatly enhanced;
- The work has greatly contributed to the introduction of integrated water resources management, by dealing with issues such as water quantity, water quality, environment, socio-economic conditions and gender;
- Cooperation of the Netherlands has paved the way for other donors to deal with the MWRI in an effective and efficient way.

3   Planning

EPADP's Planning Department is responsible for setting up the five-year and annual execution plans, along with the financing of projects. Negotiations with financiers of EPADP projects are done through this Department. A key element in the planning is the policy to carry out projects in clusters or land blocks, which at present are around 3 500 to 8 500 ha in size.

3.1   Investigation and design

Designing begins by obtaining surveying maps of the project area from the Egyptian Survey Authority (ESA), with updated information on villages, towns and built-up structures. Following the preparation of project maps, the field investigation programme is prepared for site sampling locations (generally forming a grid of 500 x 500 m). Groundwater levels, soil permeability and salinity are measured in the field and soils samples are collected and sent to DRI for analysis. Based on the soil permeability and groundwater levels, the layout of the subsurface drainage system is prepared and then longitudinal profiles of the collectors are made.

3.2   Tendering and contracting

Once the design album and the lists of quantities have been prepared, the project is tendered among pre-qualified drainage contractors. Local public and private sector contractors do the earthwork for remodelling open drains and installing subsurface drains. Structures to be rebuilt in open drains are awarded to local contractors in the private and public sectors, following local procedures for tendering.

The Irrigation Department was responsible for the installation of subsurface drainage systems that were constructed on a limited scale - mostly manually - until the end of the 1960s. Then, in the 1970s, Public Excavation Companies (PEC) were established for the mechanical excavation and construction of both canals and drains. These companies that belonged to the MWRI until recently are now fully owned by the Minister of Business Development, as a step towards privatisation, and are part of a separate holding company: Public Holding Company for Public Works. The introduction of mechanised installation involved several public sector companies capable of handling this technology. Gradually, more contractors from both public and private sectors joined in. The private sector companies started work as sub-contractors (for labour) to public main contractors, and later executed complete projects on their own. To facilitate this, EPADP supplies the contractors where necessary, together with the drainage machinery to get the job done. Contractors have to pay for the machinery from the instalments due for their work in the projects. When mechanised installation of subsurface drainage systems began 90% of the contractors were public contractors. Nowadays, the balance has shifted in favour of private contractors.

4   Drainage materials

Since the inception of pipe drainage projects in the 1930s, important developments have taken place in the use of drainage materials. The development of new materials and the development of new installation techniques are interdependent. This section contains a summary of the developments in drainage materials.

4.1   Pipes

At first there were clay pipes that were 100 mm in diameter and 0.30 m in length which were installed manually. Then in the 1950s came cement pipes of the same diameter but 0.50 m in length. With the introduction of mechanical laying[1] in the early 1960s, shorter cement pipes of length 0.30 m were found to be more convenient both for handling and for providing additional water entry surface. When in 1979 the production of corrugated plastic PVC pipes started it significantly helped to boost the progress of Egypt's large-scale drainage projects. The PVC pipes used nowadays for the field drains have an outside diameter of 80 mm and an inside diameter of 72 mm and are produced in government owned and managed factories.

Plastic pipes
The production of plastic pipes is a rather complex process whereby the parent material (i.e., PVC powder or PE pebbles) is heated and melted to form the correct shape and dimensions (Figure 7). This requires an industrial set-up in a factory, although for smaller diameters mobile

Figure 7   Plastic drain pipe production line

production plants have been developed. The PVC (or PE) resin, normally delivered in bags, is mixed with other additives, like fillers, heat stabilisers, lubricants, UV stabiliser and colour, in a blender at a temperature of about 100 ^{0}C. To avoid contamination of the resin with foreign matter like paper shreds from the bags and stones and so forth, it is advisable to sieve the resin before it is poured into the blender. The blended compound is fed into the barrel of the extruder via a feed screw coupled with a dosage meter. The blended compound is then plasticized at a temperature of about 200 ^{0}C and extruded through a die by means of two screw conveyors. This die delivers the pipe in a plain round shape and a corrugator attached to the end of the extruder shapes the corrugations. The pipe is cooled by heat exchange using chilled water and cold air. Finally the pipe is perforated, cut into appropriate lengths and coiled for storage and transport.

---

[1] The FAO/UNDP Pilot Drainage Project.

In 1988, a corrugated plastic production line was installed at the pipe factory in Aga[2] capable of producing HDPE pipes with diameters varying between 100 and 600 mm. In 1998, the Egyptian Public Authority of Drainage Projects decided that for all new projects collector drains pipes should be made of PVC or HDPE, 200 to 400 mm in diameter and 6 m long. Reinforced concrete pipes are still used, but only at the outlet, the flushing inlet and at places where the collector drains cross roads and irrigation canals.

Concrete pipes
The field drains until 1980 consisted of concrete pipes with a diameter of 100 mm and lenghts of 0.3 m and 0.5 m. Concrete pipes of 0.3 m were used for mechanical laying and lengths of 0.5 m for manual laying. Collector pipes are also made of concrete with diameters ranging between 150 and 600 mm and in lengths of between 0.75 and 1.00 m. The larger diameter pipes (> 400 mm) are reinforced.

Figure 8   Concrete pipe factory in Tanta in the Nile Delta (a) and a mobile production unit in a field workshop, were concrete pipes are stored in a shaded area (b)

A factory with an industrial set-up is needed to manufacture concrete pipes (Figure 8a), but they can also be made in a comparatively simple (mobile) production unit that can be easily erected in the project area (Figure 8b). The wall thickness of concrete pipes varies between 25 mm for the smaller diameter pipes and 40 mm for the larger diameter pipes. Typically, concrete pipes are made up of 500 kg cement to one m^3 of sand; the water added to this mix is about one-third of the weight of the cement. Care should be taken to use clean sand and water, certainly no brackish, saline or muddy water. The sand and cement should be properly mixed and when the water has been added it should be processed within 15 minutes.

---

[2] The Integrated Soil and Water Improvement Project (ISAWIP) in Daquahliya, North East of the Nile Delta.

The drainage contractors usually manufacture their own pipes. The equipment the contractors use is simple and easily dismantled. Contractors set up temporary field factories close to the drainage works.

Concrete pipes are manufactured in a mould that rotates and moves up and down at the same time as the cement mix is poured in so that compaction takes place (Figure 9). To ensure that good quality pipes are produced, it is necessary to regularly check that:

- The mould is circular. After being used for a long time the mould becomes oval and the connections suffer from wear and tear resulting in pipes with an irregular wall thickness over the cross section of the pipe;
- The clearance between the mould and the rotating shaft does not exceed 2 mm. A wider clearance results in an irregular wall thickness over the axis (lengthwise) of the pipe, which after installation may cause sediment to collect at the joints or obstruction of the movement of the head of a flushing machine;
- The rotating shaft is correctly set, because worn bearings will also result in irregular wall thickness;
- The correct mixture of cement, sand and water is used, otherwise the result will be an irregular surface of the inner pipe wall or even collapse of the pipe after the mould has been removed.

After the pipes are manufactured they should be stored in a roofed area in such a way that they can be thoroughly wetted daily (Figure 8b). Pipes should not be transported to the field within 28 days to allow sufficient curing.

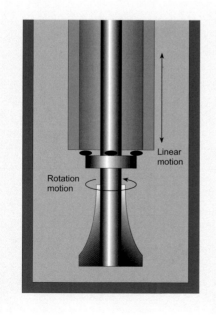

Figure 9   Concrete pipes are manufactured in a mould that simultaneously rotates and moves up and down when the cement mix is poured in the mould

4.2   Envelopes

Traditionally, a graded gravel envelope surrounded the joints of manually installed clay and cement pipes. Even after the introduction of mechanical installation of pipes, gravel envelopes continued to be installed manually along the sides and on top of the pipes as soon as they left the trench box of the machine. In the late 1970s machines were developed with funnels to evenly spread the gravel envelope, but still only along the sides and on top of the pipe. Research revealed that the cohesive clay soils of the Nile Valley and Delta do not require an envelope because they have a good structural stability. Nowadays, natural gravel is used for the envelope only if the soil is light textured with a clay content of less than 30%. Furthermore, as gravel envelopes were costly and difficult to apply, pre-wrapped synthetic envelopes were introduced in 1994. Currently, sheets of voluminous polypropylene fibres are wrapped around field drains in the factory (Figure 10).

Figure 10   PVC pipes are pre-wrapped with a voluminous envelope in the factory in Tanta

4.3 Structures

Initially, glazed crosspieces were used to connect the field drains with the smaller-diameter collector pipes and buried manholes for the larger-diameter pipes. The installation of these connections required considerable excavation and dry working conditions. Then in the 1980s, an improved connection using a plastic T-joint was introduced (Figure 11). However, though flushing inlets connected with these T-joints were tested on a pilot scale for flushing the field drains, they never achieved project status. To facilitate maintenance, concrete manholes (Ø 0.75-1.00 m) are still installed in the collector drains at every third or fourth field drain (distances varying between 150 and 200 m) and at places where there is a change in pipe diameter. The length of the hose of a flushing machine determines this distance. The last manhole is connected to an irrigation canal at the upstream end of the collector line. This so-called flushing structure can be used to flush the collector drain with irrigation water and to check whether the collector drain is functioning properly (Figure 12). At the downstream end, an outlet, normally a pitching with stones and mortar provides a safe outlet to an open main drain (Figure 13).

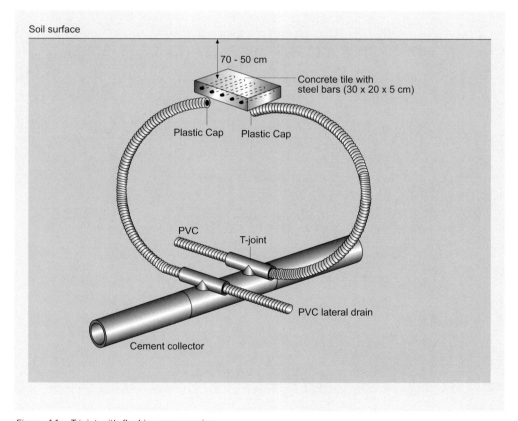

Figure 11   T-joint with flushing access pipe

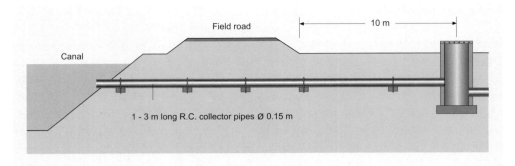

Figure 12 *Flushing structure at the upstream end of a collector drain to flush the collector drain with irrigation water*

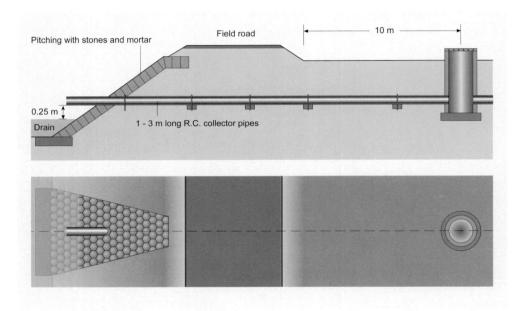

Figure 13 *Outlet Structure of a collector drain*

5   Installation

5.1   Organisation

The Egyptian Public Authority for Drainage Projects (EPADP) prepares the design of the field drainage system after thorough field investigation including in-situ measurements of the hydraulic conductivity, watertable depth and collection of soil and water samples for physical and chemical analysis. The preliminary alignment of the drains is checked for physical obstructions, inter-sections and farm boundaries. The unit design area is the catchment of a main drain or group of drains which form one interconnected hydrologic unit, averaging about 2 100 ha in size. The

final designs are tendered for bidding among drainage contractors. The contractor is responsible for checking the designs against the field conditions and requesting approval for modifications if deemed necessary. The contractor provides the materials, machinery and workmanship
necessary for implementing the project within the specified time.

The drainage contractors prepare the site and logistics such as field offices, stores and
workshops for stocking materials and producing concrete pipes. They transport the plastic pipes
from EPADP's factories to the project site. For good timing of implementation the intensive cropping system in Egypt calls for close coordination with the farmers. The rate of construction slows
down during the summer when the cotton crop is near maturation and during the rice season.
Farmers are compensated for crop damage during construction based on actual surveys of the
damaged area and the market price of the harvested crops. This compensation, which represents social support to the farmer during the construction phase, is recovered as part of the
cost recovery system adopted in Egypt. The cost of the field drainage system is recovered in
full over a period of 20 years without interest commencing five years after construction of the
drains, which allow farmers to gain full benefits.

5.2 Field Conditions

The field conditions in Egypt, namely, type of soil and agro-hydrologic conditions are uniform.
The soil consists of relatively deep alluvial soils with a high clay and silt content. However, at the
fringes of the Nile Valley and Nile Delta soils tend to contain more sand and lose their structural
stability. When the watertable is high these soils become problematic particularly under high
hydraulic gradient creating quicksand phenomena (Sherashra and Haress). In the Western Nile
Delta, some areas are characterised by calcareous hard rocks in the subsoil (Nubariya). The low
areas in the northern part of the Nile Delta are subject to artesian pressure: significant upward
seepage occurs where the resistance of the overlaying low permeable soil decreases.

Sherashra: quick sand
Implementation of the drainage system of the Sherashra catchment area, southwest of Alexan-
dria, was planned to take place in 1974. Auger holes drilled during the field investigation showed
a distinct change in the soil profile with unstable light soils below a depth of 1.0 - 1.5 m. As soon
as the auger hit the unstable soils groundwater rose under pressure to a shallow depth below
the soil surface and the auger holes caved in when digging exceeded the depth of the stable
surface soil. Further investigations of the hydro-geologic conditions revealed the prevalence in
the area of a piezometric head of around 1.0 m. A first pilot area implemented at Sherashra
produced disastrous results. The concrete pipes used for field drains were soon completely filled
with sand. The manually installed collector pipes were dislocated from their positions under the
effect of quicksand conditions. Only after the introduction of plastic pipes and mechanical
installation of collectors in 1983 did the construction of pipe drainage become a possibility in
this area. However, the results were not entirely satisfactory due to problems with the installation
of the gravel envelope.

Haress: upward pressure

The Haress area, located to the northeast of Sherishra, has a lot of marine deposits in its top profile. The layers of shells found in the subsoil significantly increases the permeability of the soil at the drain depth. A pilot area was constructed in 1993-1994: pre-wrapped PVC corrugated plastic pipes were used for the field drains and corrugated imperforated HDPE pipes for the collectors. The field drains were installed successfully and their performance was adequate. This was not the case, however, with collectors installed at a greater depth (2.0-2.5 m). Groundwater rising under pressure in the trench behind the trencher machine made the imperforated pipe (filled with air) float above the water. The problems were even greater when an attempt was made to lay the bigger pipes in a trench that was excavated with backhoe. To overcome these problems the solution was to use perforated pipes for the collectors as well: during installation these perforated pipes quickly filled with water and consequently stayed in place. A cheap type of envelope (thin sheet) was used to prevent the silt from entering the pipe. Clogging of the envelope was not a problem since the collector is not designed to have a dewatering function. The conditions in the Haress area were the motive behind the use of trenchless machines under these conditions, which proved to be successful later in 1996.

Nubariya: hard rock

The Nubaria area is part of the Nile Delta's western fringes reclaimed during the 1960s-1970s. The alluvial silty clay topsoil of the Delta diminishes towards the west and calcareous soil dominates the profile with hard rocks frequently intersecting the soil profile. Under the reclamation programme of that time a high watertable developed so that a drainage system was necessary. The normal type of trenchers operating in the Delta failed to operate under the Nubaria conditions. A partnership and cooperation between the contractor and the machine supplier yielded a special type of trencher with a more powerful engine and a different design and material for the digging mechanism (Figure 14).

Figure 14   A rock trencher installing a concrete collector drain operating in the Nubaria area

5.3   Installation Methods

Pipe drains were installed manually until the beginning of the 1960s. They were laid in ditches excavated manually with spades. Then in the early 1960s, continuous chain tile laying machines (flat trencher) were introduced for the first time in a number of pilot areas marking the beginning of Egypt's modern drainage. The objective was to test new technologies and develop design criteria for use in the large-scale post High Aswan Dam drainage projects. With the start of the World Bank funded projects in 1970, mechanical installation of pipe field drains was introduced on a large scale. By the mid-1980s there were heavy trenchers to install concrete collector drain pipes with diameters of up to 250 mm. Larger diameter pipes were still installed in trenches dug by excavators. A trenchless drainage machine was successfully tested on a pilot scale in 1995-1996. Hydraulic excavators and draglines are used for digging main open drains.

The use of imported machinery in Egypt went through a process of adjustment and modification to suite local conditions. Among these was a water tank to spray water on the cutting blades of the trencher chain and along the sides of the trench box to reduce the resistance of the cohesion forces of the sticky clays. Another modification had to do with the width of the crawlers to produce adequate pressure for the bearing capacity of the Egyptian soils. Similar adjustments were made to the length of the trench box, the arrangement and design of blades on the revolving machines and so forth. Successive development of technical specifications followed to specify the appropriate type and characteristics of machines suitable for the local conditions.

The required depth and grade of the manually installed pipe drain systems were adjusted and verified using a surveying level. Visual controls (sighting targets) were used to adjust the depth and grade of the drain pipes laid by machines. After installation the depth and grade ware checked again using a surveying level for quality control. Laser equipment was introduced in the late 1980s. In the 1990s the use of laser equipment became a compulsory condition of the construction contract. In the beginning of the 21st Century it was decided that large size diameter corrugated PVC or PE pipes would be used for the installation of collector drains (Figure 15).

While tractors and trailers transport the materials in the field, manual labour is still used to move the materials (pipes & envelopes) around and to feed the machines during operations. The use of manual labour significantly lessened with the introduction of pre-wrapped corrugated plastic pipes. The excavation for structures is either done manually or with backhoes depending on the contractor. Backfilling the trenches is mostly a manual operation although some contractors use tractors provided with a dozer blade.

The contractors own and provide the drainage machinery. However, the Government of Egypt has been helping the contractors from the beginning to purchase drainage machinery through a special arrangement under the World Bank projects. The machinery is imported by the government imported the machinery, handed over to the contractors and the cost collected in instalments while the project is being implemented. This has helped the civil contractors to build up their capacity to implement large-scale projects. Economic change and the transfer of contractors mostly to the private sector has resulted in most contractors now being able to buy their machines directly from the market, although the original arrangement is still a viable option.

Figure 15   Installation of large size corrugated PVC pipe

6   Operational Research[3]

Accurate data on capacities, efficiencies, availability of machines, equipment and contractors are needed for the planning and contracting of the drainage projects. To collect such data, an Operational Research Unit/ORU was established in 1993 within the Planning and Follow-up Department/PFD of EPADP, to carry out the following:
- Determine the work and time standards for the planning and follow-up of the drainage projects, including financial budgets;
- Analyse and support the purchase procedure of machinery and equipment for the Mechanical Department;
- Analyse and improve working methods of the various activities of EPADP.

The results of the Operational Research Unit are used to:
- Monitor the performance of individual projects;
- Assess the performance of contractors and subsequently award new contracts;

---

[3] This section is based on the Chapter Capacity and Efficiency of Drainage Machines in Egypt published in the book Drainage along the River Nile, edited by H.J. Nijland. Authors are Eng. Resk Menshawy, J. Penninkhof, Eng Omayma S. Saheen, and Ir. H.J.P. Visser.

- Determine the number of machines needed to implement EPADP's annual plans;
- Advise the Mechanical Department on the purchase of new machinery and equipment.

Some results of the operational research activities are presented in the following sections.

6.1 Capacity and Efficiency of Drainage machines in Egypt

An installation rate of about 75 000 ha per year implies the installation of approximately 1850 km of collector drains and 18 500 km of field drains. One of the main factors affecting the implementation rate of subsurface drainage is the number, productivity, and quality of the drainage machines. Inventories of data were made on the efficiencies and capacities of the various types of drainage machines operational in Egypt collected by the Operational Research Unit from which the efficiencies and capacities of these machines were assessed. The results are used for the planning of future projects.

Inventory
In 1994, an inventory was made of all drainage machines working all over Egypt. Three categories of data were collected:
- *Machine specifications:* chassis number, engine number, machine type, manufacturer, year of manufacture and date of purchase;
- *Project-related data:* sector, directorate, contractor;
- *Performance data:* general condition of the machine, condition of the main engine, hydraulic system, cutting system, drive shaft, traction and chassis.

A total of 144 field and 58 collector drainage machines were assessed. A specially developed 'Drainage Machine Inventory Program' processed the data. The overall condition of a machine was specified as *"good", "moderate", "bad"* or *"beyond repair"* (Figure 16). Drainage machines classified as *"good", "moderate",* or *"bad"* were considered operational machines. Most machines were not fully operational the whole year around. On a yearly basis it was estimated that about 85% of the *"moderate"* and 60% of the drainage machines in a *"bad"* condition could be

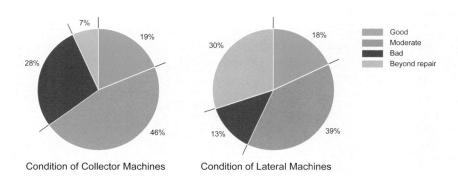

Figure 16   Result of the inventory conducted in 1994: Condition of drainage machines

considered operational. Of the machines classified as *"beyond repair"*, none would be able to work. The conclusion was that of all drainage machines in Egypt 59% of the field drainage machines and 76% of the collector drainage machines were operational.

Both field and collector drain machines were in a "good" condition up to the age of approximately 7 years, changing to a "moderate" condition between the age of 8 and 15 years. After approximately 16 years, the condition between field and collector drainage machines started to deviate. Of the field drainage machines older than 16 years nearly 75% were "beyond repair" and 14% were in a "bad" condition. Figures for collector drainage machines were 13% and 43%, respectively. Thus, collector machines have a longer lifespan than field drainage machines. But, as efficiency increases over the years the operational lifetime will drop to 10 to 12 years in the future.

Efficiencies of drainage machines
Efficiency studies were conducted by field engineers of the EPADP Directorates with the support of the ORU. Different types of field and collector drainage machines were selected in various projects. Efficiency sheets were filled in on a daily basis, indicating how many hours the machine was working and, if applicable, the reasons why it was not working. A special computer program processed the data from which it could be determined how many days per year and how many hours per day the machines were working, and the reasons for not working (Table 1). In Egypt, the average number of working days per year is 198. The non-working days are Fridays, holidays (including unofficial "days off" taken by contractors), and the "crop stoppage period" when rice or cotton are grown. Although Ministerial Law enforces the "crop stoppage period" it varies from project to project, and most drainage machines stand idle in this period even though the projects have not stopped completely. The length of a working day was 9 hours on average with an average effective time of 2.9 hours/day for collector drainage machines and 4 hours/day for field drainage machines (Table 2). There is a clear difference in time losses between the two types of machines: for collector machines, the field condition and the organisation of the work are more important, which can be explained by the higher ground pressure of the collector machines and the more demanding work organisation because of the concrete pipes. For field drainage machines, the technical breakdowns and the maintenance are more important since field drainage machines suffer more wear and tear and subsequent mechanical problems.

Table 2 represents the average situation of the machines. The efficiency, however, has a close relationship with the age of the machines: the older the machine the lower the efficiency (Table 3). The efficiency decreases from more than 4 hours per day for new machines to less than 2 hours per day after 15 years. The technical condition of the machines is the most important cause of this decrease in effective time.

Table 1   Example of a time and motion study of a field (lateral) drainage machine

Elements	Total time [cmin]	Drain length [metres]	Frequency	Time/100 m [cmin]	Time/freq [cmin]
Direct effective time					
Main element:					
- Laying pipes	441,678	39,406		1,120.0	
Indirect effective time					
Support elements:					
- Driving back	56,872	23,057		246.6	
- Lifting shoe	6,771		187		36
- Lowering shoe	5,287		145		36
- Digging connection	29,781		171		174
- Connecting outlet	12,944		102		127
- Filling water tank	3,581	39,406		9.1	
Additional elements:					
Short tech. breakdown	6,153	39,406		15.6	
Short organisational:					
- Laser	7,100	39,406		18.0	
- Pipes	70,905	39,406		179.9	
- Fuel	14,736	39,406		37.4	
- Field obstruction	7,296	39,406		18.5	
- Gravel	102,560	5,342		1,919.9	
- Field transportation	2,759	39,406		70.0	

Table 2   Daily availability times of collector and drainage machines

Time	Collectors		Field drains	
	%	(hours)	%	(hours)
Non-available time:				
* Field condition	16	1.4	9	0.8
* Technical breakdown	13	1.2	17	1.6
Subtotal non-available	29	2.6	26	2.4
Available time:				
* Non-effective				
- Maintenance	7	0.7	12	1.0
- Meal time	11	1.0	10	0.9
- Organisation	20	1.8	8	0.7
Subtotal available	38	3.5	30	2.6
* Effective time	33	2.9	44	4.0
Total time	100	9.0	100	9.0

491

Table 3   Effective time of field and collector drainage machines related to different ages

Age of machines [year]	Field drain machines [%]	[hrs/day]	Collector drain machines [%]	[hrs/day]
0 - 5	53	4.8	46	4.1
6 - 10	42	3.9	33	3.0
11 - 15	27	2.4	23	2.1
> 15	18	1.6	18	1.6

Capacities of drainage machines

Up to 1996, a total of 300 time and motion studies had been conducted. In each time and motion study, the work process of the drainage machine had been measured in a clearly defined part or activity, a so-called element (Table 4). Most elements, such as lifting and lowering the shoe, adjusting the laser and stop for gravel, were not influenced by the type of machine and the circumstances in the field. Only the element "laying pipes" (digging activity) was highly dependent on the type of machine, the condition of the soil, the type of pipes used (corrugated plastic pipes or concrete pipes), the applied envelope material (gravel or pre-wrapped synthetic envelopes), drain depth, and so forth. Assessment of the time for elements not influenced by the type of machine and the field circumstances was done by taking the average of all observations for field and collector drainage machines, respectively. The element "laying pipes" needed to be determined for each type of machine and each circumstance separately.

A specially designed "Norm Calculation Program" processed the field data. This computer program calculated the work standards for each type of drainage machine producing work and time standards, expressed in m/hour and h/km (Table 5). These standards were based on the effective time determined by the efficiency studies (Table 2). The work standards were based on the "standard" subsurface drainage system with field drain lengths of 200 m and collector lengths of 1500 m. Note, the efficiency of the machines is related to the age of the machines as well as the capacity of the machines. The results apply to field drainage machines installing corrugated PVC pipes without gravel, and collector machines installing concrete pipes.

The following conclusions were drawn based on these efficiency studies:
- Depending on the age of the machines, the capacity of field drainage machines varied between 190 and 380 m per hour, and that of collector machines between 55 and 100 m per hour;
- The capacity of the older machines was significantly lower than that of the newer machines, partly due to decreasing quality and partly due to innovations on the newer machines.

Table 4   An example of the calculation of a Work and Time Standard for laying pipe drains without envelope

Work Standard Calculation Form

Method: Laying plastic pipes of 80 mm in diameter from both sides of the collector drain

Average length of the drain 200 m

Depth of trench 1.20 to 1.50 m

Machine: All field drainage machines

Envelope: none

Elements of work process	Work standard per km field drain	
	Minutes/element	Total Minutes
1. Laying pipes		112.0
2. Turning and driving back	24.7	
Lifting shoe	1.8	
Lowering shoe	1.8	
Digging connection	8.7	
Inlet outlet connection	6.4	
Filling water tank	0.9	
Subtotal		44.3
3. Short technical breakdowns	1.6	
Subtotal		1.6
4. Short organisational breakdowns		
- Stop for pipes	18.0	
- Stop for fuel	3.7	
- Adjustment laser	1.8	
- Field obstructions	1.9	
Subtotal		25.4
- Stop for gravel		
5. Transportation in the field	0.7	
Subtotal		0.7
Total minutes per km of field drain		**184.00**
Work Standard: metres/hour [= (1000: total minutes) x 60]		**326.09**
Time Standard: hours/kilometre (= Total minutes: 60)		**3.07**

Table 5   Capacity of field and collector drainage machines based on effective time

Age of machine (years)	Field drainage machine (m/hour)	Collector drainage machine (m/hour)
0 - 5	380	100
6 - 10	320	95
11 - 15	250	85
> 15	190	55

6.2   Application of the research results

The operational research proves to be an important tool in upgrading the quality and quantity of drainage projects implemented by EPADP. It provides indicators that can be used for management support, for instance, to assess the performance of the available machinery as a planning tool or for the purchase of new machines.

Performance Assessment
The overall results of the inventory and time and motion studies revealed that in January 1997:
  • A total of 57 collector and 126 field drainage machines were operational;
  • For the implementation of subsurface drainage, about 198 working days were available per year;
  • The effective time for collector and field drainage machines was 3 and 4 hours per day, respectively;
  • The capacity of collector drainage machines decreased from 100 m/h for new machines to 55 m/h for machines that were older than 15 years. The figures for field drainage machines were 380 and 190 m/h, respectively.

Planning Tool
Results of the time and motion studies are used for planning new drainage projects. The capacity of the field drainage machines is a decisive factor for the implementation rate of drainage projects. With the available research data on field drainage machines, it was possible to calculate the total capacity of all drainage machines operational in Egypt, but also the capacities of individual contractors, and suchlike. The data can be used as a follow-up tool for individual projects. For example, say the following machines are available for a project: 3 field drainage machines, each 8 years old and 1 collector drainage machine 15 years old. Therefore, for this project the yearly capacity will be:
  • Laying of collector drains: 198 days x 1.62 hours/day x 55 m/hour = 17.6 km collector drain;
  • Laying of field drains: 198 days x 3.78 hours/day x 320 m/hour x 3 machines = 718.5 km field drain.

The research data can also be used to determine the number of new machines needed to implement EPADP's annual plan. For example, in the annual plan for 1995-96, the target was providing 108 000 ha with subsurface drainage. The available capacity, calculated by the Operational Research Unit was good for 94 000 ha, thus new machines had to be purchased for 14 000 ha. With an average capacity for new machines of 400 m/h, 198 available working days, and 4 effective hours per day, it was determined that about 10 new field drainage machines would be needed to implement the drainage in the additional 14 000 ha. So in 1995, EPADP purchased 10 new field drainage machines and 5 new collector drainage machines (3060 km of field drains requires 198 x 4.77 x 0.380 = 8.5 field drainage machines and 340 km collector drain requires 198 x 4.14 x 0.1 = 4.2 collector machines).

Purchase of Drainage Machines
Selection of suppliers can be done according to the performance of machines bought in the past. An example is presented in Table 6, in which the capacity of two types of machines has calculated from time and motion studies conducted in 1990-199. The capacity of machine X is slightly higher than the capacity of machine Y, but the differences are small indicating that the capacity does not play an important role in the selection criterion for new machines.

Table 6 *Capacity of two types of field drainage machines calculated from time and motion studies conducted in 1990-1991*

Type of drainage machine	Capacity	
	metres/hour	hours/km
Machine X	380	2.63
Machine Y	362	2.76

A breakdown of the total time (Table 7) indicated that there is no significant difference between the two machines. Although there are differences in non-available and available time as machine Y has fewer technical breakdowns, but the substantially higher time for maintenance counterbalances this advantage. The overall conclusion is that the performance and quality of both machines are good. The choice of one or other of the machines must thus be based on other selection criteria (such as price or after sales service).

Table 7 *Comparison efficiencies of two different types of field drainage machine*

Time specification	Machine X		Machine Y	
	(%)	(hours)	(%)	(hours)
Non-available time:				
* Field condition	10	0.9	8	0.7
* Technical breakdown	19	1.7	9	0.8
Subtotal non-available time	29	2.6	17	1.5
Available time:				
* Non-effective				
- Maintenance	13	1.2	22	2.0
- Meal time	10	0.9	12	1.0
- Organisation	12	1.1	9	0.8
Subtotal non-effective time	35	3.2	43	3.8
* Effective time	36	3.2	40	3.7
Total time	100	9.0	100	9.0

6.3   Quality Control: Video inspection

EPADP in cooperation with DRI is continuously looking for ways to improve existing practices, not only pertaining to design and implementation but also research. For example, to assess the performance of the drains, the Drainage Research Institute tested a video inspection unit in the Abu Matamir area in the Western Nile Delta region (Table 8). To interpret these results we recommend the classification system below:

- *No maintenance required:* Sediment on the bottom of the pipe is stirred up by the camera;
- *Need for regular maintenance (flushing):* Sediment is pushed in front of the camera occasionally, but camera can still pass. Estimated height of sediment > ¼ of pipe diameter;
- *Need for major maintenance/rehabilitation:* Camera cannot pass, amount of sediment is (i) pipe is ¼ full, (ii) pipe is ½ full, or (iii) pipe is completely blocked.

Table 8   *Some results of the video inspection of field drain with/without envelope at Abu Matamir, Western Nile Delta, Egypt*

Field drain (no.)	Manhole (no.)	Collector (no.)	Length (m)	Envelope	Status
3	2	2	86	With	No problem
4	2	2	100	Without	Camera stuck at 50 m
13	4	4	100	Without	Pipe broken at 2.5 m
14	4	4	166	With	Camera stuck at 128 m
17	5	4	121	With	Camera could not move, pipe dry
7	3	6	100	Without	Outlet broken
9	4	6	100	Without	Traces of sediment
10	4	6	175	With	Roots at 17 m
9	3	8	100	Without	Lot of sediment
10	3	8	215	With	Camera stuck at 133 m

6.4   Performance Assessment

In Egypt, performance assessment is used to establish the need for rehabilitation of a drainage system (Figure 17). The performance assessment involves three sequential steps (Figure 18). Each step is only undertaken when the previous step has confirmed its necessity and, therefore, the performance assessment process may end after a particular step. Therefore, it may not be necessary to complete all three steps or to do them in the indicated order. For example the preliminary investigation may be stopped when the complaint assessment indicates that the complaints do not require further action (and it would be resumed when the complaints persist or when other new information becomes available).

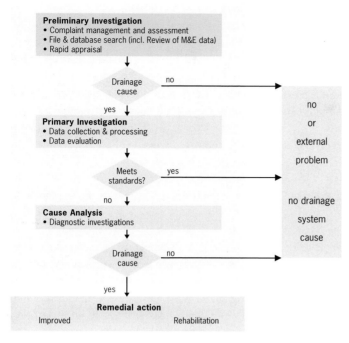

Figure 17   Performance Assessment of drainage implementation activities done by EPADP

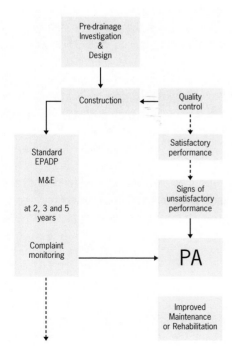

Figure 18   Standard Performance Assessment procedure used by EPADP

Step 1   Preliminary investigation based on existing information
This first step is a preliminary investigation, mainly based on analysis of the existing information and includes the following activities:
- Complaint management: review and assessment of the complaints received from the users (farmers);
- File/database search: this includes the age of the project together with the applied technology (materials and construction methods); the applied quality control; the contract documents;
- Agricultural data search: crop productivity and cropping pattern;
- Rapid appraisal: a short field survey to assess the drainage conditions.

The need for the second step is assessed based on this preliminary investigation.

Step 2   Preliminary investigation based on new data
This step requires considerable field work and expenditure and should only be undertaken when step 1 has confirmed that there are sound indications that there are indeed waterlogging and/or salinity problems in the area or in a considerable part of the area, and that these problems are most probably due to a malfunctioning of the existing drainage system. In this step, this assumption is confirmed or rejected by collecting data on watertables, soils salinity and crop yield and comparing these with the accepted standards of good performance. This step can be divided in two sub-steps:
- Data collection and processing: monitoring the selected indicator parameters followed by some form of processing to facilitate the use of the collected data;
- Data evaluation: comparing the collected indicator data with the accepted standards on the basis of which judgements can be made on the performance of the pipe drainage systems.

It is of course possible that this step reveals that there are no real waterlogging and salinity problems in the area or that the prevailing conditions are not due to malfunctioning of the pipe drainage systems. If this is the case, the performance assessment is terminated.

Step 3   Cause analysis
If step 2 has confirmed that the performance of the installed pipe drainage systems does not meet the expected standards, the cause(s) of the under-performance of the system(s) have to be identified. The outcome of this step can be either an improved maintenance programme or the rehabilitation of (part) of the system.

7   Capacity Building

7.1   Drainage Executive Management Project

In the 1970s, EPADP and the contractors faced the problems of mechanised installation of drain pipes, personnel with little experience with this drainage technology and the large scale of the projects. The enormous amount of modernised drainage machinery demanded experienced civil engineers, supervisors, operators, skilled technicians and foremen, as well as proper planning and organisation of the implementation of the projects.

Initiatives were taken to tackle these problems under the umbrella of the Egyptian-Dutch Panel on Land Drainage. The Drainage Executive Management Project (DEMP) was established aimed at strengthening the EPADP organisation and upgrading the qualifications of the staff of EPADP and the personnel of drainage contractors, improving the standards of design, implementation, operation and maintenance of drainage. Through the DEPMP project long-lasting cooperation between EPADP and Rijkswaterstaat in the Netherlands developed.

It was considered necessary to set up a training programme at various levels to acquaint EPADP engineers with the different aspects of handling and dealing with new materials and techniques, made necessary through the advancement of mechanisation. Specialised and/or additional training had to be organised for a considerable number of personnel. Only in this way could EPADP and its contractors sustain a high standard of durable construction work.

7.2   Tanta Training Centre

When the DEMP project commenced there was no training centre for trainees to go to. Moreover, it was mutually agreed that on-the-spot training would be the most practical and effective approach in the short run. The conclusion was that the trainers should go to the field, and in this way the on-the-job training for EPADP and contract field staff began. This training programme was known as *"in-service training"*, and became a regular event (Figure 19).

Figure 19   In-Service Training Team making video recordings

First, Dutch instructors together with their Egyptian counterparts visited and trained the staff of EPADP and the staff of the contractor in the directorates all over Egypt. Gradually, the Egyptian instructors took over the training *("train the trainers")*. The *"in-service training"* proved to be an instrument not only to train staff successfully in mechanised drainage implementation, but also to introduce new techniques, such as using laser equipment and rodding equipment for quality control. Training of EPADP staff in the Netherlands was also part of the DEMP project. However, after a few years it was felt that the range of training was still too limited. The need for more specific training courses became evident during the *"in-service training"* visits and ultimately the visits of EPADP staff to vocational training centres in the Netherlands convinced the EPADP management of the need for a permanent training centre. This led to the establishment of the Drainage Training Centre in Tanta.

The Drainage Training Centre in Tanta was established in 1991 to secure specific training and/or refresher courses for different levels of responsibility in land drainage projects. The DTC is currently a fully operational vocational training centre and an integrated part of the EPADP organisation. The DTC contributes to strengthening and upgrading the entire organisation. The training activities at the DTC focus on personnel of the EPADP organisation and contractors, in order to:
- Increase their skills for the job;
- Obtain essential knowledge to perform their job;
- Improve the quality and the quantity of their performance.

The DTC has all the facilities to conduct practical training courses (Figure 20). Besides the theoretical lessons much attention is paid to practical training of the trainees. All the instructors at the DTC are engineers with many years of experience in drainage practice in Egypt. The Annual training programme includes: field engineer execution courses, maintenance engineer courses, laser courses, surveying courses, operating drainage machines courses, channel maintenance with mowing buckets and so forth. The *"in-service training"* has become an integrated part of DTC's course programme.

Figure 20   Training activity at the Drainage Training Centre

Case Study - India

Case Study - India

1   Background

Subsurface drainage practices were introduced to India only recently. Thus far, only about 18 000 ha waterlogged saline land in canal irrigation commands have been provided with subsurface drainage systems, the majority of which is less than 10 years old. The bulk of the coverage is in Rajasthan (15 000 ha), Haryana (1 500 ha) and Karnataka (2 000 ha). Therefore, much of the drainage experiences in the country are related to these three areas (Figure 1).

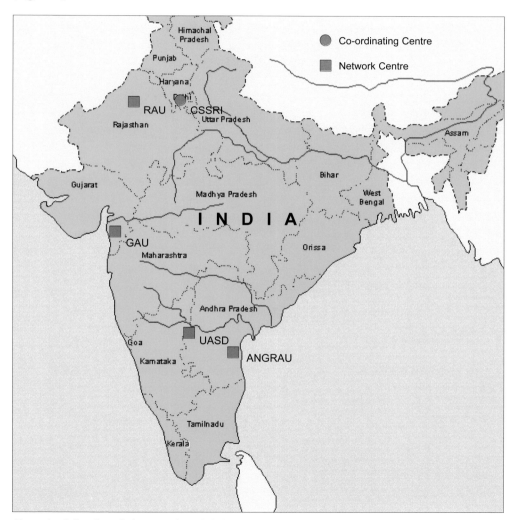

Figure 1   Subsurface drainage projects in India

India experiences a wide range of climatic and physiographic conditions and a correspondingly wide range of waterlogging and soil salinity problems. These problems are broadly classified into the following three groups:

- *Rainfed induced waterlogging* is found naturally in imperfectly drained land in much of the country during the monsoon season, with the exception of the arid parts of Gujarat and Rajasthan;
- *Natural salinity* occurs in various locations in the semi-arid parts of the north-western and western part of the Gangetic plain under the prevailing hydrologic and geochemical conditions of the land. Natural salinity is also found in the plains and deltaic areas along the coast;
- *Irrigation-induced waterlogging and salinity* is a relatively recent feature that developed in the late 19th century when large-scale canal irrigation was introduced. These problems are found in different command areas throughout the country, either in the form of waterlogging only, or a combination of waterlogging and soil salinity.

It is estimated that some 8.4 million ha is affected by soil salinity and alkalinity, of which about 5.5 million ha is also waterlogged, mainly in the irrigation canal commands and 2.5 million ha in the coastal areas. Even though some surface drainage improvements have been undertaken in rainfed and irrigation-induced waterlogged areas, the drainage requirements of much of the farmland are yet to receive any attention. Control of waterlogging and soil salinity through subsurface drainage has been gaining ground in recent years. Large expansions in this field may come up in the coming decades to safeguard the sustainability of agro-economy in the canal-irrigated areas that are seriously threatened by waterlogging and soil salinity. Research for the control of waterlogging and soil salinity received a big boost under the Canada aided Rajasthan Agricultural Drainage Research (RAJAD) project and the Netherlands aided Haryana Operational Pilot Project (HOPP) and Indo-Dutch Network Project (INDP). The necessary research developments for large-scale expansion of subsurface drainage have emerged from these projects.

2   Organisation

The improvement of drainage in India is largely planned and implemented as a flood control measure. As a result most of the attention has been on the construction of flood protection embankments along the rivers and major surface drains. Nevertheless, on-farm drainage has started to receive some attention in irrigation command areas. The development of water resources and their use is a state issue. The Central Government through the Ministry of Water Resources provides the policy, directions and expertise for planning, development and use of water resources within the states as well as among the states. International projects on Water Resources are also dealt with by the Central Government. The Command Area Development Wing, headed by a Commissioner, looks after the water and land management issues in irrigation commands. Under the Command Area Development Programme, the construction of irrigation systems up to tertiary levels, land development, drainage improvement and construction of road networks are taken up in an integrated manner. The Agriculture Departments of the State

Governments, supported by the Agriculture Department of the Central Government, are responsible for the appropriate agriculture practices to the farming community as well as land reclamation and soil and water conservation activities.

Water management and drainage research is conducted at both central and state level under the Indian Council of Agricultural Research (ICAR) through its own specialised research institutes and the various state agricultural universities. The research mainly pertains to crop drainage requirements and land reclamation practices. The construction aspects of drainage have received very little attention.

In some states like Haryana subsurface drainage is considered to be a measure for land reclamation and, therefore, executed by the Agriculture Department. The surface drainage network and the canal water supply, distribution and management are, however, under the purview of Irrigation Department. Thus the improvement of on-farm (subsurface) drainage is not integrated with the improvement of the main irrigation and drainage systems and improvements in management.

Drainage improvements within an irrigation command are entrusted to the Command Area Development Authority (CADA) in some states like Rajasthan. CADA is headed by Area Development Commissioner (ADC) under whom come the wings of irrigation, agricultural extension, agricultural research, land development and revenue, all under the overall responsibility of the Department of Command Area Development and Water Use. The major drainage and irrigation networks are operated and maintained, scheme-by-scheme, by the Irrigation Wing and the on-farm drainage improvements by the Land Development Wing. Outside the command areas, the improvement of drainage is the responsibility of the Irrigation Department. Thus there is no integrated and centralised organisation for improving drainage and the policy and practices also suffer as they vary with each department.

3   Planning

As there are no centralised organisation in India to diagnose, monitor and implement drainage measures there is also no systematic planning to address the drainage problems. The drainage improvements are limited to waterlogged areas in the form of open drainage and subsurface drainage for waterlogged saline areas. The monitoring activities, identification and implementation are spread over several departments.

4 Drainage materials

Pipes
The principal materials that have been used for subsurface drainage systems are clay pipes in South India and PVC pipes in the North India.

Clay pipes
Bell-mouthed clay pipes with a row of eight perforations on the underside, 60 cm in length and 100 mm diameter for field drains and 150 mm diameter for collectors, were used in South India in the 1970s and 1980s because plastic pipes were not available. The material cost was three times the cost of installation. Furthermore, the performance of drainage systems was severely affected by the displacement of the pipes and choking of drain lines. At present there are a few pilot projects in progress with corrugated PVC drain pipes that may gradually replace clay pipes.

Concrete pipes
Concrete pipes have been used only for collector and field drains on a pilot scale. For example in the Sampla and Mundlana pilot areas in Haryana (Figure 2).

Figure 2   Concrete pipes (Ø 100 mm) used in Sampla Pilot Area, Haryana

PVC pipes
The production of corrugated PVC drain pipe only commenced in the early 1990s and then only up to 100 mm in diameter conforming to DIN specifications. These corrugated PVC pipes were used for field drains and reinforced cement, concrete or PVC rigid pipes for collector drains. Then, in the mid-1990s under the RAJAD project, corrugated PVC drain pipes of seven sizes became available, ranging in diameter from 80 mm to 450 mm (Table 1).

Envelopes
In the large drainage installation projects both granular and synthetic envelope materials have been used. In areas where clay pipes were used sand blinding, namely, backfill with sand around the pipe was practised (Figure 3). A considerable amount of testing of envelope materials has

been done in sandy loam soils under the HOPP and IDNP projects and in clay soils under the RAJAD Project. Field investigations under RAJAD and laboratory investigations at the Central Soil Salinity Research Institute (see Box 1) showed the soil texture (clay percentage) and sodium absorption ratio (SAR) to be the significant determinants of the need for an envelope. The criteria for deciding on the need for envelope were as follows:
- Clay > 40%   Envelope not required
- Clay 30 - 40% & SAR > 16   Envelope required
- Clay < 30%   Envelope required

The specifications for the envelope adopted by respectively the HOPP and RAJAD project material were as follows.
- *Sandy Soils:* For sandy loam soils, non-woven polypropylene material of a minimum thickness of 3 mm weighing 300 gm/m^2 or more with a pore size of O_{90} and between 350 and 550 microns is recommended. The envelope should be strong enough for manual or machine wrapping and for transport and installation by hand or machine;
- *Clay Soils:* For clay soils, non-woven polypropylene material of a minimum thickness of 0.9 mm when compressed and a weight of at least of 240 gm/m^2 is recommended. The permeability of the envelope should be at least 20 m/day and 95% of the openings of the fabric should be smaller than 150 microns but not smaller than 100 microns. The tensile strength of the envelope should be at least 360 N.

Table 1   Technical specifications of corrugated PVC drain pipes

Nominal diameter in mm		80	100	160	200	294	355	455
Inside diameter in mm		72	88	144	178	258	315	401
Depth of corrugation in mm		4.2	6.0	7.6	10.3	17.1	19.0	24.6
Pipe coil length in metres		100	75	30	6	6	6	6
No. of perforations per metres		120	140	-	-	-	-	-
No. of perforations in cross section		3	4	-	-	-	-	-
Width of perforation in mm		1.8	1.8	-	-	-	-	-
Length of perforation in mm	Min	8.5	8.5	-	-	-	-	-
	Max	15.0	15.0	-	-	-	-	-
Water inlet area in cm^2/m	Min	18.4	21.4	-	-	-	-	-
	Max	32.4	37.8	-	-	-	-	-
Bending radius at 0 ^{0}C in mm approximately		240	300	480	600	882	1065	1365

Figure 3   Installation of a sand envelope in the ACRIP Appikalta Pilot Area, Andhra Pradesh: a) sealing the joint; b) sand filter around a concrete drain and c & d) around a plastic drain

5   Installation equipment

Large-scale subsurface drainage installation is relatively new in India. International contractors imported the drainage machinery and undertook the bulk of the installation under RAJAD project. For HOPP, the Netherlands Government provided a trencher, with which about 1000 ha area has been covered so far.

6   Examples of large-scale drainage projects

6.1   Rajasthan Agricultural Drainage Research Project

The Rajasthan Agricultural Drainage Research Project (RAJAD) was the first major project to install subsurface drainage systems at a large-scale in India. The project was a joint undertaking funded by the Government of Canada, Government of India and the State Government of Rajasthan. The project was a large-scale, applied research project on the use of horizontal subsurface drainage and associated water management techniques to control soil salinity and waterlogging problems in irrigated agricultural lands. The project was located in the Chambal Command area in Rajasthan. The total Chambal Command area is 385 000 ha, of which 229 000 ha is under irrigation. Waterlogging and salinity problems followed the introduction of irrigation in the area in the 1960's. The project aimed at:

- Capacity building of the state government and farmers to address the problems of waterlogging and soil salinity;
- Development of design criteria for subsurface drainage through pilot area research;
- Establishment of facilities for drain pipe supply;
- Demonstration and implementation of large-scale mechanised subsurface drainage installation;
- Construction of subsurface drainage using local machines and persons;
- Pilot testing of Integrated Water and Agriculture Management.

The project started in 1991 and by the end of 1998 an area of about 15 000 ha was provided with subsurface drainage at an overall costs of € 41.3 million (2000 prices). The overall crop yield increased about 25%.

Project organization
The Government of Canada designated the Canadian International Development Agency (CIDA) as the agency responsible for the implementation of the project and CIDA appointed a Canadian Project Executing Agency. The Commissioner of the Chambal Command Area Authority appointed the Project Manager (Figure 4). A Project Steering Committee (PSC) was responsible for the programme review, policy, budget approval, external institutions coordination and report review. A Technical Coordination Committee (TCC) coordinated the Pilot Research and design criteria recommendations.

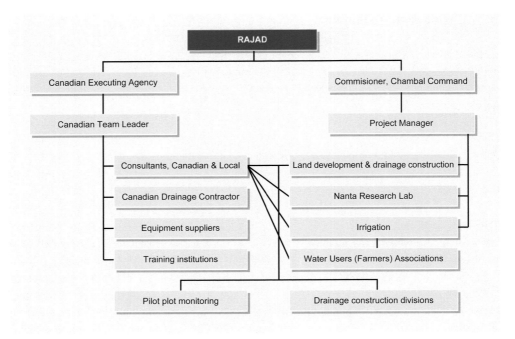

Figure 4   Project organisation of RAJAD

Planning

RAJAD was an integrated project in which both research through pilot studies and implementation of subsurface drainage in large areas took place. The following schedule was followed:

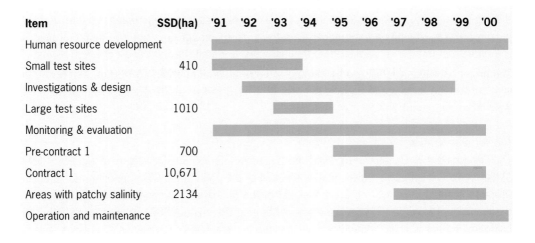

Item	SSD(ha)	'91	'92	'93	'94	'95	'96	'97	'98	'99	'00
Human resource development											
Small test sites	410										
Investigations & design											
Large test sites	1010										
Monitoring & evaluation											
Pre-contract 1	700										
Contract 1	10,671										
Areas with patchy salinity	2134										
Operation and maintenance											

Delineation of saline areas was done by EM38-survey on a 77 ha grid. In the affected areas, soil samples were collected on an 8.5 ha grid and analysed on mechanical and chemical properties. For classification of salt affected soils the following criteria were used:

Class	EC_e (dS/m)	ESP	PH
Saline soil	>4	<15	<8.5
Saline-alkali soil	>4	>15	>8.5
Alkali soil	<4	>15	>8.5

Layout
A composite subsurface drainage system was installed with field drains at an average depth of 1.2 m and 60 m spacing connected to collector drains that discharge by gravity in open main drains.

Drainage materials
Corrugated PVC drain pipes of seven sizes were used. The pipes were locally produced by a private company and were subject to stringent quality testing prior to use.

Envelopes
Synthetic fabric envelope materials were used in case the criteria for use of envelope mentioned in Chapter 4 required to do so.

Installation equipment
Four trenchless machines and one trencher were used. Initially only field drains were installed by the trenchless ploughs and collectors were installed using excavators. The first machine to be used was a trenchless plough equipped with a 400 HP diesel engine and an operating weight of 40 Mt. Its overall length when operating was 10.5 m with a width of 3.30 m and a height of 7.0 m (3.0 m laser light receiver mast in the upright position). The second machine was a bulldozer with a drainage plough added on the rear. In the international contract, in which subsurface drainage system has been installed in about 10,600 ha, two trenchless machines (one vertical plough and a V- plough) and a trencher were used. The V-plough was used to install drains of Ø 80 and 100 mm. The vertical plough was used to install the field and collector drains of Ø 160, 200 and 294 mm. Local equipment included: backhoe for excavating at joints, junctions, outlets and the like; bulldozers for removal of abrupt grade changes and restoration work; tractors, trucks etc. for transportation of material and hydraulic vibrators for compaction.

Construction practices
Prior to installation, a laser transmitter was set up, calibrated to the nearest benchmarks and checked to ascertain that the existing topography and proposed depth of the field and collector drains was indeed correct. First the collector drain was installed. An excavator/backhoe then excavated down to the collector and a T-joint was connected to the collector pipe. The field drain pipe was fed through the plough boot, the connection elevation confirmed, connected to the T-joint, plough boot elevation set to design grade and finally installed by the plough. After completing the drain line, the machine returned over the same line to compact the soil and then moved on to the next line. A bulldozer followed the machine to compact the soil once more. Finally, the farmers levelled their fields in preparation for the subsequent crop season. A small

crew restored the bunds, drains and watercourses disturbed by the machinery. As-built construction drawings were prepared for operation and maintenance requirements. Under extreme wet conditions and during the monsoon season the work was suspended. Sometimes, however, it was required to pull the trencher by a bulldozer when and where local wet conditions prevailed. The trenchless installation under wet conditions caused smearing and clogging of the synthetic envelopes resulting in less than optimal performance of the drainage systems. In such cases, additional field drains had to be installed to alleviate wet conditions in the fields. The rate of installation varies from 500 m/day for the combined mechanical/manual installation to more than 5000 m/day for installation by trenchless drainage machine (Table 2).

Table 2   Installation rates of the different installation techniques achieved at RAJAD

Method	Installation rate (m/day)
Manual installation with one backhoe and 20 labourers	500
Installation by excavator	1500
Installation by trenchless drainage machine	5000 - 6000

Experiences gained during installation resulted in the following list of precautions:
- Construction management staff should be given comprehensive training in effective inspection and reporting techniques prior to the start of the installation;
- A Construction Management Organisation with the clear division of responsibilities is essential;
- Laboratory testing and field inspection of PVC pipe and fittings must be a continuous, well documented process of quality control to avoid installation problems and failures of the system;
- All faulty material should be rejected;
- Laser set-up should always be double checked against control points and ground elevations prior to starting the actual installation of the drain pipes;
- Grade control on collector and field drains is fundamental to the success of installation;
- Installation work should start from the outlet drain and installation should then proceed upstream to prevent drainage water collecting in trenches;
- Restoration work should start within 24 hours of the pipe installation.

6.2   Haryana Operational Pilot Project

Project objectives
The Haryana Operational Pilot Project (HOPP) for the reclamation of waterlogged and saline lands of Haryana came into being in 1994 with the assistance of the Government of the Netherlands. The long-term objective of the project was to *"build and strengthen the capacity of the Department of Agriculture (DOA) of Haryana to implement the subsurface drainage technology in the*

state and to create/act as a resource/knowledge base for the future interventions of subsurface drainage technology in waterlogged and salt affected areas of Haryana (and later in north-west India) including playing an active facilitating role in the development of a drainage policy in the state and possibly in neighbouring states". The specific (short-term) objectives were:
- Transfer of technology (equipment, knowledge and skills) relating to the reclamation of waterlogged and saline lands in Haryana;
- Construction and operation of two horizontal subsurface drainage schemes, each of about 1000 ha;
- Creation in Haryana of a nucleus organisation capable of:
  - Implementing subsurface drainage systems on about 2500 ha per year and maintaining the resulting drainage network;
  - Attracting sufficient funds for the purchase of additional equipment, the actual construction of drainage systems and for hiring the necessary staff.
- The participation of farmers in the planning, construction, operation and maintenance of the subsurface drainage systems;
- The environmentally sound disposal of the saline drainage effluent of the pilot areas.

Project organisation
The organisations responsible for managing and implementing the HOPP were the Department of Agriculture, Government of Haryana, India and the Directorate General of International Co-operation, The Netherlands. The overall supervision and guidance was in the hands of two committees whose members belonged to a number of organisations involved in drainage in Haryana (Department of Agriculture, Department of Irrigation, CSSRI, Haryana Agricultural University, and others), as follows:
- Steering Committee headed by the Secretary of Agriculture of DOA in Chandigarh, for guidance on policy matters meeting at least twice a year;
- Technical Committee headed by the Director of CSSRI in Karnal to guide the Haryana OPP on the technical details meeting at least four times a year.

Consultancy was provided by the Netherlands through an Indo-Dutch consortium of consulting companies. To implement HOPP an organisational unit under the DOA was established with deputations from other departments within Haryana (Figure 5). Based on a process approach, a Knowledge Management Unit (KMU) was established at Chandigarh together with a Technical Assistance Team to ensure the sustainability of the institutional memory from project experiences. In addition to assuming Monitoring and Evaluation (M&E) responsibilities, the KMU guided the implementing department (Subsurface Drainage Cell) to develop capacity building packages, co-ordinate training on data collection, work processing and planning, gender sensitisation and farmers participation for field teams, farmers and contractors. The KMU was also responsible for cultivating links with other agencies (e.g. Department of Irrigation) and assists in the development of drainage policy initiatives in Haryana and elsewhere as appropriate. The project activities were grouped under the following work components:
- Project management;
- Planning and design;
- Construction of subsurface drainage and other field activities;

- Machinery maintenance;
- Farmers participation and O&M;
- Monitoring and evaluation.

The work programme was designed to ensure that full integration of all the components took place and that human resource development and training was linked to all components.

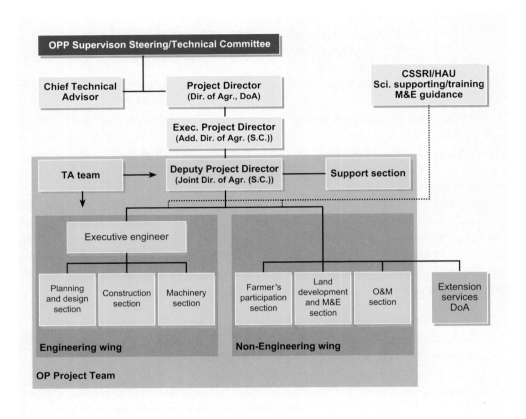

Figure 5   Organogram of the Haryana Operational Pilot Project

Planning
Before HOPP started, CSSRI and Haryana Agriculture University conducted operational research on waterlogging and soil salinity in sandy soils of Haryana. The recommendations of these studies provided the required inputs for undertaking subsurface drainage construction under HOPP. The sequence of activities was as follows:
- Participatory Rural Appraisal (PRA) in the pilot areas, mapping the social landscape;
- Rough layouts for the blocks based on maximum size of the drainage blocks, boundaries of villages, minors, dirt roads, open drains and so forth;

- Motivational activities including the development of communication materials, orientation visits to nearby mini pilot schemes and farmer field days;
- Detailed designs;
- Verification of the designs in consultation with the farmers, changes in the designs were made when feasible;
- Obtain farmers' consent for the construction of the subsurface drainage system;
- Formation of Farmers Drainage Societies including elections for the executive committee and official registration according to the Societies Registration Act (1860) and bye-laws. The executive committee included one ex-officio member of HOPP;
- Construction of the subsurface drainage system with conflict resolution by the Farmers Participation Section (FPS) staff;
- Handing over of (electric) pumps operation to the registered Farmer Drainage Societies.

The first subsurface drainage systems were installed in April 1997 in the Gohana area: in three seasons about 1000 ha divided into 23 blocks with one pumping unit in each block were provided with subsurface drainage. The drains were installed mechanically using imported trencher machines. All blocks were handed over to the farmers' drainage societies in phases for operation and maintenance.

Then, the construction activities were shifted from government constructing units to a private contractor. Identification of areas requiring drainage, their prioritisation, undertaking investigations, design and planning were carried out by the government and its own staff, while the construction was carried out by contractors and the systems operated and maintained by the farmers' drainage societies.

Layout
Composite subsurface drainage systems were installed with corrugated PVC pipes for both the field (Ø 80 & 100 mm) and collector (Ø 200 & 294 mm) drains. The field drains connect on both sides to a collector pipe that discharge into a sump. Each sump serves around 50 ha, an area of approximately 40 - 50 farmers being the maximum size of group that can organise themselves. From the sump, the drainage water is lifted by pumping and disposed of into a surface drainage system. To prevent the inflow of fine soil particles into the pipes, nylon socks (for the collectors) and polypropylene non-woven fibres (thickness >2 mm and an apparent opening size O_{90} > 300 microns) are used for the collector and field drains, respectively. Both pipe and envelope materials were produced locally (Figure 6). The field drains are about 315 m in length and have an average depth of 1.7 m. The maximum depth of the collectors at the sump is 3 m. The design discharge is 2 mm/day, which has been reduced to 1.5 mm/day for the new projects, resulting in a drain spacing of 60 to 67 m.

Equipment
The Netherlands Government provided a trencher, with which about 1000 ha area has been covered so far (Figure 7).

Figure 6   Wrapping the non-woven polypropylene envelope around the drain pipe

Figure 7   Trencher installing pre-wrapped corrugated drain pipe in Gohana area

Costs

Based on the actual expenditure for the first 983 ha in Gohana (1997-1999) the total cost of installing subsurface drainage amounted to € 770 per hectare at 2000 prices (Table 3).

Table 3   Actual cost of installing subsurface drainage systems in Haryana, India

Item			Cost per ha (€)	(%)
Materials	•	Pipes	238	(31%)
	•	Envelopes	132	(17%)
	•	Structures [a]	59	(8 %)
Machinery	•	Fixed [b]	174	(23%)
	•	Variable [c]	131	(17%)
Miscellaneous			37	(5%)
Total			**770**	**(100%)**

[a] Structures include sump, pump house, pumps, electrification, manholes, labour, disposal (surface) drainage;

[b] Fixed machine costs include interest (15%) and depreciation based on a lifetime of 7 - 10 years. A working time of 70 machine hours have been used for one block with an average working time of the construction plant (trencher, excavator, bulldozer, tractors and trailers) of 800 hrs per year;

[c] Variable costs include spare parts (estimated over lifetime), repairs (partly estimated), diesel and oil (actual).

6.3   Indo-Dutch Network Project

This third project is not an example of large-scale implementation but of applied research and small-scale implementation. To support the research activities in subsurface drainage design and small-scale implementation, the Indo-Dutch Project for waterlogging and soil salinity was in operation for about 17 years (1985 - 2002). Between 1996 and 2002 this project was converted into a Network Operational Research Programme on Drainage and Water Management for Salinity Control in Canal Commands (IDNP). The overall objectives of the project were (i) to strengthen research capacity of CSSRI and the four State Centres, especially in the field of waterlogging and salinity control, and (ii) to enhance awareness on drainage and related water management for the control of waterlogging and soil salinity at State and Central level. The objective of the drainage pilot area research component was to conduct operational research on drainage methods for reclamation of waterlogged and salt affected agricultural land in different agro-climate zones of India. Eight pilot areas, ranging in size from 20-188 ha, were implemented in 5 agro-climate zones. Monitoring included one large-scale monitoring area of 2000 ha out of which nearly 1200 ha were provided with subsurface drainage.

Project Organisation

The IDNP project was implemented jointly by the Government of India through the Indian Council of Agricultural Research (ICAR) and the Government of the Netherlands through the Royal Netherlands Embassy (RNE) in India. The Implementing agencies in India were:
Central Soil Salinity Research Institute (CSSRI), Karnal, Haryana (Box 1);
- Acharya N G Ranga Agricultural University (ANGRAU), Indo-Dutch Network Project, Bapatla, Andhra Pradesh;
- Gujarat Agricultural University (GAU), Soil and Water Management Research Institute, Navsari, Gujarat;

- University of Agricultural Sciences Dharwad(UASD), Agricultural Research Station, Bhee-marayanagudi, Karnataka;
- Rajasthan Agricultural University (RAU), Agricultural Research Sub-Station, Hanumangarh, Rajasthan.

Box 1   Central Soil Salinity Research Institute

The Central Soil Salinity Research Institute (CSSRI), established in 1969 under ICAR, is a central research institute located at Karnal, Haryana. It is a leading research centre in India in the fields of salt affected soils and waterlogging. Besides the main centre at Karnal, the institute has regional stations at Canning Town in West Bengal for coastal soils, at Anand in Gujarat for black soils and at Lucknow in Uttar Pradesh for alkaline soils of the Gangetic plains. It is also the headquarters of the All India Coordinated Research Project on Management of Salt Affected Soils and Use of Saline Water for Agriculture, which has seven network centres located in different agro-climatic regions of the country. The multi-disciplinary research at CSSRI is organised under the four following divisions:

- Drainage and Water Management Engineering;
- Soils and Crop Management;
- Crop Improvement, and;
- Technology Evaluation and Extension.

The research on drainage concentrates on development of design criteria, testing of drainage materials, recycling of drainage water and socio-economic aspects through field research and modelling.

CSSRI was the coordinating agency and focal point for all the other network centres and the International Institute for Land Reclamation and Improvement (Alterra-ILRI), Wageningen, The Netherlands, provided technical assistance to the project. The four state agricultural universities, often in cooperation with state departments or CADAs, had already started operational research.

Output

The project provided the guidance for identifying problems, developing research programme, undertaking pilot research in farmers' fields, and analysis of results to develop solutions to water-logging and soil salinity. Multidisciplinary scientific teams under a chief scientist at each centre conducted the studies. The outputs were synthesised into recommendations for field depart-ments for implementation. The research activities resulted in major developments on the fol-lowing issues (for more details see Bibliography):

- Two methodologies, one based on visual and one for digital interpretation, were recom-mended for the identification of waterlogging and soil salinity conditions using remote sensing: These were based on eight studies covering areas ranging between 5 000 and 350 000 ha in the Indo-Gangetic plains (3), heavy clay or black soils (3) and sandy soils (2);
- Recommendations on Waterlogging and Salinity Control were based on the research findings of 7 drainage pilot areas (of between 20 and 188 ha, Table 4), covering 5 agro-ecological sub-regions in India with soils ranging from sandy loam to heavy clay. Sugges-tions for open and pipe drains were presented for each sub-region specifications for subsurface drainage systems;
- Computer modelling for irrigation and drainage: four computer simulation models, SWAP, UNSATCHEM, SALTMOD and SURDEV, were tested to assess the short and long-term

impacts of water management options on the land and water productivity and the environment;
- Human resource development and the establishment of a training centre: the report included discussion of the adopted approach in technology transfer, capacity building and institution strengthening of the four network centres.

Table 4   *Summary of the various drainage systems in the pilot areas*

Pilot Area	State	Size (ha)	Type of Drainage System	Outfall conditions
Konanki	Andhra Pradesh	20	• Composite pipe drainage • Composite open drainage	Gravity
Uppugunduru	Andhra Pradesh	21	• Composite pipe drainage • Composite open drainage	Pumped
Segwa	Gujarat	188	• Composite pipe drainage • Singular pipe drainage	Gravity
Sisodra	Gujarat	160	• Composite open drainage	Gravity
Gohana	Haryana	1200	• Composite pipe drainage	Pumped
Sampla	Haryana	100	• Composite pipe drainage	Pumped
Islampur/ Devapur	Karnataka	180	• Composite pipe drainage • Singular pipe drainage • Singular open drainage	Gravity
Lakhuwali	Rajasthan	75	• Composite pipe drainage	Pumped

Combined Mechanical and Manual Installation in Andhra Pradesh
In Andhra Pradesh in the Krishna Delta, two drainage pilot areas were constructed in 1999/2000: one in Konanki (22 ha) and one in Uppunguduru (21 ha). Installation was done semi-mechanically : the excavation and backfill was done by excavators, and activities like pipe-laying were done by hand.

First, the collector line was set out and the ends marked with ranging rods. Then, the field drains were set out perpendicular to the collector drain using an optical square and again the ends were marked with ranging rods. All lines were marked with white chalk powder to make certain that the trenches were dug as straight as possible.

The trenches were dug mechanically using an excavator, the drain pipes were installed manually and the backfill was done mechanically using a tractor with a front blade. The excavator had a bucket with a width of 40 cm. Cleaning and smoothening of the trenches was done manually.

The collectors, rigid PVC pipes (160 mm and 6 m length), were made watertight with solvent cement. The field drains (80 mm and 100 m length) were uncoiled on the ground and laid parallel to the trench and then the envelope (a geotextile and a nylon mesh) was wrapped around the pipe in the field before the pipe was placed in the trench. Four labourers could wrap and place about 250 m of pipe per day (Figure 8). Before the soil was backfilled it was crushed using the tractor blade.

Figure 8
Wrapping of envelope material (nylon mesh) around the pipe in Uppugunduru Pilot Area, Andhra Pradesh

Problems encountered during the installation and lessons learned were:
- It was hard for one labourer to do the wrapping, therefore teams of four labourers were engaged to do the job;
- The binding wire used for wrapping the envelope material got easily twisted;
- Delays in installing the pipes were often caused as a result of standing water in the trenches. Pumping was required to discharge this excess water;
- Stability of the trench walls was poor and therefore the drain pipes needed to be installed as soon as possible after excavation.

Combined Mechanical and Manual Installation in Gujarat
In Gujarat in the Kakrapar irrigation command area, a 188 ha drainage pilot area was established in Segwa to test several layouts and configurations of subsurface drainage systems, namely, singular and composite systems and various drain depths and spacings. The following methods were tried:
- Manual installation in a 9.1 ha block: drains were installed manually at a depth of 0.90 m. The tools used for the manual installation included: hoes, sticks, hand scrappers, rope, metal and wooden compactors, metal buckets and vessels and bailing buckets;
- Semi-mechanical installation in two blocks (18.9 ha): an excavator was used to dig the trench up to 10-15 cm above the design level, all other activities such as levelling, grading, envelope wrapping, pipe-laying, backfill, were done manually (Figure 9).

Figure 9 In Segwa, the drain trench was excavated mechanically and all other activities were done manually: a) excavating the trench; b) checking the level; c) preparing the bed; d) checking the final level; e) checking the level at the outlet and f) laying the pipe

Time studies were conducted to establish the labour requirements (Table 5). The overall labour requirements in the manually installed block were 52 working days per 100 m drain (or 1.9 m/day). For preparatory activities like setting out the alignment and levels, the labour requirements were between 1 and 2 man-days per 100 m of drain, and for supporting activities like levelling, grading and smoothening the trench bottom, pipe-laying and backfill they were between 5 and 11 man-days. Thus the actual excavation of the drain trench took about 39 man-days per 100 m or 2.5 m/manday. The overall cost of installation of the completely manually installed system (approximately € 495/ha at 2000 prices) was 27% higher than the cost of the semi-mechanically installed system (approximately € 385/ha).

Table 5   *Labour requirements for the manual installation of pipe drains in Segwa Pilot Area*

| | Labour requirements per 100 m of drain | |
| | [man-days] | |
	Field drain	Collector drain
Preparation:		
Setting-out alignment	0.3	0.5
Pegging	0.1	0.2
Cleaning alignment	0.9	0.0
Marking	0.5	0.6
Subtotal - Preparation	1.8	1.3
Supporting activities:		
Setting out levels	0.1	0.1
Placement of boning rods	0.1	0.0
Levelling and smoothing trench bottom	6.2	0.0
Pipe inspection	0.1	0.1
Laying of pipe	0.5	0.5
Backfill	2.6	2.4
Compaction	1.5	1.5
Subtotal - Supporting activities	11.1	4.6
Excavation of drain trench	39.2	Done by excavator
Grand total	**52.1**	**5.9**
Additional activities:		
Wrapping envelope	1.3	
Gypsum application [a]	5.3	
Dewatering [b]	4.9	

[a] In several trenches the backfill was mixed with gypsum to study the effect of gypsum application on sedimentation in the drain pipes in these unstable soils (high SAR).

[b] In several trenches dewatering was required because of the inflow of excess irrigation water.

The major problems encountered with the manually installation of the pipe drains, the adopted methods to overcome these problems and the lessons learned were:

- In the block where the system was installed semi-mechanically, the installation of the pipes could not follow the digging of the trenches. This problem was caused by the rather high labour requirements for supporting activities (5 - 11 labour days per 100 m of drain, see Table 5) as well as insufficient labour availability;
- Extra time was needed to train the labours in the specific tasks, like wrapping, grading & smoothening the trench bottom, pipe laying and backfill. It was difficult to find enough skilled labourers;
- A high labour input requires a higher input in supervision. The large number of labourers and the long distances in the field necessitated the use of walkie-talkies;
- The soils in Segwa Pilot area are rather heavy (clay content about 44%), when these soils dry up manually excavation is hard and difficult. It was especially hard to get good quality (fine and crumbled soil particles) for the backfill on top of the pipe;
- On the other hand, these soils become sticky under wet conditions. Therefore, to avoid waterlogged conditions, installation was not done in the monsoon season, but only in the summer season (January - May) when rainfall is limited;
- Neighbouring farmers did not want to interrupt their irrigation practices, which on several occasions resulted in inflow of water in the trenches;
- In the deeper trenches or those parts of the area where the groundwater table was high, trench walls were unstable due to in-flowing groundwater. This resulted in sudden collapse of (part) of the trench, which not only caused extra work but also created a safety hazard for the labourers working in the trench.

Manual Installation in Karnataka

In Karnataka, 180 ha operational research pilot area was constructed in Islampur-Devapur along the Naraynapur Left Bank Canal. A singular open and pipe drainage system was installed in a 14.9 ha block and a composite pipe drainage system in a 14.4 ha block. All installation activities, namely, excavation of the trench, laying of the pipes and backfill, were done by local labours. PVC corrugated pipes (Ø 80 and 100 mm) were installed at a spacing of 30 and 50 m, a depth varying between 1.1-1.2 m (for the field drains) and 1.4-1.5 m (for the collector drains) and wrapped with nylon socks in part of the area. The installation technique was similar to the method used in Segwa (see above), again with special emphasis on grade control. The only major difference was that topsoil was used for the first layer of backfill (0.20 to 0.30 m on top of the pipe), as this was more stable than the excavated subsoil. This layer was compacted lightly using wooden flats. Overall labour requirements for the installation of the composite system in the 14.4 ha block was 127 days/ha at a cost of Rs. 5200 to Rs. 5500 per ha (1999-2000 prices). Labour requirements per 100 m of drain line corresponded to the Segwa Pilot area, namely, 49.8 man-days per 100 m for Islampur-Devapur (Table 6) and 52.1 man-days per 100 m for Segwa (Table 5).

Table 6   Labour requirements for the manual installation of a composite pipe drainage system in 14.4 ha in Islampur-Devapur Pilot Area

Activity	Labour input [man-days]			Labour requirement
	Men	Women	Total	[man-days per 100 m of drain]
Land clearing:				
- Collector line and outlets	50		50	6.4
- Field drain lines		75	75	2.6
Installation:				
- Field drains (2890 m)	510	430	940	32.5
- Collector drains (782 m)	234		234	29.9
Construction of outlets and manholes:				
- Mason	40		40	1.1
- Labour	60	50	110	3.0
Transport of pipes & materials	60		60	1.6
Watchman on site	90		90	2.5
Assistance to engineers (setting out levels etc.)	150		150	4.1
Miscellaneous	30	50	80	2.2
Grand Total	**1224**	**605**	**1829**	**49.8**

On average a male labourer could install 6 to 8 m of field drain (excavation, installation and backfill) per day and 4 to 5 m of collector drain. A couple (consisting of a female and male labourer) could install 9 to 11 m of field drains per day. The labour requirements doubled on rainy days.

Case Study - The Netherlands

Case Study - The Netherlands

1   Background

1.1   Historical developments

In the Netherlands, 25% of the land is below sea level and about 65% of it would be flooded where it not for the dykes (Figure 1). The climate is relatively mild with an average annual rainfall of about 750 mm and an annual evaporation of about 475 mm. The removal of excess rainfall in combination with the low elevation, the lowest area is 6.5 m below mean sea level, requires an intensive drainage system to keep one's feet dry, both man and crops. The expansion of agriculture in the Netherlands started some 1000 years ago with a gradual change from shifting cultivation towards a more permanent development and occupation of the land. Farmers had to learn to organise themselves to mobilise enough labour and capital under evolving authorities: abbeys (1000-1200 AD), feudal rulers (1200-1500), locally organised groups (1300-1500) and water boards (1300-present). Moreover the water management was influenced by private or municipal land reclamation companies and peat mining companies (1500-1700), companies to drain and reclaim lakes (1500-1900), and governmental services to reclaim lakes, swamps and heath lands (1900-2000). Field drainage has always been the responsibility of the land user and the main drainage systems the responsibility of the above-mentioned institutions. Exceptions are the large-scale, government-supported, land reclamation and land consolidation projects in the second half of the 20th century: in these projects both the field and main drainage systems were implemented.

1.2   Large-scale reclamations in the 20th century

The generally felt need for better agricultural production conditions in the 20th century resulted in a number of government-financed, long-term programmes in which the construction of subsurface drainage systems was a significant part. Important programmes were the land reclamation programme in the former Zuiderzee area and the rural development programmes on the *"old lands"*, the so-called land consolidation projects. The public organisations involved in these programmes were the IJsselmeerpolders Development Authority (for the newly reclaimed areas) and the Government Service for Land and Water Use (for the *"old lands"*). Both organisations were multi-purpose organisations whose tasks included drainage installation. The IJsselmeerpolders Development Authority carried out most of the works themselves in forced account. The construction of drainage systems in the land consolidation projects was carried out by consultants and contractors under contract with Government Service for Land and Water.

1.3   Commonly used subsurface drainage system

In the Netherlands, subsurface drainage systems are used in almost all agricultural lands, except in the peat areas, where a high groundwater table is require to reduce subsidence and only shal-

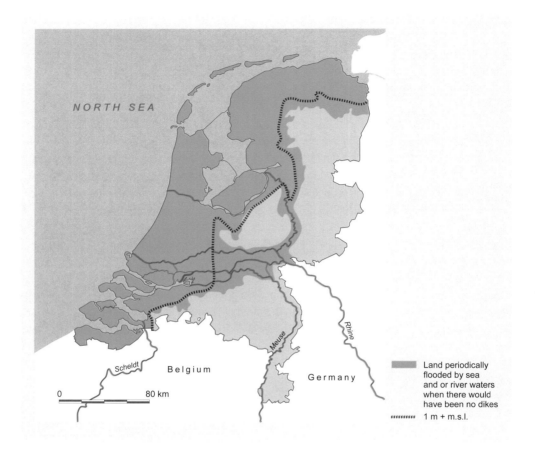

Figure 1   Land periodically flooded by sea and river

low open drainage systems are used. The most commonly installed subsurface drainage system is a singular system with piped field drains discharging into open collector drains (Figure 2). The main function of the field drains is to control the watertable level. The corrugated plastic field drains (Ø 60 mm) are installed at a depth of 1.0 to 1.3 m. In fine or reduced (risk of ochre formation) soil layers, voluminous organic (coconut fibres) envelopes were used in the past, but they have been replaced by synthetic pre-wrapped envelopes. Depending on the drain depth and soil texture, installation is done by either trencher or trenchless drainage machines (Part I Figure 5.8). The discharge from the subsurface field drains and the surface runoff is removed by gravity through a system of open collector drains.

1.4   Present status of drainage in the Netherlands

As mentioned above, an intensive drainage programme was carried out in the Netherlands during the second part of the 20th century. In total some 750 000 ha in the *"old lands"* and 150 000 ha

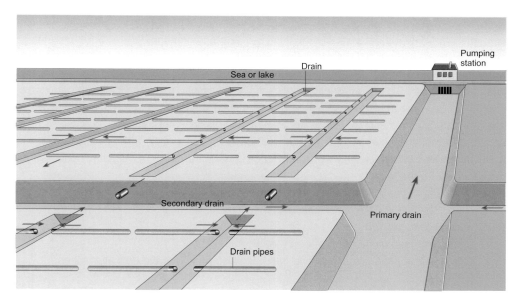

Figure 2   The single subsurface drainage system in the Netherlands consists of pipe field drains, open collector, secondary and primary drains and a pumping station

in the new polders were equipped with subsurface drainage systems. Generally speaking all agricultural lands that require drainage have been provided with subsurface drainage, except the peat lands. The peat lands that are mainly used for pasture can only be superficially drained to avoid oxidation and the subsequent subsidence. Therefore these areas are only equipped with a shallow open drainage system that maintains water levels at around 0.5 m below the surface. Currently, most of the drainage installation in the Netherlands is replacement of defunct systems, improvements of drainage in case change of land use and drainage of urban and industrial sites.

2   Organisation of the water management

2.1   Water Boards

Water boards emerged in the 13th Century when land reclamation and protection against flooding became essential for survival. These water boards are an example of an effective and sustainable self-managed organisation for the construction, management and maintenance of dykes and drainage systems. Protection against floods and the agricultural development in many parts of the Netherlands was accomplished through cooperation among groups of landowners with a common interest in drainage, thus engaged in community undertakings to remove excess water from their holdings. These efforts eventually resulted in the creation of water boards. Within the water board organisation, the farmers and landowners are responsible for the local water management engineering works such as the smaller dykes, watercourses and roads.

Overall responsibility for proper water management throughout the country rests with the national government that exercises authority over the provinces. The national government, in the person of the Minister of Transport, Public Works and Water management, is responsible for water management affairs of national concern. This Ministry has its own executive body for this job: the Directorate General for Public Works and Water management. The local and regional responsibility for water management, as laid down in the constitution, rests with the water boards. The provincial governments supervise the work and the finances of the water boards: they set up and abolish water boards, determine the water management tasks to be undertaken by the water board, the area in which it will work, the composition of the governing body and how its members will be elected.

Traditionally, the tasks of the water boards in the Netherlands were:
- Flood protection;
- Conveyance and disposal of drainage water;
- Maintaining of agreed minimum and maximum water levels in the drainage system.

These tasks have now been extended to include water quality management, ecological management, water conservation and flood prevention. Nowadays, the water boards may be charged with the following tasks:
- *Water control:* providing protection against flooding by means of dunes, dykes and quays;
- *Water quantity:* managing the amount of water and ensuring that it is kept at the right level;
- *Water quality:* combating water pollution and improving the quality of surface waters;
- *Management* of the inland water ways and roads.

The role of the water boards as far as subsurface drainage is concerned is a normative and a controlling one. If a farmer or a group of farmers wants to install a subsurface drainage system they need to obtain permission from the water boards. An application for the installation of a subsurface drainage system is judged on the basis of the following criteria:
- The effect on the neighbouring areas;
- The discharge;
- The quality of the drainage water.

Water boards always had to serve the interests (= functions of water) of different groups. In the past, little conflict arose between agriculture and other sectors because the pressure on the land was not yet dominant. If any conflicts presented between agriculture and peat mining, for instance, an extensive jurisprudence offered a verdict most of the time. Potential conflicts between sub-sectors of agriculture over water management urged farmers to participate and de facto they became the only interest group represented in the water boards. During the 20th century, the parallel interdependency in drainage has grown considerably and water boards are now the arena of decision making on all functions of water, in which besides the farmers all concerned parties, like households, municipalities, industries, recreation and nature organisations have a say.

2.2   Government Service for Land and Water Use

The main task of the Government Service for Land and Water Use is the planning, preparation and supervision of the execution of land consolidation projects[1]. These projects embody multiple aims: besides improving the production conditions for agriculture, they include the preservation and development of nature, improvement of living conditions in rural areas, and development of green belts around cities. Sectoral improvement of water management and a more rational arrangement of agriculture land use is part of the programme. Central to the objectives to improve the water management is meeting water control requirements for agriculture and nature areas. Adjustments have to be made to the groundwater level as both land use and drainage requirements change as years go by. Lowering the groundwater level is important in order to increase productivity when growing agricultural crops. In addition, it increases the load-bearing capacity of the soil to accommodate the heavier agricultural machines driven on the land, even during wet periods. Conversely, in certain areas where the soil is sensitive to drought, it may be necessary to maintain high groundwater levels in order to maximise crop growth, taking into account (adjacent) nature areas that usually require a higher groundwater level than the surrounding agricultural land. In a rural development project, both agriculture and nature interests are considered in the planning process. An appropriate water control system is designed for the project area to achieve the desired groundwater levels by means of fixed or moveable weirs, thereby ensuring the best possible water levels in the drainage system (Figure 3). The field drainage is usually improved by constructing a new subsurface drainage system or modifying the existing one, but it also includes enlarging watercourses and renovating existing pumping stations.

2.3   IJsselmeerpolders Development Authority

Initially, the IJsselmeerpolders Development Authority[2] had no other task than to cultivate the newly reclaimed land. Over the years, its task has evolved from land reclamation primarily for agriculture, to an integrated development of agriculture, urban settlement, forests, recreational facilities and nature reserves. This experience has given the IJsselmeerpolders Development Authority worldwide recognition in the reclamation and development of new lands.

Reclamation Process
The first step in reclaiming land for the sea or lakes includes the construction of a ring dike, one or more pumping stations and the dredging of the main drainage channels to the pumping

---

[1] In the past decade nature development and realisation of the ecological main structure as part of spatial planning and redevelopment of the rural areas has become an important part of the tasks of the Government Service for Land and Water Use.

[2] The tasks of the IJsselmeerpolders Development Authority came to an end in 1997 with the completion of the Southern Flevoland polder. The organisation merged into the Regional Directorate IJsselmeerpolders of the Directorate General of Public Works and Water Management.

a

b

c

Figure 3   Fixed (a), adjustable (b) and movable (c) weirs are used to maintain the water level in the open drainage system at the desired level

stations. After these works are completed, the water is pumped out of the new polder. Once the polder is drained, the land developers take over from the civil engineers. The tasks of the land developers are to prepare the new land for agriculture (Land Use Department) and to pave the way for further development (Urban Development Department and the Socio-Economic Development Department). The Land Use Department is responsible for the rural development and for the implementation of the works in the agricultural sector, including the land drainage systems, infrastructural works, rural roads and bridges, mechanised farming and afforestation. The next step is preparing the land for agriculture that starts with the aerial sowing of reed on the exposed mud flats. Reed speeds up the ripening process of soil with the result that the area becomes accessible on foot and at a later stage by vehicle. The third and final step is the progressive implementation of the field drainage system, an essential measure to further ripen the soil and to progressively transform the reclaimed area into agricultural land. The first field drains are open ditches usually spaced at intervals of 48 m. These ditches facilitate the drainage of surface water and the water in the surface layers. One year before cultivation starts, extra ditches are dug between existing ones at intervals of about 12 m. Finally, after a few years of cultivation, the ditches are replaced by subsurface drainage pipes (Figure 4).

Finally the drainage of the polders consists of the following elements:
- Open ditches that after some years were replaced by piped subsurface drainage;
- Open collector drains;
- Secondary drains;
- Primary drains;
- Pumping stations.

2.4   The Drainage industry

The activities in both the large land consolidation projects and the reclamation of the IJsselmeer polders prompted the development of modern mechanised drainage techniques. The need for efficient and reliable installation of pipe drains in large areas coupled with increasing labour cost and labour scarcity facilitated and gave an economic basis to the development of modern drainage trenchers and later trenchless drainage machines. The switch from the cumbersome heavy tile drains to the corrugated plastic drain pipes was made in the same period thanks to the development of the plastic industry and the large volumes of pipes required that made investment in development and production of machinery attractive. The development of pre-wrapped envelopes, first made of voluminous coconut fibres and later on of voluminous synthetic fibres, was prompted by the need for envelopes in most soils and the high price of gravel.

These developments were the result of a rather unique cooperation between the government services, the research departments of universities and of these government services, the machine building industry, the plastic industry, the land development companies and consultants. This cooperation resulted in:
- Modern drainage techniques that with adjustments are now applied world-wide;
- A specialised industry for the production of drainage machines;

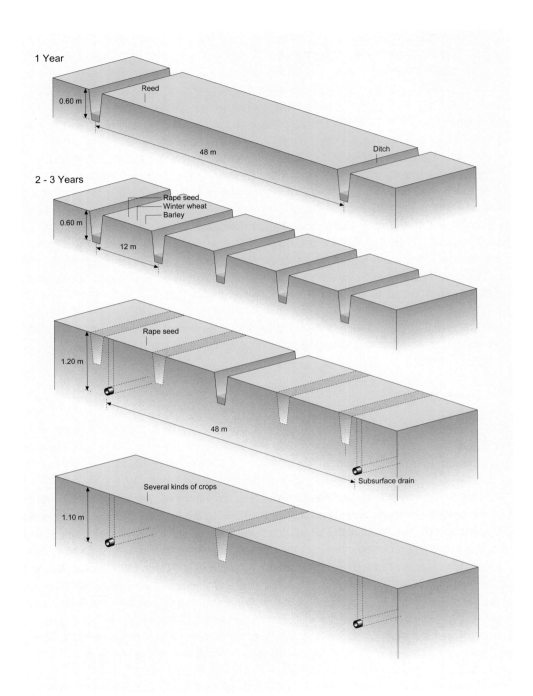

1 Year

0.60 m

Reed

48 m

Ditch

2 - 3 Years

0.60 m

Rape seed
Winter wheat
Barley

12 m

1.20 m

Rape seed

48 m

Subsurface drain

1.10 m

Several kinds of crops

Figure 4   Sequence of drainage measures during the reclamation of Southern Flevoland

- Specialised drainage contractors, and;
- A specialised industry for the production of drain pipes and accessories as well as pre-wrapped envelopes.

2.5   Drainage Contact Group

To enhance to cooperation between the various partners involved in agricultural land drainage the so-called Drainage Contact Group was formed. This group organised study and extension meetings on a regular basis to ensure that all parties are kept up-to-date with the latest developments in the sector and that their interests were taken into consideration. While the initiative to organise these meetings came from (semi-) government organisations, farmers, manufactures and consultant organisations also played an important role. During the meetings they had the opportunity to express their views on recent developments, new rules and regulations and discuss the difficulties encountered by the implementation. The (semi-) government organisations, on the other hand, could sound out the general feeling for proposed changes in the existing rules and regulations and got feedback on new developments. The Drainage Contact Group also played an important role in setting up applied research, and improving the quality of work and setting higher quality standards.

2.6   Research institutes

An important factor in the resources management system is the scientific knowledge complex, through which new and existing knowledge from research is disseminated via education, publications and extension services. This scientific knowledge complex (including drainage research) has changed considerably over the past decades as itemised below:

- The number of research institutes has been drastically reduced through successive rounds of merges: for instance, in Wageningen, the main centre for agricultural research in the Netherlands, the seven research institutes and the departments of Wageningen Agricultural University involved in agricultural water management have merged into one Knowledge Centre under the umbrella of Wageningen University and Research Centre, of which Alterra-ILRI is part of;
- The same applies to the institutions for secondary and higher vocational training, which also have gone through a round of mergers and concentration;
- Research programmes have evolved from single-disciplinary research on basic plant-soil-water relationships to interdisciplinary research involving all aspects of the effects of interventions in the complex natural resources systems;
- The change from a government-sponsored and owned research complex in to a privatised organisation where research programmes have become demand driven instead;
- The integration of research and education and society as a whole. The introduction of demand-driven research has improved the representation of all stakeholders and reduced the accumulation of power (as knowledge is power) with only a few privileged groups left.

The mandate of Alterra-ILRI is to collect and disseminate knowledge for better and sustainable use of land and water resources. This includes the following tasks:
- To collect information on land reclamation and improvement all over the world;
- To disseminate this knowledge through publication, courses, and consultancies;
- To contribute -by supplementary research- towards a better understanding of the land and water problems in developing countries.

2.7   Farmers

As mentioned before, farmers always have been responsible for the installation of a subsurface drainage system on their land. A farmer who wants to install a system needs to obtain permission from the Government, in particular the water board. The water board will check whether the proposed system is in line with the current regional rules and regulations that, for example, stipulate that the system should not exceed the maximum permissible lowering of the water table, quantity and quality of drainage. Once permission has been obtained, the farmer will engage a drainage contractor. The drainage contractor guarantees that the drainage system is installed according to the Standard Rules and Regulations for the implementation of drainage works.

3   Drainage materials

3.1   Pipes

The diameter of the PVC corrugated pipes used for subsurface drains ranges between 50 and 200 mm. As the length of the field drains of the singular systems used in the Netherlands is most times limited to about 200 mm, pipes of 60 and 80 mm diameter are mainly used. Dimensions, quality criteria and testing methods are standardised, under the authority of the *"Nederlands Normalisatie Instituut"* (Netherlands Normalisation Institute). There are several standards available for drain pipes and envelopes (Table 1). Quality certification is done by an independent organisation: *"Stichting voor Onderzoek, Beoordeling en Keuring van Materialen en Constructies/KOMO"* (Institute for Research, Judgement and Testing of Materials and Constructions).

Table 1   Netherlands standards for drain pipes and envelopes (in Dutch) [a]

Standard	Subject
NEN 7036	Corrugated unplastised PVC pipes for sub-soil drainage
NEN 7047	Wrapping material made of coconut fibre for land drainage pipes
NEN 7048	Wrapping material made of peat-fibre for land drainage pipes
NEN 7090	Wrapping material made of polypropylene fibres for land drainage pipes

[a] *Nederlands Normalisatie Instituut,* P.O. Box 5059, 2600 GB Delft, The Netherlands

3.2   Envelopes

Most of the soils in the Netherlands require an envelope. Apart from their hydraulic and filter function, envelopes are also useful in areas where the formation of iron ochre is likely to occur. The most widely used envelope materials were organic materials such as coconut and peat fibres, but they have been gradually replaced by voluminous envelopes made of polypropylene fibres. On a smaller scale, especially on sandy and loamy soils, thin synthetic envelopes are also used. Gravel envelopes are only used in exceptional cases, e.g. in urban and industrial sites and in areas where quick sand problems are encountered (Box 1), as gravel is scarce in the Netherlands and hence the supply and transport is very expensive. Similar to drain pipes, the composition, quality and testing methods are standardised (Table 1)

Box 1   Planning the supply of gravel for subsurface drains in the Lauwerszee project area

The planning of the gravel supply in a subsurface drainage area is illustrated by an example of the installation of subsurface drains in the Lauwerszee project area in the northern part of the Netherlands. Gravel was used because of the unique soil and hydrological conditions (quick sand) and the proposed land use (recreation and military training ground). The gravel had to be transported by ship to the project area over a rather long distance, more than 250 km (Figure 5). The gravel was a by-product of the gravel used for housing and road construction and its availability is limited. The supply rate of gravel was less than the amount needed during the period of drain installation. Therefore, a rather large amount of gravel had to be in kept in stock (Table 2 and Figure 6). The required amount of gravel was based on envelope of 40 cm of gravel around a drain of 200 m length. The amount of gravel required was 26 m^3, namely, 9 loads of 3 m^3 each drain. The calculation shows that at least 3600 m^3 of gravel had to be in stock before the drain installation could start and that the supply had to start at least 12 weeks before the drain installation begins.

Table 2   Calculation of amount of gravel needed in Sub-area no.5 Lauwerszee

Total drain length	60 km
Average amount of gravel needed per km	100 m^3
Total amount of gravel	6000 m^3
Drain installation per week	7.5 km
Amount of gravel per week	750 m^3
Supply of gravel per week	300 m^3
Duration of drain installation	8 weeks
Duration of gravel supply	20 weeks

From the temporary storage the gravel was transported to the drainage machine in so-called dump-carts and via a gravel trailer with a conveyor belt into the container on the trench box of the drainage machine. The speed of the gravel trailer needed to be the same as the speed of the drainage machine, because stopping the drainage machine waiting for gravel supply had to be avoided, as this had a negative effect on the drain alignment. The total number of equipment needed and the time needed for the supply of gravel from temporary storage to the drainage machine is presented in Figure 7.

Figures of box 1 on the next pages.

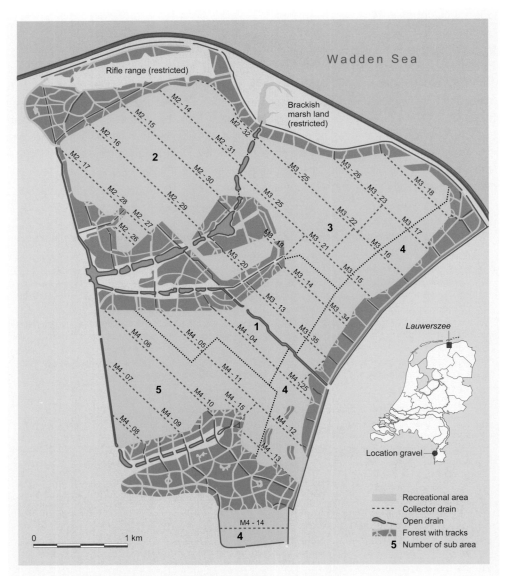

Figure 5   The Lauwerszee project area and the location of the gravel supply site

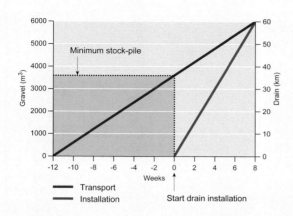

Figure 6   Duration of gravel transport from the gravel pit to the project area

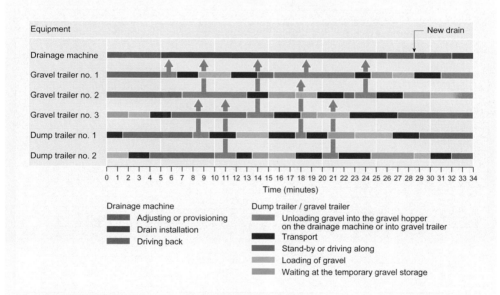

Figure 7   Schedule of activities of gravel supply equipment and duration

539

3.3 Structures

As was mentioned before, most subsurface drainage systems in the Netherlands are singular, thus only a limited number of structures are needed, mostly confined to special conditions, such as:
- Drain bridges, and;
- Manholes for flushing and control.

The other accessories for pipe drains are standardized:
- Couplings to connect pipes with the same and different diameters;
- T-joint and cross-joints;
- End caps;
- End chutes to avoid erosion of the banks of the collector drain (Figure 8).

Figure 8   End chute to protect the side slope of the open collector drain against erosion

4   Installation

4.1   Manual installation

Nowadays, manual installation of pipe drains is obsolete in the Netherlands, but in the first half of the 20th century, most drains were installed by hand. In that period a wealth of experience with manual installation was built up and realistic and precise standards for a large variety of conditions were developed. The amount of earthwork a labourer can handle varies considerably from place to place, mainly depending on the type of soil (Table 3). On average, digging a trench requires a labour input of about one labourer-day per metre per hour. A word of caution: in other countries, especially in the tropics, conditions are often much more difficult, so these figures serve only as a guideline.

Table 3   Guidelines for labour input earth movement using manual labour

Activity	Labour input hours/m^3	
	Sand	Clay
Excavation, including loading the spoil in a wheelbarrow:		
• Up to 0.75 m depth	0.4	0.5
• 1.0 - 1.5 m depth	0.5	0.8

4.2   Mechanical installation

Mechanized drain laying was introduced in the 1950s. Initially American wheel diggers were experimented with. These machines had a low production per hour and therefore soon chain digging machine were developed. The performance and the capacities of trenchers has been further improved and developed since then (Figure 9). A modern trencher with laser control can install 400 - 500 m of corrugated drain pipe (Ø 60 mm) per hour, at a depth of 1-1.4 m.

Figure 9   Development of drainage machines in The Netherlands

The use of trenchless drain techniques has expanded since the 1980s. Approximately 2/3 of lateral drains are installed by trenchless drainage machines. With trenchless installation 500 to 750 m of drain can be installed per hour. Large part of the agricultural land in the Netherlands is used as pasture. Trenchless drain installation is causing very little damage to the grass land. Moreover, installation costs are lower and the production is higher.

In newly reclaimed areas trenchers are preferred. Clay in the reclamation areas is highly saturated with water. Leaving the trench open for some time after digging will increase evaporation and the ripening process is accelerated. The trenchers are equipped with a knife at the trench box to scrape off a small portion of the ripened topsoil into the trench (*"blinding"*) on top of the drain pipe (Figure 10)

Figure 10   Trencher operation in reclamation area with blinding knife at the trench box

5   Quality control

5.1   Certification

In The Netherlands, a system of certification has been set up for quality control of the drainage materials. The quality check of the production is carried out by an independent inspection institute. Manufacturers can participate on a voluntarily basis and if they do and their products constantly meet the quality standards they have the right to market their products as certified by the institute. To the implementation authority this quality certificate means a guarantee of the quality of the product. The manufacturers are obliged to check the quality of their products continuously and the results are entered in a logbook. An inspector from the inspection institute visits the manufacturing plants about 6 times a year. These visits are unexpected and irregular. During these visits the inspector makes random checks of the production quality, and compares the results with those in the logbook. As the visits are unexpected, the manufacturer needs to ensure that the quality is good at all times. The cost of this certification system amounts to about 0.5% of total drainage costs. Nowadays, these standards include an internal quality control system based on the international standard ISO 9000-series.

5.2 Organisation of Quality Control

In large-scale drainage projects (100 - 1000 km of drains) the (semi-) government organisations usually commissions the implementation works. The work is put out to tender and carried out according to specifications that also include the quality standards. Certification is the most appropriate way of guaranteeing that the materials are up to standard. Checking the workmanship by means of rodding or continuous depth recording is also be specified on the basis of random checks. If errors are detected in the random checks the intensity of the random checks is increased according to fixed rules. The consulting company in charge of supervision of the work normally does these checks. An indication of the cost involved based on experiences in the Netherlands is presented in Table 4.

Table 4   Cost of quality control expressed as a percentage of the total cost of drainage in large projects

Item	Cost of checking all drains (%)	Intensity of random checks (%)	Cost of random check (%)
Certification of materials[a]			0.5
Rodding	6	15	0.9
Continuous depth recording	50	3	1.5
All three methods			3

[a] Excluding cost of internal quality control by manufacturer.

In small-scale projects commissioned by private farmers (2.5 and 10 km of drain), the tender documents normally do not include rules and regulations concerning the quality of the work. This may result in poor quality work. To improve the quality the Government Service for Land and Water Use issued a model for a standard contract for private drainage works in 1984. This standard contract contains the quality control methods discussed above. In another development, the farmers' and drainage contractors' organisations decided in 1987 - on the farmers' initiative - to establish a foundation to improve the quality of drainage work. The procedure is more or less analogous to the procedure for certification of materials discussed above. Contractors have their work supervised by this foundation and if their work is up to standard they receive a certificate. The cost of this system comes to about 2% of drainage costs. The possibility to apply this system in the whole of the Netherlands is being studied.

Case Study - Pakistan

Case Study Pakistan

1   Background

Waterlogging and salinity is a serious threat to irrigated agriculture in Pakistan: of the 16.7 million ha in the Indus Basin about 2 million ha are waterlogged and 6 million ha salt affected. The major parts of the irrigated areas in Pakistan where drainage is needed have little slope. Therefore the disposal of the drainage effluent by gravity is in general not possible. The standard subsurface drainage system is a composite system, with buried field and collector drains. Sumps are used to pump the drainage water from several collector drains in open main drains. Figure 1 shows the location of the major pipe drainage projects in Pakistan.

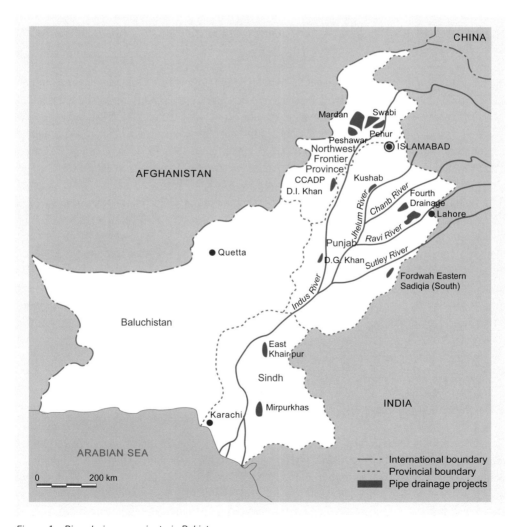

Figure 1   Pipe drainage projects in Pakistan

2 Organisation

2.1 Historical developments

Drainage in Pakistan is generally executed within the canal irrigation commands. In 1958, the Water and Power Development Authority (WAPDA) was established as the agency responsible for the coordination of design, construction and initial operation of the engineering works. After decades of irrigation development, the enormous protective irrigation systems of Pakistan began to experience problems with rising groundwater tables caused by inefficient water delivery systems and inequitable water distribution. In the 1960's WAPDA launched some 51 Salinity Control and Land Reclamation projects (SCARP's) to provide vertical drainage to combat these problems. The SCARP projects were initiated with loans from the World Bank. WAPDA was responsible for the design, construction and initial operation and monitoring of these deep tubewell projects, after which the Provincial Irrigation Departments (PID's) took over operation and maintenance.

As the drainage fees cover only around 20% of the actual expenses of O&M, the financial burden to operate and maintain the public tubewell systems became gradually too much for the PID's. These problems were aggravated because the life expectancy of most SCARP's proved to be less than half the expected life time. To overcome these problems, the irrigation and drainage sector was reformed and in 1997 Provincial Irrigation and Drainage Authorities (PIDA's) were established in all four provinces. System management is to be decentralised and farmers are to take part in the system development and to take over O & M. This is realised by the creation of Area Water Boards (AWB's) and Farmer Organisations (FO's). PIDA's facilitate and promote the formation of AWB's, which compose of farmers, government and PIDA representatives. AWB's on its turn facilitate and promote the formation of FO's. The PIDA's are responsible for the planning, construction, operation and maintenance of the system at main and secondary level. At tertiary level, the FO's are responsible for O & M of the system. All these organisations have to become financial autonomous by levying water charges and drainage fees. The establishment of FO's and AWB's is however hampered by (i) a lack of farmers' involvement in policy reforms; (ii) the weak legal framework (the PIDA Acts) to implement reforms; (iii) lack of knowledge within the FO's and AWB's to develop and implement strategies to deal with the systems' problems and (iv) to make the shift from engineering to institutional solutions.

2.2 International Waterlogging and Salinity Research Institute

To counteract the waterlogging and salinity problems, the Ministry of Water and Power, under the umbrella of WAPDA, and with the assistance of the UN, established the International Waterlogging and Salinity Research Institute/IWASRI, in Lahore, Punjab in 1985. The overall objectives of IWASRI are to co-ordinate and to conduct research on waterlogging and salinity in Pakistan. Over the years IWASRI's mandate has evolved but its intentions and functions have largely remained the same. End-users of IWASRI's research include farmers, planners and designers, policy makers, national research institutes and the drainage industry.

To assist IWASRI, The Governments of Pakistan and The Netherlands in 1988 initiated the Netherlands Research Assistance Project/NRAP, a collaboration between IWASRI and Altera-ILRI. The main aim of NRAP, which covered the period 1988-2000, was to conduct a multidisciplinary research programme on waterlogging and salinity with special attention to drainage engineering, groundwater hydrology and land reclamation. In the second phase of the project, the development of a participatory approach to drainage was included. The project yield valuable results in the following fields:

- *Technical lessons learned,* in particular: (i) design criteria for gravel and synthetic envelope materials; (ii) drainage design with computer simulations; (iii) drainage design criteria; (iv) salinity measurements by magnetic induction; (v) interceptor drainage; (vi) groundwater approach to drainage design; (vii) operation and maintenance of drainage systems (viii) benefits of shallow drainage, and (ix) the use of poor quality water for crop production and reclamation;
- *Participatory drainage development:* lessons learned on development and implementation of Bahawalnagar Subsurface Drainage Pilot Area (112 ha) in the Fordwah Eastern Sadiqia Irrigation and Drainage Project;
- *Institutional development,* including capacity building at ISWARI, through training and the execution and dissemination of research.

2.3   Implementation of subsurface drainage projects

Most subsurface drainage works are implemented on the project basis. For each project a consortium is formed under the authority of WAPA. Such a consortium normally consists of a private (most times foreign) or public contractor and a consulting engineering firm (both local and foreign) to assist with the design and supervision. Salient features of some major projects are discussed in Chapter 5.

3   Drainage materials

Field drains
In Pakistan, corrugated perforated PVC pipes are used for subsurface field drains. As the hydraulic conductivity of the soil is relatively high (e.g. in Mardan Scarp in the Northwest Frontier Province the hydraulic conductivity ranges between 1 and 3 m/d), the spacing between field drains is large and consequently the pipe diameters are rather big (> 100 mm, Table 1).

Table 1 Materials used in some major drainage projects in Pakistan

Project	EKTDP [a]	FDP [b]	Mardan	Khusab
Size of the unit	280 - 450 ha	380 - 400 ha	100 - 300 ha	
Field drains	100 mm corrugated PVC pipe	100 - 200 mm PVC pipe	100 mm PVC pipe	100 & 150 mm PVC pipe
Envelope	Gravel	Natural river run gravel with Hydraulic Conductivity >15m/d	Mainly gravel but for some collectors synthetic fabric envelope was used	Gravel mainly but for IWASRI research synthetic envelope was used on one sump
Collector drains	225 - 450 mm CC and 250 - 300 mm PE pipes	Perforated 250 - 375 mm PVC pipes	Perforated 100, 150, 188, 250 & 300 mm PVC pipe	100, 150, 200, 250, 300 & 380 mm PVC pipe
Sumps	Pumps provided	79 numbers circular 3.05 m diameter masonry well on RCC base slab. One to three pumps of each 2.25 cfs capacity	Outflow was by gravity and therefore no Sump required	Total 56 sumps. 45 circular and 11 rectangular

[a] East Khairpur Tile Drainage Project, Sindh Province

[b] Fourth Drainage Projects, Faisalabad, Punjab Province

Collector drains

In the first major subsurface drainage project, EKTDP, concrete pipes were used as collectors but their installation under the prevailing high water table and unstable subsoil conditions proved to be extremely difficult and the work progressed slowly. The concrete collector drains did not always perform well due to dislocation of the pipes. Therefore, perforated large diameter PE pipes with gravel envelope were installed in the remaining part of the EKTDP project. In all the following projects, perforated plastic PVC pipes are being used. Nowadays, plastic T-joints are used to connect the field and collector drains (Figure 2).

Envelopes

Most soils in Pakistan are fine-textured (silty loam, sandy loam, silty clay etc.) and require an envelope material. No well-established criteria to determine the need and type of envelope existed, mainly gravel envelopes were installed (Table 1) generally based on design criteria developed in the USA (USBR, SCS and others). Serious problems occurred with the crushed rock envelope at the FDP although it was designed according to the specifications (Chapter 5.4). River-run gravel envelopes (having rounded particles) of the same specifications performed better, stressing the need for local verification of these rather site-specific criteria.

Figure 2   Before the field drains are installed, the field drain is connected to the collector drain using a plastic T-joint

Sumps
Sumps are provided for the collection of effluent from the collectors. These sumps are generally a circular brick masonry structure, with a depth of 5 to 7 m (15 to 20 feet) below the soil surface. One to three pumps are installed in a sump for the evacuation of drainage effluent to the surface drain. Electric sensors are provided for automatic operation of the pumps.

4   Installation

Dewatering
Subsurface pipe drains are generally installed when the groundwater table is high. Moreover, in large areas the soil conditions are such that the subsoil is unstable. Therefore, before the construction at a particular unit starts, the contractor will install dewatering equipment (vertical well pointing) and diesel pumps to dewater the site of the sump. The sump is constructed before laying the collector and field drains. Dewatering of the sump starts immediately when the installation of the collector starts. Diesel pumps are also operated to dewater the sites where connections between field drains and collector are made.

Installation of Gravel Envelopes
As the field drains have a comparatively large diameter (Chapter 1.3) it was observed that gravel was not laid uniformly around the pipe in the earlier projects. Therefore, a modification was made in the trench box with an addition of auger which was moving around the pipe below the gravel box feeder (Figure 3). The speed of the gravel auger is automatically adjusted to the speed of the trencher during drain installation. This modification was first time introduced in Fourth Drainage Project and subsequently in the Chashma Command Development (CCAR) (Chapter 5.3) and

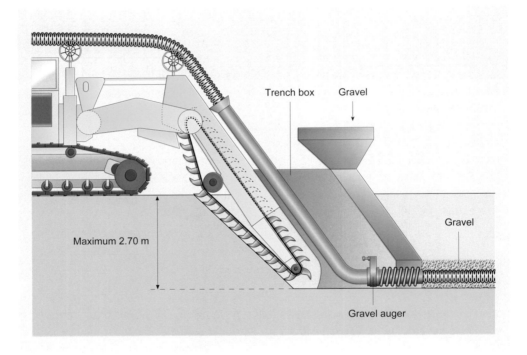

Figure 3   Gravel auger in the trench box

the Fordwah Eastern Sadiqia South (FESS) projects. The results were encouraging and gravel was laid comparatively uniformly.

Installation of Deep Collector Drains

In the Fourth Drainage Project, drain spacing is wide and consequently the collector drains are very deep, up to 4 m below the ground surface, especially at the downstream sections near the sumps. It was not possible for the trencher to lay the collector drains at that depth. For these particular sections, the top layer of about 0.30 m was scraped away from alignment of collector drain.

Trench Backfill and Pipe Stretch

In several projects, sink holes appeared after the installation of drains. The reasons were that, although the consolidation of the top layer was reasonably good after backfill, the conditions immediately above the drain pipe were poor and did not improve in time. This was because:

- Consolidation of the backfill on top of the drain pipe in semi-saturated conditions was not possible, as no equipment would go deeper than 1.5 m;
- Just after installation, the trench often collapsed resulting in large humps of soil on top of the drain pipe leaving big voids.

The sink holes appeared as the result of piping after irrigation and rainfall events. Sink holes appeared even after two to three years after construction especially when the trench backfill had not been exposed to irrigation and/or a heavy rainfall event which are needed to consolidate the trench properly.

Sink holes damaged or misplaced pipe couplings and gravel envelopes. To reduce the risks of sink holes, excessive gradients were avoided by reducing pumping from the sumps during construction. Pumping was resumed only after trench backfill has been exposed to one cropping season irrigation and/or to a heavy rainfall event. Furthermore, additional measures like rollers (Figure 4), puddling, extra soil, blinding, slow water table draw down and deep tillage were used to overcome this problem.

a

b

c

Figure 4
Rollers to compact the back-fill were use in the Mardan SCARP project: (a) site view; (b) detail roller and (c) rear view

5 Salient features of some large-scale drainage projects

5.1 East Khaipur Tile Drainage Project[1]

East Khaipur Tile Drainage Project (EKTDP) was the first major subsurface drainage project to combat waterlogging and salinity in Pakistan. This World Bank-financed project covered 18 000 ha in the Sindh Province, of which 14 000 ha were provided with subsurface drainage systems. The subsurface drainage system of a unit (varying in size between 280 and 450 ha) consists of plastic field drains, concrete collector drains and a sump through which the excess drainage water is pumped into a shallow open main drain. The project execution started in 1981 and was completed in 1986.

a

b

c

Figure 5 Dewatering of collector drain section, (a) horizontal dewatering by diesel pumps (b) and installation of concrete collector pipes (c) in the EKTDP project area

---

[1] Based on Ochs, W.J and B.G. Bishay. 1992. Drainage Guidelines. World Bank Technical Paper Number 195, ISSN 0253-7494.

The corrugated PVC field drains (Ø 100 mm) were manufactured in Pakistan and were installed at a average depth of 1.8 m with an average spacing of 115 m (range between 50 and 175 m). All field drains were installed with a trench drainage machine and provided with a gravel envelope (0.1 m^3/m). The concrete collector pipes were manufactured also locally but within the project area. The diameters ranged between 230 and 460 mm and the maximum installation depth at the outlet was 3 m. Installation was done by a hydraulic excavator after previous dewatering.

The total installation cost, excluding extra and indirect costs, was about € 1183/ha at 1981 prices (Table 2). The extra and indirect costs totalled 44%: i.e. contingencies (10%), contractor's overhead (10%), contractor's profit & risk (10%), foreign technicians (2%), supervision and accounting (5%) and crop compensation for farmers (7%).

Table 2 Cost of subsurface drainage system in EKTDP (1981 prices)

	Cost	
	(€ per m of drain)	(€ per ha)
Field drains:		
Pipe material (ex factory)	2.25	
Transport of pipes to site	0.04	
Gravel filter including transport	1.95	
Installation pipe & gravel	0.95	
Land clearing and backfill	0.15	
Repair of crossings with roads, canals, etc.	0.25	
Transport of equipment	0.15	
Sub-total field drains	5.74	603
Collector drains:		
Dewatering	13.30	
Concrete pipes	5.75	
Transport	1.60	
Excavation, installation and backfill	7.05	
Land clearing and levelling	0.50	
Sub-total collector drains	28.20	412
Manholes (connections field - collector drains)		20
Sumps and pumping stations		43
Open main drains:		
- Excavation	12.00	
- Structures	20.00	
Sub-total open drains	32.00	106
Total per hectare		**1,183**

Lessons learned

The installation of the concrete collector drain pipes was a cumbersome and costly job. Prior to the installation of the collector pipes sections of the collector line had to be dewatered by horizontal dewatering and some sections even by vertical well pointing due to the unstable soil conditions in the area. It became clear after the installation and operation of a number of collector units that the performance of the concrete collector drain pipes was unsatisfactory. The unstable subsoil caused dislocation of the concrete pipes, sink holes appeared, and costly repairs were necessary. So, it was decided to install large diameter perforated PE pipes with an gravel envelope in the remaining collector units (Figure 6). The PE pipes had to be imported, as large diameter PE or PVC pipes were not yet locally made. The installation and performance of the PE collector drain pipes proved to be successful in unstable soil. So, in unstable subsoil no concrete drain pipes are to be used but only perforated collector drain pipes with envelope material.

5.2   Mardan Salinity Control and Reclamation Project

The Mardan Salinity Control and Reclamation Project encompasses 52 000 ha of the Lower Swat Canal Command in the Northwest Frontier Province, of which about 30 000 ha were provided with subsurface drainage. The project was funded by the Governments of Pakistan and Canada through a World Bank loan and a Canadian International Development Agency (CIDA) grant. The project was carried out under a general agreement for consulting engineering services between WAPDA (representing the owners) and two associated Canadian and Pakistan Engineering Companies (Engineer). Actual implemented was done under contract; the first contract utilized Canadian contracting practices, while the second followed an international contracting format. The overall project consisted of an extensive program of civil works, including the construction of surface and subsurface drainage, irrigation canal remodelling, road improvements, land level-

Figure 6   Installation of large diameter perforated corrugated PE collector drain pipe with gravel envelope

ling, reclamation and agricultural development programmes. The project started in 1987 and was completed in 1991. The main activities and players in the implementation of the subsurface drainage systems are presented in Table 3. Prior to the installation of subsurface drainage the area had relative high watertables: pre-drainage watertables fluctuated between 0.3 and 1.2 m.

Table 3   Main activities and responsible actors in the implementation of MARDAN SCARP

Activity	Responsible actor/player
1. Pre-construction:	
1.1 Acquisition of construction access	Owner
1.2 Drain layout surveys	Contractor
1.3 Layout adjustment (if required)	Engineer
1.4 Certification of layouts	Engineer
1.5 Control of irrigation water	Owner - Irrigation Department
1.6 Supply of drain pipes	Owner
1.7 Supply of gravel envelope	Owner
2. Construction:	
2.1 Site stockpiling drain pipes and gravel envelope materials	Contractor
2.2 Clearing trees from drain lines	Contractor
2.3 Smooth and prepare right of way for installation	Contractor
2.4 Installation of drain pipes and gravel envelope	Contractor
2.5 Restoration of disturbed lands and water canals	Contractor
2.6 Construction of related structure, i.e. outlets, culverts, manholes, etc.	Contractor
2.7 Inspection of all works to verify construction in accordance with contract	Engineer
3. Post-construction:	
3.1 Measurement of all installed items	Engineer
3.2 Invoice for interim payments	Contractor
3.3 Check of all measurements (3.1) and certify invoices for payment	Engineer
3.4 Approve and payment of contract invoices	Owner

Drainage Materials

Corrugated PVC pipes were used for both the field and collector drains, varying in size from 100 to 300 mm. Gravel envelopes were used for the field drains and a thin synthetic envelope for the collector drains. The gravity system had relatively deep field drains (1.8 - 2.0 m) resulting in wide spacing (> 100 m) and very deep collectors (up to 3 m).

Equipment

For the installation of the field drains (Ø 100 mm) two types of drainage machines were used:

- A trenchless plough: a double roller, imaginary hitch-point type with gravel box and drain pipe chute mounted on a crawler tractor (410 HP). Due to the traction conditions, tow services of an additional crawler tractor (300 HP) were normally required (Figure 7);
- A chain-type trencher.

Figure 7   Trenchless drain installation in the Mardan SCARP project area

For the installation of the collector drains (Ø 160 - 300 mm) two chain-type trenchers with gravel box and pipe chute were used. Under wet ground conditions a crawler-type tow tractor had to be used to provide extra power.

All these machines were equipped with laser controlled hydraulic systems. The average rate of drain pipe installation varied from 2 500 m/day for the field drainage machines and 540 m/day for the collector drainage machines.

Quality control during installation

As poor construction quality was regarded as one of the main causes of drain failure, an intensive inspection routine was pursued. The inspection team, which included a survey team, undertook the following activities:

- Grade inspection at 30 m intervals along the installed field and collector lines. Although all the drainage machines were laser controlled, numerous deviations were observed mainly due to the response time required for the adjustment of the trench box and to a less extent due to adjustment of the laser and system control linkages;

- Visual inspection of the pipe couplings, end caps either on the surface (pipe couplings and end caps) or in excavations (field - collector drain couplings, see Figure 2);
- In the second contract, inspection also included the pulling of a ball (with a diameter 12.5 mm less than the diameter of the pipe) through the line to check for loose couplings and deformed (compressed) pipe sections;
- In-situ measurements of the thickness of the graded gravel in inspection pits.

Jointly procedures and measurements between the Engineer and the Contractor were introduced, although not contractually required, to minimize later disputes.

Lessons learned
Some of the major lessons learned during the installation of subsurface drainage in the Mardan SCARP are:
- Discontinuation of irrigation a few days before and during installation is required to obtain sufficient grip for the drainage machines;
- In areas that are intensively cropped and have many (small) farm holdings, a good coordination between the landowners, farmers, contractor and engineer is essential for a smooth work process;
- Frequent and jointly organised (between the contractor and the engineer) inspections are essential to ensure good quality installation practices;
- Specifications of construction requirements, inspection procedures, etc. have to fully and carefully define the requirements of the works. They must also address any unique problems that are likely to be encountered during the work. Again these specifications should be developed in close cooperation between the consultant and the contractor.

Effects of the subsurface drainage system
The waterlogged conditions reduced considerably after the project was completed: a monitoring programme revealed that the post drainage watertable fluctuates between 1.2 and 2.5 m, compared to a pre-drainage fluctuation between 0.3 and 1.2 m.

5.3   Chashma Command Area Development Project

The Chashma Command Area Development (CCAD) Project encompasses about 60 000 ha served by the Chashma Right Bank Canal (CRB) in the Dera Ismail Khan District of the Northwest Frontier Province. Three types of subsurface drainage were installed to combat the waterlogging and salinity problems:
- Interceptor drains along an unlined section of the CRB Canal in the upstream part of the project area (7 700 ha);
- Subsurface pipe drainage systems in the middle section of the project area (29 000 ha), and;
- Surface drainage in combination with subsurface drainage in the perched watertable zones in the downstream section of the command (23 000 ha).

Organisation

The executing agency was the Water and Power Development Authority and a international consultant consortium served as consultants during the implementation. The project was financed by the Asian Development Bank using international competitive bidding with pre-qualified contractors. Three contractors tendered for the job and the tender was awarded to the 2nd lowest bidder as the lowest bidder was declared non-responsive. The project started in 1985 and was completed in 1995.

Subsurface drainage system

The subsurface drainage system consists of locally produced PVC corrugated field and collector drains of 150, 200, 250, 300 and 350 mm diameter. The field drains were installed at a minimum depth of 1.70 m and 610 m spacing, only in the fine-textured soils of the downstream part spacings of 200 to 300 m were used. A river-run gravel envelope (thickness 100 mm), based on Soil Conservation Services (SCS) criteria, was placed around the drains. The collector drains convey the water into a circular reinforced brick masonry sump (Ø 3.0 & 3.6 m, with a 7.7 m depth) form where the water was pumped in to a disposal drain using electric pumps.

Equipment

A specially designed drainage trencher was purchased: with a 464 horsepower Caterpillar, hydraulic motor-driven gravel compacting screw, wide tracks, a track-mounted gravel feeder and laser control. Track-mounted feeders and trailers with float tyres for maximum bearing were used to transport the gravel to the drainage machine (Figure 8). The manufacturer provided the contractor an experienced expatriate trenching machine operator for in-service training of local machine operators.

Figure 8   Track-mounted gravel feeders and gravel trailers with float tyres for maximum bearing were used in the Chashma CAD Project

The equipment suffered excessive wear and tear due to the extremely wet conditions. The digging chains and allied parts of the trencher machine wore very rapidly due to the abrasive action of sand. Replacement of these digging chains in the CCAD project was eight times more than for similar projects in Pakistan: after digging 3.5 - 4 km of trench in the CCAD project area compared to e.g. 30 km of trench in Nawabshah. Another reason for this was the contractor's procurement of locally manufactured chains. Replacement of a digging chain costs 2 working days.

Lessons learned
- Because of the emergency from flooding and the resulting local pressure on the Government to initiate the works, a feasibility study was not conducted and the project was commissioned based on the limited available information. Investigations, surveys and designs were only carried out after the project execution started. This resulted in many changes of the original plans. Although this delayed the project for several months, millions of rupees were saved that would otherwise have been wasted on unnecessary drains if the project had been in its original scope;
- Contracts also started without adequate surveys, acquisition of land rights, or complete plans and specifications, seriously hampering the construction activities later on;
- The surveys of the large area were very time consuming and were not always very accurate. This resulted in poor quality base maps and unreliable topographical maps;
- The deep installation depth of the drain caused frequent breakdowns of the trencher, excessive dewatering efforts and slow installation rates. These problems were rectified only after the design was revised to reduce depth of drains by splitting the larger sump units to smaller ones (170 - 250 ha);
- The initial implementation schedule developed by the Engineer was not realistic: time required to import equipment, the assembly and adjustment to local soil conditions should have been included;
- A visit of the manufacturer of the trencher to the site at a early stage in the project resulted in valuable modifications to the equipment to make them more suitable for the local conditions, e.g. wider tracks and the introduction of the power auger for the gravel placement;
- The supply of gravel under the wet conditions encountered in the project area was problematic: although the trencher with its wide tracks performed satisfactorily, the performance of the auxiliary equipment like gravel trailers and excavators was poor. The option to use a much lighter synthetic envelope instead of gravel should be considered under such wet conditions;
- The contract was awarded to the second lowest bidder, although this bid was considerable lower than the highest. During construction the contractor who was awarded the job always complained of heavy financial losses and had constant difficulties to make sufficient funds available to procure sufficient materials and auxiliary equipment, resulting in many delays. The contactor who submitted the highest bid had gained experience in similar projects (Mardan SCARP) and should probably have completed the project in time. Thus in contracts requiring specialized services, the bidder's experience in similar works should also be weighed during the tender evaluation.

- A monitoring programme, in particular on watertables (and soil salinity) should be initiated at the start of the project and continue afterwards to assess the benefits of drainage.

5.4   Fourth Drainage project

The Fourth Drainage project (FDP) located in the Faisalabad District of the Punjab included the installation of subsurface drainage in an area of 31 500 ha. The project was launched by WAPDA in 1984 and only completed after many delays in June 1994. One of the main problems faced was due to the use of crushed gravel as envelope. The subsurface drainage system consists of corrugated plastic (PVC) field (Ø 100, 150 & 200 mm) and collector (Ø 250, 300 & 375 mm) drains. The design specifications, which were based on the United Stated Bureau of Reclamation (USBR) criteria, specified that well-graded gravel with a minimum thickness of 100 mm should be placed around all field and collector pipe drains. The contract stated that *"the envelope material shall consist of a uniform well graded mixture of sand and gravel. It should be sound, stable, clear, free of vegetable matter, clay and other deleterious matter. The minimum hydraulic conductivity of the envelope shall be 50 ft. per day (15 m/d)"*. Normally river-run gravel is used in Pakistan, but because river-run gravel was not available in the vicinity of the FDP area, the use of crushed gravel was proposed by the contractor and accepted by the engineer. Soon after installation started it became clear that the drain lines for which the crushed gravel was used did not perform satisfactorily: drain pipes were chocked by soil that had entered the pipe. The execution was stopped to investigate the cause of the problem. Drains were excavated and it was discovered that a lot of fine soil had moved into the drains (Figure 9). Subsequent laboratory tests revealed that the hydraulic conductivity of the crushed gravel (> 900 m/d) was much higher than river-run gravel (75 - 250 m/d) of the same gradation. It was concluded that the resulting higher hydraulic gradient had allowed the finer soil particles to enter the pipe.

Figure 9   Fourth Drainage Project: excavations revealed that the drain pipes were blocked by fine sediments

Following these field and laboratory tests, the designers reviewed the specifications and, although the gravel gradation was kept according to its previous graduation, it was decided that only river-run material should be used. Different quarries were visited and gravel samples were collected for laboratory and field tests. After these tests proved to be successful three new quarry sites were selected and the use of river-run gravel was specified for the remaining part of the contract. The consequences on the project implementation process were that:

- The temporary stoppage of the execution delayed the project by about 5 months;
- The cost of gravel increased about 3 times due to the longer haulage distance.

Lessons learned

The main lesson learned from this experience is that specifications based on knowledge that was developed elsewhere (in this case the USBR criteria) should be locally verified during the project's preparation phase.

Bibliography

Drainage of clay soils

1995   Rycroft, D.W. and M.H. Amer. *Prospects for the Drainage of Clay Soils*. Irrigation and Drainage Paper No. 51. FAO, Rome. 52 pp.

This bulletin discusses the drainage of clay soils. The book starts with a discussion of the physical and chemical properties of clay soils, the movement of water and salts in these soils and then reviews the techniques to drain and reclaim heavy clay soils. Case studies of drainage of heavy clay soils in Yugoslavia, Portugal, Spain and Egypt are included.

Drainage design

1984   Framji, K.K., B.C. Garg, and S.P. Kaushish. *Design Practices of Open Drainage Channels in an Agricultural Land Drainage System: A Worldwide Survey*. ICID, New Delhi. 343 pp.

This volume on open drainage channels consists of two parts: Part I is devoted to a general review of the design aspects of open drainage channels: system lay-out, design capacity, channel shape, roughness coefficient, permissible channel velocity, longitudinal channel slope, side slope; Part II contains the country reports of Australia, Bangladesh, Canada, Colombia, Czechoslovakia, Egypt, France, Federal Republic of Germany, German Democratic Republic, Great Britain, Greece, India, Iraq, Ireland, Japan, Malaysia, Morocco, Portugal, Saudi Arabia, Sudan, and the U.S.A.

1980   Food and Agriculture Organisation of the United Nations. *Drainage Design Factors*. Irrigation and Drainage Paper No. 38. 1980. FAO, Rome. 52 pp.

This manual, which is based on an expert consultation, gives 28 questions and answers regarding drainage design factors.

1978   U.S. Department of the Interior, Bureau of Reclamation. *Drainage Manual - A guide to integrated plant, soil, and water relationships for drainage of irrigated lands*. U.S. Government Printing Office, Washington, 286 p.

The manual contains the engineering tools and concepts that have proven useful in planning, constructing, and maintaining drainage systems for successful long-term irrigation projects. Although the manual is not a textbook, it provides drainage engineering with a ready reference and guide for making accurate estimates of drainage requirements. All the methods and techniques covered in the manual have proven to be very satisfactory through observed field conditions on irrigated lands in the USA but also in other parts of the world.

Drainage guidelines

1992   Ochs, Walter J. and Bishay G. Bishay. *Drainage Guidelines*. 1992. World Bank Technical Paper Number 1995, The World Bank, Washington. 186 pp.

This paper provides research results for and experiences with agricultural drainage and related subjects. It has been developed to guide Bank staff, consultants, and borrowing-country technicians as they work through the project cycle, seeking to assist planners and designers, as well as those responsible for implementation and follow-up, when projects involve drainage measure.

1990   Schultz, B. *Guidelines on the Construction of Horizontal Subsurface Drainage Systems.* International Commission on Irrigation and Drainage, New Delhi. 236 pp.
These guidelines give general criteria and recommendations for the construction of horizontal subsurface drainage systems. The book starts with an inventory of subsurface drainage systems and then briefly reviews design aspects. It gives attention to drainage materials and to equipment to install the drains. It then recommends construction methods, and describes operation and maintenance. Finally, it treats the cost benefit analysis of projects. Includes a glossary.

1987   Pavelis, G.A. (Ed.). *Farm Drainage in the United States: History, Status and Prospects.* Miscellaneous Publication No. 1455, United States Department of Agriculture, Economic Research Service, Washington DC, 170 p.
This publication covers the historical, technological, economic, and environmental aspects of agricultural drainage in the USA. The main purpose is to review the evolution of modern farm drainage and to identify farm drainage objectives for agricultural extension specialists and agents, environmental specialists, drainage consultants, installation contractors, and educators. Farm production, water management, and other benefits and costs associated with the drainage of wet soils on farms are described within the context of existing USDA programs and other Federal policies for protecting wetlands. The publication, which draws from the combined knowledge of academic and USDA professionals, covers subjects: 1) A framework for future farm drainage policy: the environmental and economic setting; 2) A history of drainage and drainage methods; 3) Advances in drainage technology: 1955-85; 4) Purposes and benefits of drainage; 5) Preserving environmental values; 6) Principles of drainage; 7) Drainage system elements; 8) Planning farm and project drainage; 9) Drainage for irrigation: managing soil salinity and drain-water quality; 10) Drainage institutions; 11) Economic survey of farm drainage; 12) Drainage potential and information needs, and: 13) Drainage challenges and opportunities.

1983   Food and Agriculture Organisation of the United Nations. *Guidelines for the Preparation of Irrigation and Drainage Projects.* Revised Edition. FAO, Rome. 31 pp.
Gives guidelines for the main text of a feasibility study, which provides the answers to questions that might be raised in the course of project appraisal.

Drainage materials

2001   Vlotman, W.F., L.S. Willardson, and W. Dierickx. 2001. *Envelope Design for Subsurface Drains.* ILRI Publication 56, ILRI, Wageningen, 358 p.
The book is a compilation of the most recent information on how to design and select envelope materials for agricultural drains. It is especially valuable for drainage engin-

eers, contractors, drainage equipment manufacturers, students, teachers, and researchers who need to understand soil hydraulic conditions and how to prevent soil particles from moving into drains so that they can design successful subsurface drainage systems. The publication consists of two parts. In part one, guidelines for the design of envelopes for subsurface drains are presented, it includes the following subjects: the needs for a drain envelope, material selection, design, cost, implementation, maintenance and evaluation. Part two, the "resources" section, presents the background of drain envelope design, the theory and testing of existing design criteria and experiences.

2000 Stuyt, L.C.P.M., W. Dierickx and J. M. Beltrán. *Materials for subsurface land drainage systems.* Irrigation and Drainage Paper No. 60. FAO, Rome, 183 p.
This paper provides practical information to drainage engineers and contractors for the selection, installation and maintenance of drainage materials as well as specifications and standards for such materials. In addition, the manual also contains practical guidelines for the implementation of laboratory and field investigations to evaluate the performance of drainage materials.

1970 Food and Agriculture Organisation of the United Nations. *Drainage Materials.* Irrigation and Drainage Paper No. 9. FAO, Rome. 122 pp.
This manual gives an overview of the materials used in the construction of pipe drainage systems.

Drainage planning, design and management
2004 Smedema, L.K., W.F. Vlotman and D.W. Rycroft. *Modern Land Drainage: Planning, Design and Management of Agricultural Drainage systems.* 450pp.
New edition of the publication Land Drainage (published in 1983). The book is based on traditional drainage methods for rainfed agriculture in the humid temperate zone. Significant parts are devoted to drainage for salinity control of irrigated lands in (semi-) arid zones, and to drainage of rice land in the humid tropics. Institutional, management and maintenance aspects are covered, as well as the mitigation of adverse impacts of drainage interventions on the environment. Moreover, various applications for drainage design and management are treated. The book is intended for use both as a university level textbook and as a professional handbook.

1983 Smedema, L.K., and D. Rycroft. *Land Drainage: Planning and Design of Agricultural Drainage Systems.* Batsford Academic and Educational Ltd., London, United Kingdom. 376 pp.
The text discusses the diagnosis of agricultural drainage problems and their solutions, based on an understanding of the physical principles involved. Land drainage is treated as being a field of applied soil physics and applied hydrology. All major drainage problems are covered, each in its particular environment and field of application: Groundwater Drainage; Watertable Control; Surface Drainage of Sloping and Flat Lands; Shallow Drainage of Heavy Land; Drainage for Salinity Control in Irrigated Land; Drain-

age and Reclamation of Polders; Drainage for Seepage Control; Main Drainage: Design Discharges, Canal Design, Outlets. The book stresses the universal relationships between the main design variables and soil, climatology, and other relevant environmental conditions.

Drainage principles and applications

1994   Ritzema, H.P. (Editor-in-Chief). *Drainage Principles and Applications, Second, Completely Revised Edition.* ILRI Publication 16, ILRI, Wageningen, 1125p.

This completely revised second edition on drainage principles and applications is based on lectures delivered at the International Course on Land Drainage, which is held annually by the International Institute for Land Reclamation and Improvement, Wageningen, The Netherlands. The book presents the basic principles of land drainage with applications. The book provides a coverage of all the various topics useful to those engaged in drainage engineering. Includes a glossary.

Also available is a Spanish version published in 1977, entitled: Principios y Aplicaciones del Drenaje (en cuatro volúmenes).

Drainage systems

1999   Skaggs, R.W., J. van Schilfgaarde (Ed.). *Agricultural Drainage.* Number 38 in the series Agronomy, American Society of Agronomy, Madison, USA, 1328 p.

This monograph summarises the information developed during the past two decades and deals with the many aspects of contemporary agricultural irrigation and drainage systems, placing these systems into the perspective of comprehensive water management. It can serve as the scientific basis for decision-makers in developing management strategies to improve the soil conditions of the field and protect water quality from contamination by cropping practices. The 42 chapters which contributions from 71 scientists and professions are presented in 12 sections: I) Introduction; II) Overview of drainage and crop production; III) Soil water movement in drained lands; IV) Movement and fate of solutes in drained lands; V) Modelling in the performance of drainage systems; VI) Drainage for salinity control and reclamation; VII) Water table control; VIII) Hydrology and water quality impacts of drainage; IX) Planning and design of drainage systems; X) Drainage methods and materials; XII) Special drainage problems; XII) Determination of soil properties for drainage design, and; XII) Socio-economic impacts of agricultural water management systems.

Drainage testing

1976   Food and Agriculture Organisation of the United Nations. *Drainage Testing.* Irrigation and Drainage Paper No. 28. FAO, Rome. 172 pp.

This publication gives guidelines on how to test the functioning and adequacy of single drains and drainage systems.

Drainage training manuals

1996   Ritzema, H.P., R.A.L. Kselik and F. Chanduvi. *Drainage of Irrigated Lands.* Irrigation Water Management Training Manual No. 9. Food and Agricultural Organisation of the

United Nations, Rome, 74 p.

Drainage of Irrigated Lands is the ninth in a series of training manuals on irrigation. The manual is intended for use by field assistants in agricultural extension services and irrigation & drainage technicians at the village and district levels who want to increase their ability to deal with farm-level irrigation and drainage issues. It discusses the needs for drainage in irrigated areas, focusing on drainage at farm level. It reviews the systems that are available to drain irrigated lands and explains which factors of soil and hydrology influence drainage. It touches briefly upon the design, construction, operation and management of field drainage systems.

Case studies
China
1987   Ministry of Water Resources and Electric Power. *Irrigation and Drainage in China*. China Water Resources and Electric Power Press, 107p.

This publication gives an overview of the status of irrigation and drainage in China and the developments since the Chinese revolution in 1948.

2004   Fang Sheng and Chen Xiuling. *Comprehensive Control of Drought, Waterlogging and Salinity and its Technological and Economic Effects* (in Chinese and English). China Agricultural Science and Technology Press, China, 84 p.

This publication summarises the research and observations on, and the experiences with the implementation of the research results over a period of 20 years with controlling waterlogging and salinity in the North China Plain. One of the conclusions is that with a proper waterlogging and salinity control, the effects of drought can be substantially reduced.

Egypt
2003   Advisory Panel Project on Water Management. *Precious Water: a celebration of 27 years of Egyptian- Dutch Cooperation*. APP Central Office, Cairo, Egypt, 84 p.

The booklet published through the Secretariat of the Egyptian-Dutch Advisory Panel on Water Management, on the occasion of the Third World Water Forum, March 2003, presents an overview of an unique 27-year cooperation between the Governments of Egypt and the Netherlands in the Egyptian-Dutch Advisory Panel on Water Management. This bilateral cooperation on water started, in 1975, on drainage, with a main focus on design and implementation of large-scale drainage systems. Throughout the years of the bilateral co-operation, the Advisory Panel successfully widened its scope from drainage specific issues to water management topics and gradually changed from technical support to policy advice. The main objective of the Panel in its present set-up is to assist the Ministry of Water Resources and Irrigation in carrying out its responsibilities towards managing the quality and quantity of Egypt's freshwater resources more efficiently and effectively. This task is accomplished with an Annual Panel Meeting, Workshops, consultant missions (local and international), Working Group Meetings, Task Forces, etc., coordinated by a Secretariat, based in Cairo, Egypt, and Wageningen, The Netherlands.

In the booklet the "nuts and bolts" of the Panel as well as many of the achievements of the last 27 years are described in 13 interviews with Panel members, Officials of the Netherlands Embassy in Cairo, and the Panel's Secretariat.

2003   El Guindy, S., M. Salah El Deen, A. Bazaraa & W. Wolters. *"Seminar on Water Management Development in Egypt, Results of Long-term Egyptian-Dutch Cooperation".* Proceedings seminar on water management development, 12-14 December 2002, in Hurghada, Egypt. Advisory Panel Project on Water Management, Cairo, Egypt.
The proceedings highlight the results of the long-term, 27 years from 1975-2002, Egyptian-Dutch cooperation on water management. The objectives of the Seminar were threefold:
- To highlight the achievements of more than 25 years of Egyptian-Dutch cooperation;
- To reflect on the evolution of the cooperation programme from technology transfer in land drainage towards integrated water management and planning, institutional reform, capacity building and environmental management;
- To exchange experiences, lessons learned, vision for the future of Egypt's water sector and coordination issues of donor cooperation.

The proceedings include the critical success factors for such a bilateral cooperation programme as well as the Main Findings and Recommendations of the Seminar. A CD with all papers and presentations completes the Proceedings.

2001   Drainage Research Project I & II. 2001. *Drainage Research Project I & II, Final Report, Dec 1994 - June 2001.* Drainage Research Institute, Kanater, Cairo, Egypt, 172 p.
The report presents the results of the long-term co-operation of drainage research in Egypt between the Drainage Research Institute (DRI), Egypt and the International Institute for Land Reclamation and Improvement (ILRI), the Netherlands. After a brief sketch of agriculture and agricultural research in Egypt, with emphasis on the activities by DRI, the achievements in the field of design criteria are described in 6 sections: I) Project details; II) Research on design criteria; III) Monitoring and evaluation; IV) Research on drainage technology; V) Crop production and water management; VI) Research Management. The report concludes with a list of publications by the project.

2000   H.J. Nijland (Ed.) *Drainage along the River Nile.* RIZA Nota nr. 2000.052, Ministry of Public Works and Water Resources, Egypt, Ministry of Transport, Public Works and Water Management, Directorate-General of Public Works and Water Management, The Netherlands, 323 p.
This publication presents the achievements of 15 years of co-operation on institutional and technical aspects of Agricultural Land Drainage in Egypt between the Egyptian Public Authority of Drainage Projects (EPADP) and the Netherlands Directorate General of Public Works and Water Management (RWS). It presents various aspects of large-scale implementation of drainage, covering subjects that are technical, economic, and organisational, or that concern operation research, and institutional and human resources development. The contributions of 40 authors are presented in 5 parts: I)

Drainage in Egypt and The Netherlands; II) Training: III) Planning and Organisation; IV) Information Technology, and; V) Drainage Technology.

1989 Amer, M.H. and N.A. de Ridder (Eds.) *Land Drainage in Egypt.* Drainage Research Institute, Cairo, Egypt and the International Institute for Land Reclamation and Improvement (ILRI), The Netherlands, 377 p.

The project presents the achievements of 14 years of technical co-operation between Egypt and The Netherlands on agricultural land drainage. The book summarises the knowledge gained in research studies that were conducted to combat waterlogging and salinity in the Nile Delta and Valley with the aim to provide some 2.1 million hectares with subsurface drainage systems. The results are presented in seven: 1) Drainage survey and design practices; 2) Drainage technology; 3) Operation and maintenance of drainage systems; 4) Vertical drainage feasibility in the Nile Valley; 5) Reuse of drainage water for irrigation; 6) Economic evaluation of drainage projects, and 7) Institutional and management aspects of drainage projects. The book provides in depth guidance to practising engineers in planning and designing drainage systems.

India

2003 Indo-Dutch Network Project on Drainage and Water Management for Salinity Control in Canal Commands in India. *Research on the control of waterlogging and salinization in irrigated agricultural lands.* Central Soil salinity Research Institute, Karnal, India and Alterra-International Institute for Land Reclamation and Improvement, Wageningen, The Netherlands, 4 Volumes, 380p.

This report presents the findings of the Indo-Dutch Network Project on research on the control of waterlogging and salinization in irrigated agricultural lands in India. The project, covering the period 1995 - 2002, was a collaboration between the Central Soil Salinity Research Institute, Karnal , the four State Agricultural Universities of Andhra Pradesh, Gujarat, Karnataka and Rajasthan and Alterra-ILRI. The four volumes of the report cover the following issues:

- A methodology for identification of waterlogging and soil salinity conditions using remote sensing: Based on eight studies covering areas ranging from 5 000 to 350 000 ha in the Indo-Gangetic plains (3), heavy clay or black soils (3) and sandy soils (2), two methodology, one based on visual and another for digital interpretation are recommended;

- Recommendations on Waterlogging and Salinity Control based on pilot area drainage research: presenting the research findings of 7 drainage pilot areas (ranging in size from 20 to 188 ha), covering 5 agro-ecological sub-regions in India with soils ranging from sandy loam to heavy clay. For each sub-region specifications for subsurface drainage systems, both open and pipe drains, are presented;

- Computer modelling in irrigation and drainage: four computer simulation models, SWAP, UNSATCHEM, SALTMOD and SURDEV, were tested to assess the short and longterm impacts of water management options on the land and water productivity and the environment;

- Human resource development and the establishment of a training centre: the report discusses the adopted approach in technology transfer, capacity building and institution strengthening of the four network centres.

1995   Rajasthan Agricultural Drainage Research Project. 1995. *Analysis of Subsurface Drainage Design Criteria.* Chambal Command Area Development Authority, Rajasthan, India, 260 p.

The report presents an intensive review of the present state of scientific knowledge and technology in the subsurface drainage research activities undertaken by the Rajasthan Agricultural Drainage Research Project (RAJAD) during1991-1994. These activities have resulted in the development of criteria and guidelines for subsurface drainage installation to assist with the formulation of large-scale subsurface drainage procedures for the installation of subsurface drainage in about 25 000 ha in the Chambal Command Area, Kota, Rajasthan, India. The information is presented in 10 chapters: 1) Project description; 2) Background information on Chambal Command Area; 3) Salinity and waterlogging; 4) Description of the experimental drainage test sites; 5) Subsurface drainage design criteria development; 6) Multidisciplinary aspects of subsurface drainage; 7) Hydraulics of subsurface drainage systems; 8) Subsurface drain envelope requirements; 9) Subsurface drainage installation costing procedures; 10) Design guidelines for subsurface drainage.

The Netherlands

1993   Ven, G.P.van de (Editor). *Man-made lowlands: history of water management and land reclamation in the Netherlands.* Matrijs, Utrecht, 293 p.

Man-made lowlands presents a comprehensive and richly illustrated picture of the way the Dutch have made and kept their lowlands habitable. A indispensable standard work for anyone interested in the Dutch history of water management and land reclamation. The publication covers subjects: 1) The Netherlands, the country and its inhabitants; 2) Water management from about 800 to about 1250; 3) Water management from about 1250 to about 1600; 4) Water management from 1600 to about 1800; 5) The Netherlands, its inhabitants and water management administration from 1800 till present; 6) Water management in 'Laag-Nederland' from about 1800 till present; 7) Water management in 'Hoog-Nederland' from about 1800 till present; 8) Improvement of the large rivers; 9) The Zuiderzee and the Delta projects; 10) Epilogue and the prospects of water management in the Netherlands

Pakistan

2001   Alterra-ILRI. *Netherlands Research Assistance Project: a bilateral cooperation in drainage between IWASRI and ILRI - Final Report 1988-2000. Alterra-ILRI Rapport 354,* Wageningen, 90 p.

This is the final report of the Netherlands Research Assistance Project, a joint undertaking by the International Waterlogging and Salinity Research Institute (IWASRI), Lahore, Pakistan and the International Institute for Land Reclamation and Improvement (ILRI), Wageningen, The Netherlands. The project, with covered the period 1988-2000, had two main activities: work on technical aspects of drainage and the development of a participatory approach to drainage. The report discussed three main issues.

1. Technical lessons learned, in particular: (i) envelope materials; (ii) drainage design with computer simulations; (iii) drainage design criteria; (iv) salinity measurements by magnetic induction; (v) interceptor drainage; (vi) groundwater approach to drainage design; (vii) operation and maintenance of drainage systems (viii) benefits of shallow drainage, and (ix) the use of poor quality water for crop production and reclamation;

2. Participatory drainage development: lessons learned on development and implementation, and;

3. Institutional development, including capacity building through training and the execution and dissemination of research.

1984   MARDAN SCARP. 1984. *MARDAN SCARP Subsurface Drainage Design Analysis.* Water and Power Development Authority, Pakistan, 224 p.

This reports presents the subsurface drainage design analysis for the Mardan Salinity Control and Reclamation Project (SCARP) carried out by the Pakistan Water and Power Development Authority (WAPDA) and consulting engineering companies Engineering with assistance by the Canadian International Development Agency (CIDA). The Mardan SCARP project encompasses 123 600 acres of the Culturable Command Area of the Lower Swat irrigation canal in the Northwest Frontier Province of Pakistan. The achievements are presented in 8 chapters: 1) Background information; 2) Design drainage rates, drain depths and spacings; 3) Subsurface drainage pipework; 4) drain envelopes; 5) Cost estimates; 6) Economic analysis; 7) Subsurface drainage plans, and; 8) Evaluating the performance of subsurface drainage.

Glossary

Alignment
(1) The fixing of points on the ground in the correct lines for setting out a canal, drain or pipeline, etc. (2) A ground plan showing a route, as opposed to a profile or section, which shows levels and elevations.

Augerhole method
A technique to determine the saturated hydraulic conductivity of a soil at a certain depth by augering a cylindrical hole in the soil, bailing water from it, and measuring the rate of water-level rise in the hole.

Backfill
Soil excavated from a drain trench that is to be placed back into the trench after the drain pipe has been installed.

Backfilling
Replacement of excavated material from a trench into the trench directly after the drain pipe has been installed. Backfilling is a three-step operation: blinding (backfilling directly after installation to fix the pipe in its position) - backfilling - compaction.

Bar chart schedule
A chart on which the start and finish of activities are represented as bars on a time scale. A bar chart schedule is a simplification of the planning prepared in a net work planning or an independent planning method (see also **Network planning**).

Benchmark
A relatively fixed point whose level is known and used as a *reference* for levelling.

Bill of quantities
List of specifications of activities, including labour and materials, for a project or work to be carried out, expressed in measurable quantities, e.g. area (ha, m^2), length (m, km), weight (kg, ton) or volume (litres, m^3), labour days, including simplified technical specifications of the materials and methods to be used and references to the more elaborate technical specifications.

Blinding
First step in backfilling a trench by carefully replacing the excavated soil around and over the drain pipe, mainly used to fix the drain pipe in its position.

Boning Rod
A rod or stake with a cross bar with variable length to indicate a reference level (Figure C 1301).

Critical path
The longest path of the network in terms of time requirements for a sequence of activities that have to be implemented one after another (see also **Network planning**).

Centrifugal pump
A roto-dynamic pump with radial flow, its inlet opening being near the centre of the impeller and its outlet along its periphery. The water follows the curved impeller vanes away from the centre.

Collector drain
A drain that collects water from the field drainage system and carries it to the main drain for disposal. It may be either an open ditch or a pipe drain.

Compaction
Artificial increase of the dry density of a granular soil by mechanical means such as rolling the surface layers.

Composite drainage system
A drainage system in which both field drains and collectors are buried.

Concrete
A mixture of water, sand, stone and a binder (nowadays usually Portland cement) which hardens to a stone like mass.

Consultant
A registered architect, chartered engineer or specialist who acts for a client. For construction projects the duties of a consultant often go much further than giving advice. The consultant and his staff can provide the complete design and supervision of the construction (acting as the Clients or employers representative) up to and including final handing-over of the project.

Contract
Binding agreement (between persons, groups, states) to supply goods or equipment, to carry out works, etc. at a fixed price.

Contractor
A person who signs a *contract* to carry out certain specified work at certain rates of payment, generally within a stated time.

Culvert
A square, oval, or round closed conduit used to transport water horizontally under a highway, railway, canal, or embankment.

Deflection
The deflection or elastic change of a pipe under stress or pressure.

Deformation
The deformation or plastic, non-recoverable, change of a pipe which is under stress or under extreme temperatures.

Design discharge
A specific value of the flow rate that, after the frequency and the duration of exceedance have been considered, is selected for designing the dimensions of a structure, a drainage system, or a part thereof.

Drain
A channel, pipe, or duct for conveying surface water or groundwater.

Drain pipe
See **Drain.**

Drain spacing
The horizontal distance between the centre lines of adjacent parallel drains.

Drainage base
The water level at the outlet of a drained area.

Drainage basin
The entire area drained by a stream in such a way that all stream flow originating in the area is discharged through a single outlet.

Drainage coefficient
The discharge of a drainage system, expressed as a depth of water that must be removed within a certain time.

Drainage criterion
A specified numerical value of one or more drainage parameters that allow a design to be calculated with drainage equations.

Drainage effluent
The water flowing out of a drainage system which must be disposed of, either by gravity flow or by pumping.

Drainage gate
A gravity outlet fitted with a vertically moving gate or with a horizontally hinged door or plate (flap gate).

Drainage sluice
A gravity outlet fitted with vertically-hinged doors, opening if the inner water level is higher than the outer water level, and vice versa, so that drainage takes place during low tides.

Drainage survey
An inventory of conditions that affect the drainage of an area, made at various levels, ranging from reconnaissance to design level.

Drainage system
(1) A natural system of streams and/or water bodies by which an area is drained. (2) An artificial system of land forming, surface and subsurface conduits, related structures, and pumps (if any), by which excess water is removed from an area.

Drainage techniques
The various physical methods that have been devised to improve the drainage of an area.

Dumpy level
See **Level.**

Elongation
See **Deflection.**

Entrance resistance
The extra resistance to water flow in the vicinity of a drain pipe, due to a decreased permeability of the material around the drain and/or to a contraction of the flow lines resulting from the small drain openings.

Envelope
Filter material placed around pipe drains to serve one or a combination of the following functions: (i) to prevent the movement of soil particles into the drain; (ii) to lower entrance resistances in the immediate vicinity of the drain openings by providing material that is more permeable than the surrounding soil; (iii) to provide suitable bedding for the drain; (iv) to stabilise the soil material on which the drain is being laid.

Evaluation
The assessment of the degree of success of a planned project or process, often undertaken at a specific moment (e.g. upon or after completion).

Excavator
A power-driven digging machine, mounted on crawler tracks or wheels. The backacter, dragline, face shovel, grab, and skimmer are fittings which can be attached to give a different function to the jib of the standard excavator.

FIDIC
"Federation International des Ingenieurs Conseil" (International Federation of Consulting engineers) an international organisation that has prepared standards contracts often referred to as FIDIC contracts.

Feasibility study
A study of the existing and future parameters of a drainage or other project in such detail that a reasonable estimate of its profitability can be made.

Field drain
(1) In surface drainage, a shallow graded channel, usually with relatively flat side slopes, which collects water within a field. (2) In subsurface drainage, a field ditch, a mole drain, or a pipe drain that collects groundwater within a field.

Field drainage system
A network that gathers the excess water from the land by means of field drains, possibly supplemented by measures to promote the flow of excess water to these drains.

Field lateral
See **Field drain**.

Filter
A layer or combination of layers of pervious materials designed and installed so as to provide drainage, yet prevent the movement of soil particles in the flowing water (see also **Envelope**).

Flushing
Method by which sediment is removed by flushing a pipe drain from the downstream end with water.

Free water surface
See **Watertable.**

Grade
See **Gradient**.

Gradient
The rise or fall per unit horizontal length of a pipe.

Granular envelope
See **Gravel envelope**.

Gravel envelope
Envelope made of untreated or only slightly washed, rounded, natural building aggregate, larger than 5 mm, graded to a pre-described texture to match the prevailing soil type.

Gravity outlet structure
A drainage structure in an area with variable outer water levels, so that drainage can take place by gravity when outside water levels are low.

Grey Literature
Written information that is not officially published and has a limited distribution, e.g. project reports, feasibility studies, research reports, etc. Often the content of these reports is confidential.

Groundwater
Water in land beneath the soil surface, under conditions where the pressure in the water is equal to, or greater than, atmospheric pressure, and where all the voids are filled with water.

Horizontal drainage
A method of groundwater drainage in which low watertables are maintained by pipe drains or open ditches.

Hydraulic conductivity
The constant of proportionality in Darcy's Law, defined as the volume of water that will move through a porous medium in unit time, under a unit hydraulic gradient, through a unit area, measured at right angles to the direction of flow.

Hydraulic excavator
See **Excavator**.

Impact test
A test to measure the brittleness of the pipe material, in particular its sensitivity to the notch effect.

Interflow
Water that has infiltrated into a soil and moves laterally through the upper soil horizons towards ditches or streams as shallow perched groundwater above the main groundwater level.

Irrigation
Controlled applications of water to agricultural land to allow the cultivation of crops, where otherwise, owing to a deficiency of rainfall, agriculture would be impossible.

K-value
See **Hydraulic conductivity**.

Land reclamation
Making land capable of more intensive use by changing its general character: (1) by draining excessively wet land; (2) by reclamation of submerged land from seas, lakes, and rivers, and; (3) by modification of its saline, sodic, or acid character.

Laser equipment for drain installation

Equipment consisting of a transmitter which emits a plane of invisible light, horizontal or under a slope, and a mast with receptors on the drainage machine. The receptors are connected to the hydraulics of the drainage machine. The transmitted light assures semi automatically the installation grade and level of the drainage pipe is according to the set plane of the transmitter.

Layout

A drawing showing the general arrangement of a proposed drainage system.

Level

(1) The elevation of a point; (2) an instrument with a telescope and bubble tube which enable the surveyor to take level sights over considerable distances, shots of 30 - 50 m being normal practice.

Levelling staff

Staff with a graduation in centimetres used in combination with a level (or levelling instrument) to determine the level of a spot removed from the levelling instrument.

Longitudinal profile

An annotated design drawing of a canal along its centre line, showing original ground levels, canal bank levels, design water levels, bed levels, and other relevant engineering information.

Main drain

The principal drain of an area, receiving water from collectors, diversion drains, or interceptor drains, and conveying this water to an outlet for disposal outside the area.

Main drainage system

A water conveyance system that receives water from the field drainage systems, surface runoff, interflow, and groundwater flow, and transports it to the outlet point.

Manhole

An access hole to a pipe collector, just large enough for a man to enter. It is normally covered with a concrete cover.

Mechanical analysis

Determining the particle size distribution of a soil or gravel envelope by screening, sieving, or other means of mechanical separation.

Mean Sea Level (MSL)

The average water level in a tidal area.

Mole drain
An unlined underground drainage channel, formed by pulling a solid object, usually a solid cylinder with a wedge-shaped point at one end, through the soil at the proper slope and depth, without a trench having to be dug.

Network planning
Planning method in which all activities are placed in a diagram in such a way that all activities are listed in a realistic order (some activities can only start when other activities have been completed).

Observation well
A small diameter pipe, at least 25 mm in diameter, in which the depth of the watertable can be observed. It is placed in the soil and perforated over a length equal to the distance over which the watertable is expected to fluctuate.

Open drain
A channel with an exposed water surface for removing and/or conveying surface and ground-water.

Outlet
The terminal point of the entire drainage system, where it discharges into a major element of the natural open water system of the region (e.g. river, lake, or sea).

Outlet drain
A drain that conveys collected water away from the drained area or project, either in the form of a natural channel or as a constructed drain.

Overland flow
Water flowing over the soil surface towards rills, rivulets, channels, and rivers. It is the main source of direct runoff.

Peg
A wooden or metal pin, usually pointed at one end, used to mark the location and/or level of an item to be constructed (same as stake).

Performance assessment
A tool to determine the functioning of a drainage system compared to the design criteria and to identify the causes of malfunctioning (if applicable).

Piezometer
A small diameter pipe used to observe the hydraulic head of groundwater. It is placed in, or driven into, the subsoil so that there is no leakage around the pipe. Water can only enter the pipe through a short screen at the bottom of the pipe, or through the bottom only.

Pipe drain
A buried pipe - regardless of material, size, or shape - which collects and conveys drainage water from a piece of land to a collector or to a main drain.

Pre-wrapped envelope
Envelope, often a synthetic envelope, which is pre-wrapped around the drain pipe before it is delivered to the site. Pre-wrapping is normally done in the factory.

Ranging Rod
A bar or stick of 2-3 m height that is used by surveyors to mark an alignment in the field. Ranging rods are often painted red and white each colour part indicating a height of 50 cm (Figure C 1301).

Reconnaissance study
An initial, exploratory study into the conditions affecting an existing problem. Its results should allow the extent of the problem to be weighed and possible solutions in general terms to be found.

Rodding
A method to check a newly installed drain line by pushing a glass fibre rod through the pipe outlet into the drain pipe over its entire length.

Sighting rod
A rod or stake with a cross bar at the top (Figure C 1301).

Singular drainage system
A drainage system in which the field drains are buried and discharge into open collectors.

Soil survey
The systematic examination of soils in the field, including the laboratory analysis of specific samples, their description, and mapping.

Soil texture
The relative proportions of the various sized groups of individual soil grains in a mass of soil. Specifically, it refers to the proportions of clay, silt, and sand below 2 mm in size (fine earth fraction).

Specifications
Written description of work to be done. Specifications form part of a contract and describe the quality of material mode of construction and also giving dimensions and other information not shown in the drawings.

Stake
A strong, pointed length of wood or metal (to be) driven into the ground to indicate in the field the location and/or level of an item to be constructed (same as peg).

Subsurface drainage
The removal of excess water and salts from soils via groundwater flow to the drains, so that the watertable and rootzone salinity are controlled.

Subsurface drainage system
A man-made system that induces excess water and salts to flow via the soil to wells, mole drains, pipe drains, and/or open drains, and be evacuated.

Sump
A pit often made of pre-cast concrete rings or brickwork, in which water collects before being pumped out.

Supervisor
Person who supervises and directs the work carried out by the contractor.

Surface drainage
The diversion or orderly removal of excess water from the surface of the land by means of improved natural or constructed channels, supplemented when necessary by the shaping and grading of land surfaces to such channels.

Surface drainage system
A system of drainage measures such as channels and land forming meant to divert excess surface water away from an agricultural area in order to prevent waterlogging.

Survey
(1) Examine the general condition of an area, a drainage system, structure, etc.; (2) Measure and map out the position, level, size, boundaries, etc. of an area; (3) A map or drawing showing the layout of an area.

Synthetic envelope
Envelope made of artificial (often plastic) material, nowadays most times pre-wrapped in the factory.

Tender
Statement of the price which one offers to supply goods or services, or to undertake a specific work.

Tender procedure
Process in which suppliers or contractors are invited to make an offer (to carry out work, supply goods, etc) at a stated price.

Terms of Reference (TOR)

Scope or range given to a person or authority specifying the duties to be performed.

Textural class

The name of a soil group with a particular range of sand, silt and clay percentages, of which the sum is 100% (e.g. sandy clay is: 45 - 65% sand, 0 - 20% silt, 35 - 55% clay).

Tidal drainage

The removal of excess water from an area, by gravity, to outer water which has periodic low water levels owing to tides.

Tile drain

See **Pipe drain**.

Total float

The difference in time between the time that is available for implementing an activity and the time needed to do this activity (see also **Network planning**).

Trench box

Part of the trencher that holds the trench sides apart and contains guides for the pipes and envelope material (sometimes called tile box).

Trencher

A drainage machine that digs a trench in which a drainpipe and if required a pre-wrapped envelope or gravel filter are laid.

Trenchless machine

A drainage machine that instead of digging a trench uses a plough to lift up the soil to make room for the drain pipe.

Tubewell drainage

The control of an existing or potential high watertable or artesian groundwater through a group of adequately spaced wells.

Vertical drainage

See **Tubewell drainage**.

Vertical plough

Trenchless drainage machine equipped with a vertical plough that acts as a subsoiler.

V-plough

Trenchless drainage machine equipped with a V-plough that lifts a triangular "beam" of soil while the drain is being installed.

Watertable

The locus of points at which the pressure in the groundwater is equal to atmospheric pressure. The watertable is the upper boundary of groundwater.

Index

A

Advisory Panel Project, 472, 476
Alignments & levels, 126, 317, 318
  collectors, 318, 399
  control, 139, 326
  cost of levelling, 168, 174
  excavation by excavator, 380
  field drains, 318, 398
  field preparation, 120, 166, 168,
    317, 321
  manual installation, 299, 373
  misalignment, 416
  smoothing, 321
  starting level collector drain, 344
  quality control, 139, 298, 397,417
  setting-out costs, 168
  vertical alignment, 141
APEX plates, 102
Area boundaries, 33
As-built drawings, 147, 174, 191, 231,
  235, 512
Asian Development Bank, 47, 49, 55
  project in Pakistan, 560
Auger, 96, 240, 246, 249, 250, 551
Auxiliary equipment, *see Support equipment*
Available time, 197, 491, 495

B

Backfill, 132, 283, 355, 359, 360, 383, 400
  compaction, 377, 382
  costs, 174, 555
  dry soil, 361
  equipment, 113
  manholes, 355
  manual installation, 377, 382, 522
  quality control, 139, 400
  trench, 132, 312, 359, 400, 553
  wet soil, 361
Backhoe, 93, 486, 511, 512
Bar chart, 43, 195
Base material, 71, 215
  costs, 159, 169
  collector drains, 75
  clay pipes, 77
  field drains, 71, 164
  granular envelope, 82, 83
  synthetic envelope, 169, 170, 395
Bench mark, 168, 307, 317, 363, 380, 511

Beneficiaries, see also *Farmers*
  cost estimates, 154
  role in implementation process, 27
Benefits of drainage, 17, 143, 154, 156,
  166, 195, 549, 562
  associated benefits, 157
  direct effects, 157
  indirect effects, 153, 157
  secondary benefits, 17, 157
  "with drainage" case, 157
  "without drainage" case, 157
Bidding, 46, 485, 560
  documents, 55
Bill of quantities, 36, 37, 39, 51, 156, 168,
  175, 189, 190
Bio drainage
  China, 456
Blades, 102
  check, 246
  replacement, 249, 250
  subsoiler, 102
  trenchless machine, 102
  V-plough, 104
Blind pipe, 332, 339, 350
Blinding, 98, 132, 355, 360, 506, 542, 553
Boning rod, 127, 227, 229, 234, 299, 301,
  312, 347
Bonus, 136, 207
Budget, 27, 29, 168, 476, 488
  control, 43
  output preparation process, 35
  planning, 43, 153, 156, 158
Build-up time, 197

C

Capacity, 197, 198, 201
  drainage machinery, 106, 492
  gravel trailer, 112
  pipe production, 162, 165
  supporting equipment, 108
  trencher, 95, 197
Capacity building
  Egypt, 498
  India, 517
  Pakistan, 548
  The Netherlands, 529
Case study, 447
  China, 451

Egypt, 467
India, 501
Pakistan, 545
The Netherlands, 525
Cement pipe, see also *Concrete pipe*, 74, 479
  cost raw material, 215
  quality control, 392
Central Soil Salinity Research Institute, 517, 518
Certification, 137, 141
  The Netherlands, 536, 543
Chashma Command Area Development Project, 559
  Checking
  functionality, 143, 233, 403, 404, 423
  routine, 148, 421
China, 451
Clay pipe, 20, 70, 76, 392, 479, 506
  collector, 80
  handling, 328
  history, 20
  India, 506
  installation, 92, 129, 375, 541
  maintenance, 148
  production, 77
  quality control, 77, 392
  standards, 78
  transport, 77
Cleaning, see also *flushing*, 423, 428
Collector drain, 24, 57, 550
  alignment starting level, 318, 344
  alignment, 318
  checking performance, 404
  composite system, 62, 285
  concrete pipes, 81
  costs calculation, 163, 173, 555
  flushing, 435
  function, 80, 403, 412, 424
  grade control, 407
  installation, 299, 341, 353, 524, 552, 558
  layout options, 57
  manholes, 314
  manual installation, 382
  material, 34, 69, 80
  open, 57
  outlet, 89
  output design process, 39
  Pakistan, 550

pipe, 57, 80
plastic pipes, 80, 130, 556, 557
quality control, 397
singular system, 60
slope, 63
starting level for operator, 342, 347
sump, 341
type of pipes, 57, 80
Collins apparatus, 141, 417
Combined mechanical and manual installation, 91, 115, 116, 512
  advantages & disadvantage, 117
  India, 519, 520
Command Area Development Authority, 505
Command panel, 242, 267
Compaction, 133, 360, 361, 377, 400, 522
  manual, 382, 383
  trench, 132, 361
Composite drainage system, 22, 62, 220
  advantages & disadvantages, 63
  backfill of trench, 359
  bill of quantities, 175, 190
  China, 462
  equipment requirements, 119
  flushing provisions, 131
  functionality, 403, 421
  implementation requirements, 229
  information requirements, 219
  installation of manholes, 349, 355
  installation of pipe connectors, 353
  installation of sump, 341, 355
  monitoring, 424
  outlet, 89
  performance, 315, 403, 423, 403
  preparatory activities, 313
  site clean up, 363
  staff requirements installation, 121, 230
  starting level installation, 343
Concrete collector drain, 81, 382, 399, 550, 554, 555, 556
  quality control, 399
Concrete field drain, 74
  base material, 75
  diameters, 74
  maintenance, 148
  production, 75
  quality control, 75
Concrete pipe, 20, 71, 74, 81, 480, 506, 550
  costs, 170, 555

installation, 130, 328, 376, 382, 400
   production in Egypt, 481
   standards, 76
Connections, see also *Joints*, 353
Construction, 37, 44, 181
   activities, 192
   backfill, 132
   cost subsurface drainage, 153
   costs, 153, 168, 175
   grade control, 126
   instruction sheets, 183
   manholes, 130
   outlet, 125
   partners in construction process, 44
   placing envelopes, 130
   placing pipes, 129
   planning, 189
   post construction checking, 413
   preparation process, 44
   pumps, 174
   quality control, 135
   setting out alignments & levels, 126
   site clean-up, 133
   staff requirements, 120
   steps during installation, 124
   trench excavation, 128
Construction department
   task requirements planning, 119
   role implementation process, 54
Construction process, 27, 189
   quality control, 135
Consultant, 45, 48
   pre-qualification tender, 48
   role implementation, 27, 37, 54
Contingencies, 175, 191, 212
Continuous depth recorder, 141, 413, 417
Contract, 45, 207
   awarding the tender, 54
   conditions of payment, 156
   procedure, 46
   standards, 55
   specifications for quality control, 136
   transport, 213
Contract department
   instruction sheets, 183
   role in implementation process, 54
Contracting
   procedures, 46
   Egypt, 478
   Pakistan, 556, 560

Contractor, 44, 48
   Egypt, 485
   handing-over site, 307
   instruction sheets, 183
   role during the implementation, 44
   role quality check, 137
   specifications tender documents, 44
   tender procedure, 48
   role in implementation process, 45
   tender preparation, 53
Controlled drainage
   O & M requirements, 145
Corrugated plastic pipe, 71
   costs, 164
   diameters, 72
   handling during installation, 326
   history, 20
   installation, 263
   production, 72
   quality control, 73, 391
   reel, 98
   standards, 74
   transport, 73
Cost calculation, 153, 165, 205
   equipment, 172, 209, 207
   example, 172, 173, 212
   raw materials, 215
   staff, 207
   transport, 213
Cost components, 207
Cost control, 41, 153, 156
Cost estimate, 39, 145, 159, 205
   drainage installation unit, 163
   unit costs, 160
   accuracy, 155
   during planning process, 155
   methodologies, 160
   pre-drainage soil survey, 166
   principles, 159
Cost of transport, 213
Cost recovery, 159
Costs, 153
   comparison machines, 106
   crop compensation, 123
   construction, 168, 517
   contingencies, 175
   depreciation, 210
   drainage industry, 158, 161
   equipment, 207, 517
   levelling drain-line, 169

financing costs, 153
fixed costs, 209, 517
flushing, 151
general costs, 174
India, 516
interest rate, 210
investment costs, 153
maintenance, 60
minimising operational costs, 259
O & M, 151
O & M in Pakistan, 548
on-farm investments, 159
operational costs, 60, 209
overhead, 160
Pakistan, 555
pre-construction activities, 165
profit and risk, 175
quality control The Netherlands, 543
raw materials, 215
recurrent costs, 153
staff, 205
staff training, 161
subsurface drainage systems, 153
trencher, 261
total costs, 175
Couplers, 78, 326
Crawler tracks, 95, 239, 260
Critical depth, trenchless machine, 104
Critical path, 41, 194
Crop compensation
during installation, 107, 123
Egypt, 485
Crop rotation
China, 455
Crop yield, performance indicators, 144
Crossings, 62, 66, 173, 321
O & M, 177

D
Deep collector drains
Pakistan, 552
Depreciation, 160, 210
Depth control, 93, 107, 299, 321, 325
Design, 39, 37, 89
China, 461
criteria, 33
conditions, 55
cost estimates, 154, 156
costs, 153, 167
department, 45

Egypt, 478
input requirements, 39
layout options, 57
preparation process, 39, 311
required for planning, 189
output preparation process, 39, 189
site verification, 308
terms of reference, 39
Design department
role in implementation process, 54
Detection rod, 349, 408, 409
Dewatering equipment, 109
example network planning, 193
Pakistan, 551
vertical well-pointing technique, 126
well-sinking technique, 126
Diameters, 72, 74, 77
field drains, 72, 479, 506, 536, 549
collector drain, 74, 81, 480, 550
clay pipes, 77
Discharge site, 58
Digging chain, 95, 249
adjustment, 253
flat digger chain, 99
knives, 96
reduction of wear, 259
replacement, 249
vertical digging chain, 110
Digging knives, 96, 100, 249
adjustment, 254
replacement, 249
Digging mechanism, 95, 96, 99, 264, 268
Direct effective time, 198, 201
Discharge, 57, 58
at outlet, 35, 144
composite system, 62
in manhole, 144
singular system, 60
site, 58
sump, 87
Double-wall pipe, 72
Drain
collector drain, 57, 80
extended field drain, 63
field drain, 57
mole drain, 22
open drain, 22, 60
pipe drain, 22, 62
Drain bridge, 322, 324, 540
Drain envelopes, see also *Envelope*, 81

costs, 173
design, 39
function, 81
geo-textiles, 82
granular, 82, 83
installation, 128, 130
investment in production plant, 165
machine attachments, 96
materials, 81
organic, 82
planning, 69
pre-wrapped, 83, 85
production of granular materials, 83
quality check, 139
standards, 83
standards granular envelopes, 83
synthetic, 82, 84
synthetic, pre-wrapped, 85
synthetic, production, 84
synthetic, quality control, 86
synthetic, standards, 86
voluminous, 82
Drain installation
    preparatory activities, 307, 311
    sequence of activities, 311
    specialised machinery, 108
    support equipment, 111
    steps in installation, 124
Drain level & grade, 325, 373, 403, 407,
    413
    visual inspection, 139, 398
Drain line performance
    post construction verification, 140, 141,
    413
    vertical alignment, 141
    visual inspection, 424
Drain pipe, see also *Pipe*, 70
    base material, 71
    China, 463
    diameters, 72
    Egypt, 479
    gravel envelope installation, 365
    handling of corrugated pipes, 326
    India, 506
    installation, 263, 325
    installation, steps, 124
    installation of connections, 353
    investment production plant, 164
    manual installation, 376, 385
    The Netherlands, 536

Pakistan, 549
quality control, 391
plastic, 71, 479
poor performance, 438
post construction verification, 413
watertight joints, 357
Drain slope, see also *Drain* grade, 61, 63
    grade control, 126
    quality control, 139, 141, 408
Drain trench
    back fill, 132, 360
    excavation, 94, 117, 128
    manual installation, 373
Drainage
    benefits, 17
    China, 453
    costs, 29
    effects, 28
    Egypt, 469
    history, 18
    impact, 29
    India, 503
    mole, 22
    need, 17
    objectives, 16
    open, 22
pipe, 22
Drainage Contact Group, 535
Drainage criteria
    output of preparation process, 33
Drainage developments
    China, 459, 464
Drainage equipment, see also *Equipment*
    investment costs, 158
Drainage Executive Management Project,
    498
Drainage industry, 28, 44
    cost estimate, 155
    implementation mode, 35
    investment costs, 155, 158, 161
    The Netherlands, 533
    quality control by certification, 137
    quality control of drain pipes, 73
    role in implementation, 27, 44
    role in preparation process, 27
Drainage installation unit, 92, 118, 120, 122
    cost estimate, 163
    organisation, 120, 231, 233, 307
    quality control, 136
Drainage machinery, see *Equipment*

Drainage material, 69, 219
  China, 456
  cost estimate, 159
  cost of quality control, 174
  cost of raw material, 215
  costs, 169
  Egypt, 478
  effect on O & M, 148
  for collector drains, 69
  for field drains, 69
  India, 506
  information requirements, 32
  information requirements for envelopes,
    34, 81
  India, 511
  information requirements pipes, 34
  manufacturers, 44
  output of preparation process, 34
  Pakistan, 549, 555, 557, 560, 562
  procurement, 219
  quality control in the field, 138
  quality control, 137, 391
  selection, 69
  suppliers, 44, 69
  The Netherlands, 536
Drainage methods, 20, 57
  China, 454, 461
  Egypt, 469
  India, 511, 515
  Pakistan, 555, 557, 559
  The Netherlands, 527
Drainage policy
  preparation, 27, 28, 30, 154
  Egypt, 470
Drainage project
  cost estimate, 159
  financing, 159
  planning, 193
Drainage Research Institute, 470
Drainage system, 20, 57
  China, 461
  composite, 22, 219, 229
  Egypt, 469
  field, 20
  functioning, 143, 403, 421
  impacts, 143
  India, 511, 515, 519
  Installation, 217, 305
  malfunction, 143, 147, 438
  open, 60

  organisation of implementation, 223
  Pakistan, 555, 557, 559
  performance, 140, 403
  periodic checking, 149
  singular, 22, 219, 227
  The Netherlands, 527
  tubewell, 22

E
East Khaipur Tile Drainage Project, 554
Economic life time, 158, 162
Effective time, 107, 197, 198
Effects of drainage, 16, 28, 143, 156
  Pakistan, 559
Efficiency, 108, 197
  machinery in Egypt, 490
Egypt, 467
Egyptian Public Authority for Drainage
Projects, 473
Element, 197
End cap, 78, 175, 190, 353, 540
End chute, 540
Engine
  reduction of wear, 260
Engine power, 98, 12
Engineers estimate, 153, 156
Envelope, 81, 365,373
  China, 463
  costs, 170
  costs of granular, 165
  costs of synthetic, 165
  design criteria in India, 506
  design in Pakistan, 562
  development in China, 464
  Egypt, 482
  function, 81
  granular, 83, 365, 375, 399
  gravel trailer, 303
  India, 506
  information requirements, 34
  installation granular envelope, 130, 303,
    365, 375, 377, 382, 551
  installation organic envelope, 130
  installation synthetic envelope, 130
  investments, 164
  manual installation, 381
  manual wrapping in the field, 385
  materials, 81, 215
  Pakistan, 550, 551, 557, 560, 562
  planning of gravel transport, 537

placing, 130, 365
production plant, 164
quality control, 137, 393, 394, 398, 399
quality control installation, 139
synthetic, 84, 394
tasks of gravel manager, 236
The Netherlands, 537
wrapping, 385
Equipment, 91, 237, 262
accessibility costs, 168
backfill equipment, 113
bucket-wheel trencher, 99
capacity, 106
capacity in Egypt, 489, 492
capacity, time & motion study, 201
characteristics, 92
China, 459
cost calculation, 172
cost estimate, 160, 209
dewatering equipment, 109
economic lifetime, 162
efficiency in Egypt, 489
Egypt, 487
excavator, 93
flushing, 428, 439, 443
gravel trailer, 112
India, 509, 511, 515
information requirements, 32
investment costs, 162
maintenance requirements, 93, 245, 275
Pakistan, 551, 558, 560
planning, 91
purchase in Egypt, 495
operation, 263, 283
operational costs, 259
orchard trencher, 109
output of preparation process, 34
requirements, 91, 118
rock trencher, 108
selection criteria, 91
special-purpose, 108
support, 111
survey sheet, 201
The Netherlands, 541
transport, 113, 213
transport costs, 169
trencher machine, 91, 239
trenchless machine, 100, 271
European Union
tender procedure, 56

Excavation of trench,
by excavator, 93, 116, 128, 381
manual, 128, 374, 375
Excavator, 93, 229
advantages & disadvantage, 94
capacity, 107, 512
tasks of operator, 93, 234
Extended field drains, 63
advantages & disadvantages, 64
China, 462

F
Farmers
cost estimates, 154
instruction sheets, 183
role in implementation process, 27, 145
role in O & M, 9, 145, 149, 151, 421,
427
role in policy-preparation & decisions-
making, 28
role in handing-over process, 44, 406
role in The Netherlands, 536
Feasibility study, 155
preparation, 165
FIDIC, 51
tender procedure, 49, 55
Field allowance, 207
Field drain, 20, 57
alignment, 318
checking performance, 406
clay pipe, 77
diameters clay pipes, 77
quality control clay pipes, 77
transport of clay pipes, 77
composite system, one-sided, 62
composite system, two-sided, 62
concrete pipe, base material, 74
concrete pipe, diameters, 74
concrete pipe, production, 75
concrete pipe, quality control, 75
concrete pipe, standards, 76
concrete pipe, transport, 75
diameters of clay pipes, 77
diameters of plastic pipes, 72
extended, advantages & disadvantages, 64
extended, 63
flushing, 439, 443
function, 70
grade control, during and after installation,
335, 407

installation from open drain, 339
corrugated pipes, 72
from manhole, 314
from open drain, 335
layout options, 57
manholes, 341, 350
material, 70
outlet, 335, 339, 349
starting level for operator, 347
Pakistan, 549, 555, 557, 560
pipe, 57
plastic pipe, 71
plastic pipe, base material, 71
plastic pipe, diameters, 72
double wall pipes, 72
plastic pipe, perforations, 72
plastic pipe, production, 72
plastic pipe, quality control, 73
plastic pipe, standards, 74
plastic pipe, transport, 73
quality control, 397
required level of manhole, 345
singular system, one-sided, 60
singular system, two-sided, 60
smooth plastic pipe, 72
starting level, 343
trenchless machine, 285
types of pipes, 57, 70
Field drainage system, 20
Field investigations, 38, 166
cost estimates, 154
costs, 166
during the preparation process, 37
output of preparation process, 38
purpose, 38
Field manager, 120, 231
description of activities, 183
instruction sheets, 183
tasks, 120
tasks description, 231
Field preparation unit, 120, 122
Field staff, 120
description of activities, 183
instruction sheets, 183
tasks, 231
Financers, 45
role in implementation process, 45
Financing costs, 153, 160
Fixed costs, 209
Flat-digging-chain trencher, 99

Flushing, 149, 427, 433, 435, 439, 443
collector drain, 435
costs, 151, 177
damaged pipes, 438
equipment, 428
field drain from manhole, 443
field drain from open drain, 439
high pressure, 433
maintenance, 147, 149, 151
method, 427
principles, 427
provisions during construction, 131, 150
Forced account basis, 43
Fourth Drainage Project, 562
Fuel consumption, 146, 210, 212
Fuel price, 210

G
General costs, 155, 174
Geo-textiles, 82, 85
Government
Egypt, 470
financing of drainage projects, 159
India, 504
Pakistan, 548
role in implementation process, 27
role in policy-preparation & decisions-
making, 28
The Netherlands, 529
Grade control, 93 126, 325
checking during installation, 407
during installation, 291
equipment, 287
management, 291
manual, 299
post construction verification, 417
problems, 292
test in the field, 297
tips for operation of laser, 291
Granular envelope, 83
application, 365
China, 462
costs, 165, 170
equipment requirements, 303, 366
installation, 130, 551, 562
manual installation, 377, 382
planning, The Netherlands, 537
quality control, 139, 393
staff requirements, 366
Gravel, 20, 82, 130, 214

field depot, 393
  storage, 366
  transport, 367
Gravel envelope, *see Granular envelope*
Gravel hopper, see also *Gravel trailer*, 96
Gravel manager, 122, 172
  instruction sheets, 183
  tasks description, 236
Gravel quarry, 170, 393
Gravel trailer, 111, 112, 119, 163, 172,
  303
Gravity outlet, 58, 424
Groundwater depth, performance indicators,
  144
Guidelines, 55
  manual installation, The Netherlands, 540
  hand tools, 92
  instruction sheets, 183
  investment costs, 161
  procurement of consultants, 48

H
Handing-over process, 35, 44
  cost estimates, 154
  final check, 406
  general costs, 174
  site to contractor, 124, 307
  specifications, 35
Hard-rock trencher, 108
Haryana Operational Pilot Project, 512
History of drainage, 18
  China, 454
  Egypt, 469, 487
  India, 503
  Pakistan, 548
  The Netherlands, 527
Hydraulic excavator *see Excavator*
Hydraulic performance of drainage system,
  140, 149, 403, 413, 424

I
IJsselmeerpolder Development Authority, 531
Implementation, 15, 25, 27, 37, 115, 179,
  223, 308
  accidental stopping of engine, 264
  actual capacity, 106
  organisation, 227
  Pakistan, 549, 556, 560
  practices in India, 511
  right of way, 308

setting out of field, 317
site preparation, 321
site verification, 308
Implementation authority, 37, 45
  Construction Department, 119
  cost estimates, 154
  planning process, choice of equipment, 91
  planning process, choice of materials, 69
  planning process, choice of system, 57
  planning process, installation method, 115
  quality control, 136
  requirements, 231
  responsibilities quality control, 135
  role in actual implementation, 37, 44
  role in handing-over process, 44
  role in implementation process, 27
  role in implementation process, 45
  staff tasks, 231
Implementation conditions
  hard rock, 264, 486
  quick sand, 485
  standing water, 311, 321, 333
  saturated soil, 331
  upward pressure, Egypt, 486
  unstable soil, 331
Implementation mode, 35, 45
Implementation modes, 35, 45
Implementation practices
  Modifications, Egypt, 487
Implementation process, 25
  activities, 45
  actual implementation, 37
  administrative preparation, 30
  decisions to be taken, 45
  Egypt, 469
  handing-over, 44
  India, 504
  input requirements, 31
  layout options, 57
  main steps, 27
  material selection, 69
  O & M requirements, 145
  organisational preparation, 30, 189
  output preparation process, 33
  planning, 189
  players, 27, 45
  policy preparation and decision-making, 28
  steps, 27, 124, 311
  technical preparation, 30
Indirect effective time, 198

Indo-Dutch Network Project, 517
Information requirements, 30
  decision-making, 28
  equipment, 32
  maps, 31
  materials, 32
  objectives, 31
  outlet conditions, 31
  preparation research data, 33
  rules and regulations, 32
Installation, 115, 217, 305
  additional manholes, 314
  bottlenecks, 123
  by excavator, 379
  China, 462
  clay pipes, 328
  cleaning the site, 363
  collector drain, starting level, 344
  combined mechanical and manual, 116, 520
  composite drainage system, 227
  corrugated pipes, 326
  costs, 170
  cost of quality control, 174
  depth and grade control, 325
  drain pipe, 325, 353
  Egypt, 487
  equipment, 91, 237
  field drain, starting level, 345
  from open drain, 335
  gravel application, 365, 551
  gravel management, 370
  in saturated soils, 331
  in standing water, 321, 333
  in unstable soils, 331
  information requirements, 219
  instruction sheets, 183, 219, 220
  logistics, 123
  manhole, 355
  manual, 115, 373
  manual using excavator, 379
  mechanical, 118
  method, 115
  operation of laser, 291
  operation of trencher, 263
  organization, 119
  outlet, 339, 341
  Pakistan, 551, 554, 558, 561
  post construction verification, 413
  preparatory activities, 307

pre-wrapped envelope, 381
quality control, 135, 391, 397
saturated soil, 331
season, 123
setting out field, 317
singular system, 223
site cleanup up, 363
staff requirement, 119
standing water, 333
steps, 124, 311
sump, 341, 355
T-joint, 353
unstable soils, 331
Installation capacity
  China, 460
  Egypt, 469, 489
  India, 512
Instruction sheets
  contents, 220
  subjects, 183
  target group, 183
Instructions to tenderers, 51
Insurance, risk and profits, 160, 207, 210
  for installation, 220
Interest rates, 210
International financers
  role in implementation process, 45
International transport costs, 213
Investigation
  costs, 153, 164
  Egypt, 478
  field investigations, 31, 37, 38, 45
Irrigation, 17, 58
  installation during irrigation, 307, 333, 361
  winter irrigation in China, 456
  irrigation canal crossing, 321
International Waterlogging and Salinity
    Research Institute, 548

J
Joints, 77, 78, 130, 353, 357
  costs, 173
  installation, 129, 130, 170, 353
  quality control, 139, 148, 392, 397, 398
  watertight joints, 80, 357, 401

L
Labour costs drainpipe installation, 171
Labour requirements
  manual installation, India, 512, 522, 524,

540
Labourers
  tasks description, 235
Land reclamation
  The Netherlands, 527, 531
Landowners, 37
  investment costs, 159
Large-scale projects, 17
  China, 460
  costs, 153
  Egypt, 478, 484
  India, 509, 512
  Pakistan, 554, 556, 559, 562
  The Netherlands, 527, 531
Laser equipment, 93, 287
  batteries, 294
  beam level, 295description, 287
  control using two machines, 293
  extension mast on trencher, 295
  grade control, 287
  horizontal adjustment, 297
  level of beam, 295
  maintenance, 294
  mast on trencher, 295
  principle, 287
  receiver, 287
  tips for operation, 291
  transmitter, 297
Layout, 57, 219
  collector, 424
  comparison of options, 65
  composite system, 62
  considerations, 65
  Egypt, 469
  elements of a system, 57
  extended field drains, 63
  India, 511, 515, 519
  instruction sheets, 219
  manhole, 402
  options, 57
  output of preparation process, 34
  Pakistan, 555, 557, 560
  quality control, 397
  subsurface field drains, 57
  pumped outlet, 59
  singular system, 60
  soil conditions, 59
  The Netherlands, 527
Legislation, Egypt, 470
Lessons learned, 5

China, 459, 464
Egypt, 485, 487, 494
India, 512, 520, 523
Pakistan, 549, 556, 559, 561, 563
The Netherlands, 544
Levelling staff, 408
Levelling instrument, 93, 126, 409
Levels, quality control, 397
Life time, 158, 210, 212
Local transport costs, 213
Logistics, 123, 271
Lubricants cost, 210, 211, 212

M
Machine costs drainpipe installation, 158,
  170, 171
Main drain, 57
  layout option, main drain, 57
  O & M requirements, 145
Main drainage system, 20, 57
  investment costs, 159
Maintenance, 145, 419
  activities, 177
  checking performance, 421
  cleaning composite systems, 423
  costs, 63, 151, 177
  flushing equipment, 433
  frequency estimation, 148
  gravel trailer, 303
  integral check, 149
  minor, periodic, 149
  objectives, 146
  periodic cleaning, 149
  preventive, 151
  process, 147
  repairs, 151
  routine check, 148
  requirements drainage machine, 93
  subsurface drainage system, 147
  staff, instruction sheets, 183
  trencher machine, 245
  trenchless machine, 275
Management, cost estimate, 160
Manholes, 34, 87, 130, 350, 355, 402
  completion of installation, 355
  costs, 173
  determining the level, 343
  Egypt, 483
  installation, 314, 349, 355
  installation costs, 173

installation in field drains, 349
installation, quality control, 400
installation watertight joints, 357
levels, 343, 344
levels, composite system, 349
location, 320
lid or cover, installation, 357
quality control, 140
routine checking, 148
repairs, 151, 422, 423
sedimentation, 151
selection, 86
Manual installation, 115, 373, 379
China, 462
Egypt, 487
India, 520, 523
labour requirements India, 512, 522, 524
The Netherlands, 540
organisation, 380
using excavator, 379
tool, 116
wrapping the envelope, 385
Manufactures see Drainage Industry
Maps, information requirements, 31, 38
Mardan Salinity Control and Reclamation
    Project, 556
Market prices, 160, 169, 215
Materials
costs, 215
subsurface drainage system, 69
selection, 69
Mechanic, description of activities, 183
Mechanical installation, 91, 92, 115, 118,
    128, 305
Egypt, 487
equipment requirements, 118, 494
India, 509, 512
machinery requirements, 118
organisation, 119, 223
Pakistan, 554, 556, 559
staff requirements, 121
task requirements, 118, 231
The Netherlands, 541
Mole drainage, 22, 34
Monitoring, 197, 413, 421
performance, 424
for process control, 40
staff, description of activities, 183
staff instruction sheets, 183

N
National government see also Government
decision-making, 154
policy-preparation, 154
Need for drainage, 17
China, 453
Egypt, 469
India, 503
Pakistan, 547
The Netherlands, 527
Network diagram, 38, 193
Network planning, 41, 189
Non-available time, 197
Non-effective time, 198

O
Objectives of drainage, 16, 31
China, 457
Egypt, 469
India, 512
information requirements, 31
maintenance, 146
On-farm investments, 159
On-site camp, 169, 170, 175, 190, 192,
    321
On-site storage
gravel, costs, 169
pipes, costs, 169, 190
Open collector drain, 57, 60
Open drain, 20, 22, 32, 57
Open drainage system, 22, 57, 60, 160
Operation, 27, 44, 60, 145, 146
costs, 60, 151,153, 177, 209, 211
liftable trench box, 267
trencher, 259
trenchless machine, 283
Operation & maintenance, 27, 44, 145, 146,
    245, 275, 263, 419
cost estimates, 154
costs, 151, 153, 177
drain, 439
drainage fee, Pakistan, 548
flushing of collector drains, 435
flushing of drains, 427
flushing of field drains from manhole, 443
flushing of field drains from open
    objectives, 145
planning, 145
unit, tasks, 121
Operation in stony soils, 95, 108, 264

Operational costs, 146, 209, 211
Operational research, 108
    drainage machinery, 108
    Egypt, 488
Operator, 94, 106, 122, 233
    assistant tasks description, 234
    description of activities, 183
    excavator tasks description, 234
    starting level for collector installation, 347
    instruction sheets, 183
    starting level for field drain installation, 347
    tasks description, 236
    trencher, 233
Orchard trencher, 109
Organisation, 27, 45, 119, 181, 223
    China, 456
    Egypt, 470
    India, 504
    mechanical installation, 119
    overhead, 174
    Pakistan, 548
    quality control, 543, 558
    The Netherlands, 529
Organisation of implementation, 223, 227
    Egypt, 473, 478, 484
    India, 509, 513
    Pakistan, 554, 556, 560
Organisation of research
    Egypt, 476
    India, 517
    Pakistan, 548
    The Netherlands, 535
Outlet, 31, 34, 58, 59, 89, 125, 126, 146, 339
    composite drainage system, 89
    conditions, 31, 422
    construction, 125
    costs, 173
    gravity, layout option, 58, 125
    installation, 339
    layout options, 58
    O & M, 146, 177
    pumped, layout option, 58, 126
    pipes, 79
    quality control, 140, 422
    repairs, 151
    singular drainage system, 89
Overhead, 155, 160, 174, 207, 208
    cost estimate, 160

Overtime, 207
Owing costs, 211

P
Pakistan, 545
Participatory approach, Pakistan, 549
PE-pipes, 20, 71, 74, 82, 164
    cost of raw material, 164, 215
Penalties, 43, 136
Perforations, plastic pipes, 70, 72, 74, 391
Performance, 140, 197
    check, 140, 315, 421
    collector drain, 403
    composite drainage system, 403
    equipment, 197
Performance assessment, 143
    Egypt, 494, 496
Performance bond, 51
Performance indicators, 144
Performance methods, 403, 421
    continuous depth recording, 417
    rodding, 413
Personnel costs, 146, 210, 211
Pipe drain, 22
    accessories, costs, 169
    collector drain, 57, 80
    costs, 169
    connectors, installation, 353
    field drain, 57, 70
    information requirements of preparation, 34
    installation, 129
    installation costs, 170
    location of factory, 164
    mobile production line, 164
    production plant, capacity, 164
    production plant, costs, 164
    quality control, 137, 397
    repair of end-pipe, 151
    steps in installation, 124
    transport costs, 164
Pipe fitting
    couplers, 78, 353
    end cap, 78
    outlet pipe, 79
    standards, 80
    T-joint, 78, 353
    transport, 79
    Y-joint, 78
Pipe production line, 72, 158, 164

investment costs, 158
Pipe stretch, Pakistan, 553
Pipe-joint, see also *Joints*
  installation costs, 173
  quality control, 139
Piping, 132, 355, 359
Placing envelopes, 82, 124, 130
Placing pipes, 92, 115, 124, 128, 129
Planning, 27, 37, 40, 45, 123, 183, 189
  bar chart, 195
  critical path, 194
  Egypt, 477
  gravel supply, 537
  India, 505, 510, 514
  information requirements, 189
  need for planning, 40
  O & M requirements, 145
  quality control, 543
  selection of drainage materials, 69
  selection of manholes, 86
  selection of pumps, 86
  selection of structures, 86
  tools, bar charts, 43
  tools, network planning, 41, 189
Planning & budgeting, 27, 153
  cost estimates, 154
  during the preparation process, 40
Planning authority, 27, 38, 154, 155
  cost estimates, 154
  role in implementation process, 27
  role in preparation process, 27
Planning department
  description of activities, 183
  role in implementation process, 54
Planning tools, 41, 195, 494
Plastic drain pipe, 20, 71, 169, 170
  costs, 169
  Egypt, 479
  installation, 129
  installation, quality control, 397
  production, China, 463
  India, 506, 511, 515
  quality control, 391
Policy-preparation, 28
  cost estimates, 154
Post construction verification, 143, 156, 431
Post-installation quality control, 140, 403,
  413
Power grid system, connection, 358
Power supply, 22, 60, 73

Pre-construction activities, costs, 155, 165,
  167, 223
Pre-drainage survey, costs, 166
Pre-fabricated structures, 86
  quality control, 137, 395
Pre-installation quality control, 138
Preparation activities, 30, 223
  costs, 165
  setting out field, 317
  site preparation, 321
Preparation costs, summary, 167
Preparation, information requirements
  equipment, 32
  maps, 31
  materials, 32
  objectives, 31
  outlet conditions, 31
  research data, 33
  rules and regulations, 32
Preparation process, 27, 30, 45, 123,
  153, 165
  construction, 37
  costs, 155
  design, 37
  field investigations, 37, 168
  handing-over specifications, 35
  input information, 31
  lay-out options, 57
  planning & budgeting, 37
  policy, 27, 28
  output, area boundaries, 33
  output, budget, 35
  output, drainage criteria, 33
  output, drainage materials, 34
  output, equipment, 34
  output, implementation mode, 35
  output, layout, 34
  output, outlet, 34
  output, pumping requirements, 34
  output, type of system, 34
  tender preparation, 37, 50, 51, 167
Press pulley, 96, 130, 240
Preventive maintenance, 147, 151
Pre-wrapped envelope, 20, 32, 85, 100,
  170
  China, 464, 463
Problem soils
  China, 453
  Egypt, 485
  hard rock, Egypt, 486

quick sand, Egypt, 485
  upward pressure, Egypt, 486
Process control, 40
Production, 150
  clay pipes, 71, 77, 80
  concrete pipes, 75, 81
  cost production line, 158, 165
  capacity production line, 164
  drainage materials, 32, 34, 59, 69, 169
  investments envelope production, 165
  investment pipe plant, 164
  granular envelopes, 83
  plastic pipes, 72, 80
  quality control, 392
  synthetic envelopes, 83, 84
Profit and risk, 155, 160, 175
Project organisation, 223
  Egypt, 473, 478, 484
  India, 504, 509, 513, 517
  Pakistan, 548, 556, 560
  The Netherlands, 527, 531
Proposal
  Financial, 48
  Technical, 48
Public goods, 159
Pumps, 59, 86, 90, 124
  costs, 60, 174, 177
  diesel, O & M requirements, 146
  diesel-driven, 90
  electric, O & M requirements, 146
  electrically-driven, 90
  installation costs, 174
  layout considerations, 58
  O & M requirements, 145
  operational costs, 146
  preventive maintenance, 151
  quality control installation, 402
  repairs, 151
  selection, 86
Pump house, installation, 87, 357
Pumped drainage, power supply, 60, 126
Pumped outlet, 58
Pumping, China, 464
Pumping requirements, output of preparation
    process, 34
Purchase price, 210
PVC pipe, 20, 70, 71, 164, 215
  cost of raw material, 215
  joints, 78, 80

Q
Quality control, 135, 387
  active, 136
  after installation, 139
  clay pipes, 77, 392
  cement pipes, 392
  Collins apparatus, 141
  composite drainage system, 403
  continuous depth recorder, 141
  costs, 174
  data processing, 410
  drainage material, 391
  drainage material, procedure, 137
  during installation, 138
  envelope, 137
  grades of installed pipes, 407
  gravel envelope, 393, 562
  hydraulic performance, 140
  installation, 138, 397
  installation of gravel envelope, 366
  materials, 387
  organisation, The Netherlands, 543
  Pakistan, 558
  passive, 136
  performance assessment, 143
  pipe, 137
  planning phase, 136
  plastic pipes, 73, 391
  post installation, 140, 413
  practical aspects, 387
  prefabricated manhole, 400
  prefabricated structures, 395
  prefabricated sump, 400
  process, 135
  requirements, 136
  rodding, 140
  role during implementation, 44
  standards, 137
  structure, 137
  synthetic envelopes, 86, 394
  total quality system, 135
  tracking, 143
  unit, tasks, 121
  video inspection, 135, 140, 496
Quality of installation, 135, 148, 397
  effect on O & M, 148
  standing water, 333
Quick sand conditions, Egypt, 485

R

Rajasthan Agricultural Drainage Research
    Project, 509
Reclamation process, 17, 31, 58
    The Netherlands, 527, 531
Record sheet
    O & M trencher machine, 250
    O & M trenchless machine, 279
Recurrent costs, 153
Re-fuelling
    trencher machine, 247
    trenchless machine, 275
Regional government, see also *Government*
    cost estimates, 154
Rehabilitation need, 33, 143
Repairs, 151, 211
    composite drainage system, 423
    singular drainage system, 421
Reporting functionality, 422
Research, 31, 33, 183, 197, 413
    application of results, Egypt, 494
    China, 456
    Egypt, 476, 488
    India, 504, 512, 517, 522
    operational research 108, 488
    organisation, The Netherlands, 535
    Pakistan, 548
    information requirements, 33
    research department, 183
Residual value, cost, 210, 211
Right of way, 308
Rock trencher, 108
Rodding, 140, 413
Rules and regulations, 32, 51, 54, 55

S

Safety rules, flushing, 433
Salary, 207
Salinity, 17, 28, 31, 140, 157, 166
    China, 455
    India, 503
    Pakistan, 547
Saturated soil, installation method, 331
Secondary benefits of drainage, 15, 17, 157
Sedimentation, 141, 144, 147, 428
    maintenance needs, 149
    performance indicators, 144
Setting out
    alignments and levels, 120, 124, 126, 168
    field, 317

level of manhole, 320
    levels, 380
    manually, 373
    perpendicular line, 319
Shelter, cost, 210
Singular drainage system, 22, 60, 219,
    315, 421
    advantages & disadvantages, 62
    backfill of trench, 359
    checking performance, 315, 421
    China, 462
    equipment requirements, 119
    implementation requirements, 227
    information requirements, 219
    installation, 335
    installation, staff requirements, 122
    installation of outlet, 335
    installation, trenchless machine, 283
    minor repairs, 421
    The Netherlands, 527
    outlet, 89
    preparatory activities, 312
    site clean up, 363
Sink hole, Pakistan, 553
Site
    clean-up, 133, 363
    conditions, effect on O & M, 147
    costs of clearing, 174
    discharge, 58
    preparation, 54, 308, 321
    setting out field, 317
Site-specific conditions, 147
Soil survey, costs, 166
Spare parts, costs, 160, 210
Specifications, see also *Standards*, 136, 186
    drainage machinery, 107
    handing-over, 57
    in tender documents, 51
Sprockets
    reduction of wear, 259
    replacement, 250
Staff, 119, 231
    cost calculation, 172, 207
    cost estimate, 159
    costs, 207
    field manager, 120
    field preparation unit, 120
    implementation requirements, 229
    instruction sheets, 183
    mechanical installation, 119

O & M unit, 121
  quality control, 121, 135
  requirements installation, 121, 227
  surveying unit, 120, 232
  tasks description, 231
  training costs, 161
  trenching unit, 121, 233, 234
Standards, 49
  certification, 137
  clay pipes, 78
  concrete pipes, 76
  drain envelopes, 86, 536
  granular drain envelopes, 83, 562
  pipe fittings, 80
  plastic pipes, 74, 507, 536
  synthetic envelopes, 83, 86, 507, 536
  tender documents, 51
  The Netherlands, 536
Stone mulching, 455
Storage
  flushing equipment, 434
  gravel, 169, 366
  laser equipment in winter, 294
  pipes, 169
  trencher machine in winter, 248
  trenchless machine in winter, 277
Structures, 86, 170
  costs, 170
  information requirements, 34
  quality control, 137
  Egypt, 483
  The Netherlands, 540
  prefabricated structures, 395
  selection, 86
Sub-main drain, 57
Subsoiler blade, 102, 107, 250
Subsurface drainage system, 20, 55
  checking performance, 421
  China, 461
  collector drain, 57
  cost price, 153
  costs, 153
  Egypt, 469
  field drain, 57
  flushing, 150, 427
  flushing of damaged pipes, 438, 442, 446
  gravity outlet, 58
  India, 511, 515, 519
  installation bottlenecks, 123
  installation planning, 123

  installation preparation, 123
  installation equipment, 91
  installation method, 115
  layout options, 57
  maintenance activities, 147
  O & M objectives, 146
  O & M requirements, 146
  Outlet, 58
  Pakistan, 547, 555, 557, 559, 560
  periodic checking, 149
  pumped outlet, 58
  repairs, 151
  steps in installation, 124
  sub-main drain, 57
  The Netherlands, 527
Sump, 86, 87
  costs, 173
  determining the required level, 344
  function, 87
  in-situ installation, 342
  installation, 341, 355
  installation costs, 173
  installation, quality control, 400
  Pakistan, 551
  prefabricated sump installation, 341
  types, 87
Supervisor, 44, 121, 136, 232
  description of activities, 183
  instruction sheets, 183
  role during implementation, 44
  tasks description, 232
Suppliers, see also *Manufacturers*, 27, 44,
    215
  transport, 214
  role during the implementation, 44
Support equipment, 111
  capacity, 106
  gravel trailer, 303
Surface drain, crossing, 126, 321
Survey
  pre-drainage survey, costs, 166
  soil survey, costs, 166
  topographic survey, costs, 166
  survey sheet, 201
  survey unit, tasks, 120
Surveyor
  instruction sheets, 183
  tasks description, 235
Synthetic envelope, see also *Envelope*
  costs, 165, 170

installation, 130
quality control, 394

T

Taxes and duties, 160, 207
Tender, 44, 45
  Asian Development Bank, 55
  advantages & disadvantages, 49
  advertisement, 53
  costs, 167
  direct, 47, 48, 50, 52
  documents, contents, 44
  documents preparation, 51
  documents, 48
  European Union, 56
  evaluation, 54
  FIDIC, 55
  International, 46
  National, 47
  preparation, 44, 51, 53, 167
  preparation, cost estimates, 154
  pre qualification, 47, 50, 52
  price consultation, 47
  procedure, 45, 50
  procedure in Egypt, 478
  restricted, 47
  submission, 54
  World Bank, 55
Tenderers, 46, 47, 51
  tender preparation, 51, 53
  pre-qualification, 52
Terms of Reference, 36, 38
  FIDIC tender, 51
  for design, 39
  for field investigations, 38
The Netherlands, 525
Tile drain, see also *Pipe drain*
Tiles, see *Clay pipe*, 15, 22, 70
Time and motion study, 201
  Egypt, 490, 492
Time registration sheet, 200
Time standard, 197
Time study, 199
  Egypt, 494
  Installation, India, 512, 522, 524
T-joints, see also *Joints*, 78, 130, 353, 540
  Egypt, 483
  installation, 130, 353
Tool, manual installation, 92, 115, 374
Tools and instrument costs, 207

Topographic survey, 31, 38, 139, 166
  costs, 166
Total machine time, 197
Total quality system, 135
Tracking, quality control, 141, 143
Tracks, trenchless machine, 95, 101
Tractor driver
  instruction sheets, 183
  tasks description, 236
Training, 161
  costs, 153, 161
  Centre in Egypt, 499
Transmitter, 119, 295
Transport, 169, 207
  clay pipes, 77
  concrete pipes, 75
  costs, 213
  equipment, 111, 113, 169
  gravel, 367
  pipe fittings, 79
  plastic pipes, 73
  pipes, costs, 164, 169
  trencher machine, 260
Trench, backfill, 132, 359
  excavation, 128
  Pakistan, 553
Trench box, 95
  adjustment, 253
  changing, 264
  dimensions, 96
  installation from open drain, 335
  liftable box, 267
Trencher machine, 94, 239
  accidental stopping, 264
  advantages & disadvantage, 99
  auger, 240
  bucket-wheel type, 99
  capacity, 106, 489
  Chinese-made, 459, 465
  command panel, 242
  composition, 95
  costs comparison, 106
  description, 239
  digging chain, adjustment, 253
  engine power, 98
  extension of laser mast, 295
  flat-digging-chain type, 99
  gravel management, 370
  hard-rock type, 108
  laser mast, 295

implementation requirements, 229
installation of drain pipes, 263
maintenance, 245
maintenance precautions, 250
modifications, Egypt, 487
operation, 263
operation in stony soils, 264
operational costs, 259, 517
operator tasks description, 233
orchard-type, 109
performance monitoring, 197
press pulley, 240
reduction of wear, 260
sizes, 98
starting level manhole, 343
specifications, 107
transport wear, 260
trench box adjustment, 253
types, 99
water tank, 241
winter storage, 248
Trenchless machine, 100, 271
   advantages & disadvantage, 104
   capacity, 100, 106, 512
   composition, 101
   costs comparison, 106
   critical depth, 104
   description, 271
   engine power, 102
   installation blades, 102
   maintenance, 275
   maintenance precautions, 275
   operation, 283
   specifications, 107
   tracks, 101
Trenching unit, tasks, 121
Triple gouser plates, 101
Tubewell drainage, 22, 456
Type of pipes
   field drains, 70
   collector drains, 80

U
Unit costs, 51, 160
Unstable soil, 86, 94, 107,116
   installation method, 331

V
Vertical plough, see also *Subsoiler*, 19, 100,
   102, 271, 511

replacement of parts, 278
Video inspection, 141, 413, 496
Visual inspection, 74, 76, 93, 107, 139,
   140, 141, 149
   backfill, 400
   during installation, 398
   composite drainage system, 423
   gravel, 393, 399
   pipes, 391
   singular drainage system, 421
V-plough, 19, 100, 107, 271, 511
   blade, 104
   replacement of parts, 278

W
Warping, 455
Water board, The Netherlands, 529
Water level, manhole, 144
Water ponding, performance indicators, 144
Water tank, 98, 241
Waterlogging, 16
   China, 453
   India, 504
Wear of machine during transport, 260
Wheel tractor, 99
   driver, tasks, 236
Work standard, 197
   calculation form, 203
   Egypt, 493
World Bank
   project in Egypt, 487
   project in Pakistan, 554
   tender procedure, 55
Wrapping, 385
Wrapping machine, 85, 170

Y
Y-joint, see also *Joints*, 78
   installation, 130, 354

Colophon

This publication has been made possible with financial contributions of the following organizations:

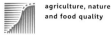 Ministry for Agriculture, Nature and Food Quality, Department of Science and Knowledge Transfer, The Netherlands

 Ministry of Transport, Public Works and Water Management, Institute for Inland Water Management and Waste Water Treatment (RIZA), Lelystad, The Netherlands

 Alterra-ILRI, Wageningen University and Research Centre, The Netherlands

 Arcadis Euroconsult, The Netherlands

 Steenbergen Hollanddrain, The Netherlands

 Mastenbroek UK, United Kingdom

 Homburg Drainage Machinery, The Netherlands

 Horman Drainagefilters, The Netherlands

Photo's: Supplied by the authors and Alterra-ILRI, except:

National Archive in Flevoland, Lelystad: page 19 (Figure 3a, 3b, 3d, 3e, 3f, 3g); page 376 (Figure C36.3)

USDA, Farm Drainage in the USA: page 19 (Figure 3c)

Steenbergen Holland Drain: page 19 (Figure 3h); page 33 (Figure 33); page 97(Figure 35a, 35e); page 103 (Figure 39); page 105 (Figure 40); page 109 (Figure 42, 43); page 110 (Figure 45), page 113 (Figure 48); page 131 (Figure 57); page 249 (Figure C5.3) ; page 261 (Figure C7.1); page 273 (Figure C10.3); page 428 (Figure E2.1, left); page 460 (Figure 4); page 472 (Figure3) ; page 486 (Figure 14); page 552 (Figure 3)

T. van Achthoven: page 516 (Figure 6 & 7)

B. Boekhoven: page 428 (Figure E2.1, right)

J. Penninkhof: page 138 (Figure 61)

English text editor: Mrs. Ninette de Zylva

Drawings: Jos Rietstap Vormgeving

Design and Layout: Graphic Design & DTP team, Alterra

Printing: Kerckebosch b.v., Zeist